THE WORLD OF ELI WHITNEY

THE MACMILLAN COMPANY
NEW YORK · CHICAGO
DALLAS · ATLANTA · SAN FRANCISCO

THE MACMILLAN COMPANY
OF CANADA, LIMITED
TORONTO

ELI WHITNEY

THE WORLD OF
ELI
WHITNEY

By Jeannette Mirsky
& Allan Nevins

THE MACMILLAN COMPANY

New York : 1952

First Printing

TS1570
WG1

"That fast, that rapid: a commodity in the land now which until now had dealt first in Indians: then in acres and sections and boundaries:—an economy: Cotton: a king: omnipotent and omnipresent: a destiny of which (obvious now) the plow and the axe had been merely the tools; not plow and axe which had effaced the wilderness, but Cotton: petty globules of Motion weightless and myriad even in the hand of a child, incapable even of wadding a rifle, let alone of charging it, yet potent enough to sever the very taproots of oak and hickory and gum, leaving the arch-shading tops to wither and vanish in one single season beneath that fierce and minted glare; not the rifle nor the plow which drove at last the bear and deer and panther into the last jungle fastnesses of the river bottoms, but Cotton; not the soaring cupola of the courthouse drawing people into the country, but the same white tide sweeping them in: that tender skim covering the winter's brown earth, burgeoning through spring and summer into September's white surf crashing against the flanks of gin and warehouse and ringing like bells on the marble counters of the banks: altering not just the face of the land, but the complexion of the town too, creating its own parasitic aristocracy not only behind the columned porticoes of the plantation houses, but in the counting-rooms of merchant and bankers and the sanctums of lawyers, and not only these last, but finally nadir complete: the county offices too: of sheriff and tax-collector and bailiff and turnkey and clerk."

WILLIAM FAULKNER

*　　*　　*

. . . "If you will at a leisure hour tell me what the world may know about your *improvements* of the steam-engine, or anything about your experiments, or calculated facts about the power of your engines, or any other *ingenious stuff* for a note, I shall with pleasure insert it [in *The Botanic Garden*]. . . . I wish the whole not to exceed 2 or 3 quarto pages, and to consist of such facts, or things, as may be rather agreeable; I mean *gentlemanlike facts,* not abstruse calculations, only fit for philosophers."

DR. ERASMUS DARWIN to MR. JAMES WATT

* * *

"Mass production is not merely quantity production; for this may be had with none of the prerequisites of mass production. Nor is it merely machine production, which may also exist without any resemblance to mass production. Mass production is the focussing upon a manufacturing project of the principles of power, accuracy, economy, system, continuity, and speed. And the normal result is a productive organization that delivers in quantities a useful commodity of standard material, workmanship, and design at minimum cost."

HENRY FORD

Authors' Note

Exactly one week before the surrender at Appomattox, Wendell Phillips wrote to Eli Whitney, Jr.: "Did I thank you for the Life of your Father. I have made lifelong search for some particular accounts of him: for he was early one of my favorites. . . . What a revelation of the callousness to right and wrong which 'the system' generates was his experience. I think there should be some more detailed account, in a more permanent form, of one whose hand was felt so forcibly on our nation's history."

The "Life" Wendell Phillips received was the slim *Memoir of Eli Whitney, Esq.*, written by Olmsted (with Silliman's all too brief supplementary remarks), published in 1846. Except for some additional facts subsequently made available by Blake and Hammond, Whitney's place in the nation's consciousness has rested on the *Memoir*. To most Americans he has been reduced to an uncluttered statement found, in one form or another, in every history book: "Eli Whitney invented the cotton gin in 1793." Our book tells his story as completely as possible; it accords Whitney his place in the making of modern America.

He was not just another clever Yankee mechanic. Whitney was a man of ideas; his real life is the life of his mind. This book tries to explore and explain it. Our main reliance, in telling the story of his life and achievements, has been on Whitney's own words (or on those of his family, close friends, or other firsthand sources). To make his efforts intelligible, we have supplied the historical and technological conditions within which he worked; we have also presented personal details—for they add color to Whitney's efforts.

When Whitney's work was comparatively new and its impact fairly unfamiliar, it attracted many Weems-like stories—they are barnacles concealing the true surface to which they have accreted, and so we have not included them. (One of the most persistent, for example, tells how Mrs. Nathanael Greene handed him a hearth-brush, saying gaily, "La! Mr. Whitney, your gin needs this." It implies that she instantly solved a mechanical problem that had baffled Whitney. If the story has an element of truth, it would be that she permitted the use of her hearth-brush when Whitney found it impossible to procure bristles to make the clearer for his model.)

Folklore such as this has its place and its uses. But Whitney, the inventor of the cotton gin, and the proponent and creator of an industrial system of irresistible potency, needs no myths to make his ideas more understandable. Now, when mass production is recognized as the mighty factor dominating our century, we turn back to Whitney for the genesis of our industrial might.

In preparing this study, the authors have incurred many obligations; to all who have helped, they wish to express their gratitude, real and profound. We are indebted to Mrs. Elizabeth Vromen-Snapper for her tireless and enthusiastic assistance in the research; to Roger Burlingame for his generosity in making his notes available; to Professors Joseph W. Roe and Harold A. Williamson, and Frank A. Taylor, Curator of Engineering, Smithsonian Institution, for their interest and their helpful discussions; to Dr. Alfred E. Mirsky for his suggestion that we read Helmholtz' *Popular Lectures on Scientific Subjects;* to Felicia J. Deyrup, Constance McL. Green, and Theodora Abel for valuable information; to Marie F. Rodell and Eleanor Daniels for beneficial criticism and editorial aid; to Sylvia Black for her accurate copying of Whitney's correspondence, and Nancy Reynolds for her skill and patience in typing the manuscript.

Miss Mirsky also wishes to thank Henry Allen Moe and the John Simon Guggenheim Foundation for twice according her a fellowship for this study.

We have relied heavily on the detailed knowledge of many specialists, and our major debts cannot be ignored. We wish to thank Mr. James T. Babb and Mrs. Zara Jones Powers of the Yale University Library; Mrs. Lilla Hawes of the Georgia Historical Society, Savannah; Miss Bess Glenn, Mr. O. W. Holmes, and Miss Elizabeth Drewry of the National Archives, Washington, D.C.; Mr. Thompson R. Harlow of the Connecticut Historical Society, and Mr. James Brewster, State Librarian, Connecticut State Library, both in Hartford; Mr. Ralph W. Thomas, Curator and Librarian of the New Haven Colony Historical Society in New Haven; Mrs. Helen Bullock of the Manuscript Division of the Library of Congress; Mr. Julian Boyd and Mr. Alexander Clark of the Princeton University Library; Mr. Sylvestre Vigilante and Mr. Igor D. Avellino of the American History Division, Mrs. Helen B. Wodrada of the Local History and Genealogy Division, and Mr. Edward B. Morrison of the Manuscript Division—all of the New York Public Library; and Mr. Penrose Hoopes for his permission to use Whitney's letter, dated March 20th, 1823, to Secretary of War Calhoun.

We are indebted to Mr. Allan Wendt for the excellence of the index.

Contents

Illustrations

ard, was the forging shop with its cluster of storehouses, and to the far right was Ithiel Town's first truss suspension bridge, a notable improvement that speeded the traffic on the Hartford Turnpike.

Here, gathered together, were the three elements that were to make the characteristic New England scene: buildings devoted to industry, mill villages, and covered bridges.

THE WORLD OF ELI WHITNEY

Two Revolutionists at an Inn

In November of 1802, two men faced each other across the table of a Washington public house. They had never met before; they were never to meet again.

"You have doubtless heard of the arrival of the notorious Tom Paine in this country— Being informed, previous to my arrival here, that he was in this neighborhood I had some curiosity to see him— I stoped at the public house where I am now writing to spend one day (it being in a central situation & convenient to the Public Offices where I have to do business)—I walked out for an hour & return'd to dinner—on entering the room—to my great surprise I found that T. Paine was there & a lodger in the house & in less than five minutes we were seated opposite each other at table—

"I was not disappointed in my expectation of his appearance—I found him the same filthy old sot that he has ever been represented—"

Tom Paine has left no record of that meeting. The man Paine saw was "a large man of rather full habit, slightly round shouldered, and doubling himself forward as he sat. His face was large and slightly oval; his nose long and hooked; his eyes deepset, black and keen; his look penetrating and prolonged. His hair was black . . . his skin smooth, sallow and pallid. Altogether his appearance was striking, the expression of his face having a deep thoughtfulness about the brow, tempered by a pleasant smile at the corners of the mouth. In conversation he was slow but his thoughts were clear and weighty. His knowledge seemed at once exact and diversified; he spoke more of science than literature; he was not discursive, but logically pursued trains of thought . . . though possessing a fine imagination, and a keen inventive faculty, he had a perseverance in pursuing his

1

plans to completion, that nothing could arrest. He was at once energetic and systematic; dignified, yet courteous; large in his views, yet
precise in detail, a profound thinker and scrutinizing nature and its
phenomena with amazing depth of thought."

No one told Paine that this was Eli Whitney, inventor of the cotton
gin and mass producer of muskets for the American government.
Whitney never knew that Paine had conceived a plan for constructing iron bridges of four-hundred-foot span, so built that they might
be shipped, fabricated and ready, to be assembled "in any part of the
world."

They failed utterly to appreciate each other. For a brief careless
moment the man who in his person and by his phrases tied together
the American and French revolutions and the man who founded the
American system of the Industrial Revolution met. In the intervening
stretch of years thought has focused sharply on the parts they played,
not on the externals they presented, and values both men as decisive
factors in making the modern world.

Eli Whitney was born on December 8, 1765, and died on January
8, 1825. The sixty years of his life were crammed with violent upheaval and dislocation, with the accelerated breaking of old patterns
and the swift birth of new.

Those decades today are labeled by phrases that imply a perceived
relationship between a combination of events—the American Revolution, the French Revolution, the Industrial Revolution—phrases
that qualify changes in tempo and temper of processes that were
long in the making and still have a powerful urgency. But to the
American who lived through those decades the phrases resolved
themselves into long defiant war years when the habitual flow of
goods was stopped and people lived in an atmosphere of scarcity and
austerity, of ingenious makeshift and hopeful manufacture; peace
years when people were magnetized by the pull of the beckoning
continent or the lure of blossoming commerce; and years when people
shuttled between embargo and enterprise, profit and panic, speculation and slump, hope and heartbreak and hope again. It was solo and
chorus, pioneer and community movement; it was colony, confederation, union.

For all letter sources, see page 333.

1 Farm and Forge

To Massachusetts, peace came like a blight. The Revolution was won, yet people were worse off than they had been: the nation, the states, and individuals struggled under debts; there was a wild longing for wealth; and speculation, like a wanton, robbed people of hope and money. Dissatisfaction flared into acrimonious interstate disputes over land; and within the state disorder and discontent led to active rebellion, as farmers, impatient of postponed reforms, again took up their muskets and followed Captain Daniel Shays.

The war was over, and with the cessation of hostilities had come a disastrous slump: hard times gripped the farms, commerce was depressed, ships stood empty and at anchor, currency was depreciated. A new nation had been declared, and yet the old social divisions persisted—a sharp line barbed with distrust and differences divided "the better kind of people" from the poor and humble; in education, speech, dress, and manners the divergence was marked. Speculation and rebellion, acute symptoms of the magnitude of the social dislocation, hastened the dissolution of the old order: the first drained off capital, the second drained off the refractory and impoverished elements, who fled the state. Neither of these solutions answered the longings of those who, like young Whitney, were ambitious and restless and poor. For such, new academies were started; their number was a measure of their need.

For in spite of rebellion and dissatisfaction, New England still walked in fear of the Lord. Massachusetts from the sea to the Berkshire frontier was profoundly committed to Puritanism. Puritan society required the outward bearing to express inner grace, just as later the business world reserved its highest praise for respectability. Respectability, a word called into being for the industrial society that was emerging,* inherited many attitudes from piety: it equated sober deportment with strict probity, it transferred its mistrust from "enthusiasm" to "impulsiveness," and the general term "sinner" splintered into a variety of words—"debtor," "drunkard," "beggar," "wastrel," "laggard"—indicating kinds and degrees of asocial behavior. The terms, still carrying the same full emotional charge of guilt, are an indication of the way society shifted its attention and energy from the godly life to the business life. By a slight but pointed adjustment of social mores to a new economy, the Puritan values of the seventeenth century were gradually transformed into the Victorian values of the nineteenth century; and as piety had had a long, absolute tenure, so did respectability.

Westborough, the town in Worcester County, Massachusetts, where Eli Whitney was born in 1765, lies within the belt of sandy soil, about forty miles inland from Boston. By horse or by wagon it was remote from the coastal towns—trading and commercial centers—that communicated easily with each other and distant ports. From the settlements of western Massachusetts that crowded into the lush bottom lands of the Connecticut Valley, Westborough was separated by a tedious line of hills that then, as now, were too poor to invite settlers. Economically and intellectually the seaboard towns looked to Boston, while the valley villages, tied together by frontier perils and frontier profits, found Hartford and New Haven more congenial, more accessible.

Boston, a metropolis of twenty thousand, was an important name among Empire ports, secure in her eminence. The hamlets that dotted the valley hid the scars of Indian massacres under the bloom and assurance of youth; theirs was an economy of plenty, theirs the excitement of rushing, booming adventures. Between those two—the sea and the river, the coast and the valley—lay Westborough. Here

---

* "The 'Candid Philosopher' was printed in 1778, without the name of the author, who was R. Lewis, a corrector of the press. At vol. i, p. 189, he uses the word [respectability], but adds in a parenthesis, 'If I may coin the word,' thus claiming to be the originator of what has become one of the sacred words of the British people." From the *Manchester Guardian*, Sept. 2, 1893.

farmers were content to make a living out of farms large enough to support them, yet too small to hold promise for their children and their children's children.

"Nathaniel Whitney," wrote Elizabeth Whitney Blake when she was an old woman and her famous brother was dead, "was a descendent of a family which came from England in the early settlement of this country, and landed at Boston and settled eight or ten miles from Boston, and Nathaniel removed from Newton to Westborough twenty years before his Tenth child, Eli, was born. Who died in the same *room* he was born in August 25th 1807 aged 66 years. Both Nathaniel and Eli were among the most respected farmers in Worcester County." As the Whitneys had pushed inland from the coast, so had the Fays. Elizabeth Fay was the first-born child of Captain Benjamin Fay, who was the son of Deacon John Fay who had purchased the "large track in Westborough called the Fay Farms. . . . Eli Whitney and Elizabeth Fay was married in January 1765—Eli Whitney [the inventor *] the first born of Eli and Elizabeth Whitney, was born December 8, 1765."

Reading her phrases with their biblical cadence, peering through the small bright keyhole of her memory, one finds the record of her brother's formative years is tantalizingly slim. Suggestive details pour out without even the mild order imposed by chronology; traits jostle talents, family gossip winds in and out in a haphazard way, incidents that illuminate personalities are casually alluded to. And yet from this careless jumble comes the authentic sound of a speaking voice—the picture of Eli as a boy and youth begins to take shape and have content. "The elaps of years, cares of a family have so far obliterated many anecdotes which would have been useful and interesting, I must pass them by. What I can recollect I will communicate with greatest pleasure . . . and I will write occurances of childhood in the language of childhood."

This letter, its cramped words packed into pages, is the only source the historian can draw on with assurance. Elizabeth limited her remembrance, restricting herself to an intimate family chronicle. To enter the world of her letter is much like following Jane Austen into

---

* Eli Whitney rightfully was Eli Whitney, Jr. Except for a few early letters he never signed his letters, business or personal, other than "Eli Whitney."

her special world: not from the details that fill the pages would the reader know that both writers record events set in times of great national activity; their quiet pages seem remote from the tremendous drama of their times. Elizabeth's account hardly mentions the Revolution, though Lexington and Concord were not too distant. It ignores the decade that had preceded hostilities. Yet Whitney was born in the year of the Stamp Act, a year made momentous by the vigorous beginning of the Revolutionary movement, when, as John Adams wrote, "That enormous engine, fabricated by the British Parliament, for battering down the rights and liberties of America, I mean the Stamp Act, has raised and spread through the whole continent a spirit that will be recorded with honor to all future generations."

Whitney was close to ten when his ears, too young to have caught the spacious, dedicated meaning of Adams's "unconquerable rage," could grasp the angry language loosed by the war against the loyalists: "Sore eyes to all Tories and a chestnut burr for an eyestone." His eyes excitedly followed minutemen drilling and volunteers hurrying off to the not so distant siege of Boston. He might have heard his father denounce speculators and monopolists (those "pestilential mushrooms of trade, which have come up in the night of public calamity," those "regrators, forestallers, engrossers, and higglers"), for, like all farmers, his father was victimized by the merciless inflation and a depreciated currency. The stories that filled Whitney's boyhood must have been true stories—the British raids on the Rhode Island and Connecticut coastal towns, the American victory at Saratoga, the French fleet sailing into Newport, and the details, long in coming from far-off Carolina, of how Nathanael Greene and his men drove the British from the last base. In the sixteen years of Whitney's boyhood and youth, by word and deed a profound change had been effected; the American colonists won their independence, and peace came.

"Our Father was a man who worked on a farm. Our Mother was after the birth of my youngest Brother sick to the day of her death— [August 18, 1777]—seven years and a half consequently we were in greate measure deprived of a mothers care at a time in life when it is most needed."

Very early Eli was inured to responsibility. The oldest child in the

family, he was but five when Josiah, the youngest brother, was born
—Elizabeth and Benjamin came in between—and his mother was
left ailing and unable to carry the load of children and household
work. Those were strenuous, uncushioned times; for a mother and
housewife it was a hard and heroic age, for a sick woman it was
catastrophic. More than fifty years later, her daughter remembered
that the hired girl had "come out from mothers room and seemed
mad because mother had told her how to do—said she would do as
she had a mind to," and in front of seven-year-old Eli had called his
mother vulgar names. Between the death of the mother and the
father's remarriage, a housekeeper, casually mentioned, looked after
the children.

For all his ponderous weight of nearly three hundred pounds (a
serious handicap to an active farmer), Eli's father remains a shadowy
figure. He "was called a good writer and was a great admirer of
good [hand]writing," hardly a quality to define a man, but a phrase
that marks him as more literate than many neighbors. Westborough
esteemed him as a prominent citizen; he often held town office, and
was justice of the peace for years. From Elizabeth's narrative it is
clear that the father was their background and home, their energy
and ambitions; he was always consulted; he was always taken for
granted.

"Our Father had a work shop and sometimes made wheels of different discriptions. He had a lathe to turn chairposts and quite a
variety of tools. This gave my Brother an opportunity of learning the
use of tools very young. He lost no time, as soon as he could handle
tools he was always making something in the shop and seemed not
to relish working on the farm." A friend remembered Whitney's own
account of how from the age of eleven his daily chore in the winter
was to fodder and water sixty head of cattle; only when his chore
was done did he make his own path for three-quarters of a mile
across the fields, through the snow, to the schoolhouse.

It is as expected that Eli Whitney should show an early gift and
preference for mechanical creativity as that Mozart at the age of
three should amuse himself by striking thirds on the clavier. But even
at a tender age Whitney was not merely dexterous with tools and
techniques; he was not merely another skillful Yankee mechanic. He

was a born manufacturer, a fledgling entrepreneur (a word coined in 1755 to designate a special class of men and activities); and in this complex of aptitudes—shrewd head, adventuresome spirit, and cunning hand—a clear continuity is traceable between his earliest efforts, as Elizabeth recalled them, and his mature work.

"In the time of the revolutionary war, nails commanding a high price, Eli proposed having a forge in the shop and making nails. Father consented. The forge was put up and Eli made nails, did his days work and gained time to make tools for his own use—put in penknife blades and do many little jobs for other people." Having done that much, Whitney, still in his early teens, expanded his venture. "As near as I can recollect it was the second winter after he began to make nails, he told me he had laid a plan to hire a man, pay his board and have the profit of his work. He wished me to say nothing about it. . . . In the evening he pretended some kind of errand at an adjoining town, asked leave of Father to take one of the horses. He rose early and was gone three days. Father became quite uneasy and inquired if I could imagine where Eli was gone. To relieve his anxiety I told him I heard him say something about hireing a man, that he was tired of working alone, that it would not consume any more coal and that he thought it would be profitable."

Suddenly, the story is no longer a boy's adventure, it is a business transaction with a mature ring. In this, his first manufacturing effort, Whitney was not playing at penny-lemonade production—he had weighed labor and overhead costs against prices and found his margin of gain. "At Eli's return he said he had traveled 40 miles out, had been in many shops had gained information enough to pay for his journey and had hired a man for a month by the name of Thayer. . . . I do not recollect that Father disapproved of anything he had done except his being absent so long without leave. Thayer come the next week and was employed three months."

Elizabeth concludes this small incident by saying, "At the end of the war making nails was no longer an object worth attending to." Since the profit had gone from nails, Eli cast about for something that was profitable. Hatpins, for instance. Ladies no longer tied on their bonnets; they "Pind [them] on with three long pins." (This skill, learned in drawing out steel into fine long pins, was used years later,

in his own shop, to make the wire teeth of the cotton gin.) At fifteen
he was already aware that he must be alert to produce for a lively
market. Why limit the forge to one product, even if it had been
bought for just such use? Of the many small household manufactories of nails, a few lingered, unlucky and profitless; most died, as
with peace, England dumped shiploads of cheap nails on the American market and killed an industry that had been born during the
war years. To switch from nails to hatpins, from hatpins to "walking
canes"; to let the forge rest and use the lathe; to discount the energy
spent and the cost of equipment; to be able to change as conditions
demand change—this rare quality Whitney possessed even as a boy.
"Whatever he undertook he seemed to have the Sagacity to perceive
probable consequences."

This considered opinion, so rare for Elizabeth, is repeated with a
slight variation: "He was remarkable for thinking and acting for
himself at the age of ten or twelve years." Then she gives her authority for her statement: "I have heard it remarked that at the age of
twelve he had more general information than *men* considered of the
first standing in the country. And the number of boys produced in
Worcester county since the birth of EW, his *Equil* may be justly considered small." But she would not have it thought that her brother
was not just as remarkable in intellectual grasp. "I recollect hearing
my Parents observe that Eli did not learn to read so quick or easily
as some of the other children but understood figures very young. I
have more than once heard [Uncle] Capt. D. Fay mention with admiration being at school when he was studying arithmetic and Eli,
being a very little boy, with his Book in one hand and the other
tucked in by the side of his apron, come and looked over his Fays
Book and whispering to himself as if he understood or was trying to
find what it meant. Fay said, 'What are you here for, you dont know
one figure from another. Go sit down.' Eli sit down. Uncle Stephen
hearing, said to Fay 'You are Mistaken. He does know something of
figures. I guess he can enumerate nine figures as quick as any one.'
Fay not thinking it possible set down nine figures on paper and asked
Eli what that meant. He answered redily and as correctly as the Master could have done."

It was June 12, 1779, when young Eli was fourteen, that his father remarried. The widowed Judith Hazeldon brought to her new home two of her ten children: Hannah, the same age as her stepsister Elizabeth, and "one of the most hairbrained creatures ever known," and Nancy, who shared birthdays with Josiah. Judith Whitney seems to have had little love for her stepchildren. From her, Eli learned that disbelief and callousness were aspects of the world he would encounter. When she was introduced into the family, she must have heard how Eli only the year before had made a violin that "was made in every part like a common fiddle and made tolerable good musick —it was examined by many—all pronounced it remarkable work for such a boy to perform." Family pride and vanity, she might have thought, puffing up the children: let them show me what he can do. "Our step mother had a case of knives which she said were very handsome. Eli would say I can make just such ones if I had tools and I could make tools if I had tools to make them with. This was repeated, and seemed rather to tease her and she disdained him and his sayings. It so happened she broke one of those knives a few months after. Eli made one exactly like the others except the stem on the blade was wanting. He said he could put on a stem but the tool would be expensive and he should never want it again. She was well pleased and I do not remember ever after hearing her deride him when he told her what he could make." It hardly seems necessary for Elizabeth to remark that "Brother Eli was when young of a mild disposition—possessed a great share of affability."

This was his home, this his background. The child who was good at figures beyond his years, the boy who mastered the workshop and engaged in serious and profitable enterprises, the youth who by himself perfected his penmanship, was not to stay with the cattle and end as a farmer. Of the three Whitney brothers, Josiah eventually settled in Boston and became a merchant; the docile Benjamin remained on the farm, possessed of his father's acres and heir to the problems posed by a lean soil; Eli chose the Connecticut Valley, with its growing industries, as the place that offered most to his talents.

II *The Emergence of the Machine*

The eighteenth century was a masterful century and it is still with us by command and continuity. It began, it might be said, in July of 1687, with the publication of a quarto volume of about five hundred pages: Newton's *Principia*. Therein order and reason, arranged mathematically, explained the mysteries of tides and firmament; motion itself was subject to the laws of nature. No longer was the earth solely a testing ground for heaven and hell; mathematics had proved it to be part of a cosmic machine—though Newton conceded that occasionally it required divine regulation. This concept set the secular tone for the century. Young men, John Aubrey noted at that time, were "in love with that Studie. Before, the Mathematical Sciences were lock't up in the Greek and latin tongues and there lay untoucht." From clerics to courtiers, young men of education sought to understand Newton; they were intoxicated by the new worlds of thought that he had made possible. Cotton Mather spoke for them when, to the Royal Society, he wrote that Newton was "the *perpetual Dictator* of the learned World."

It was the Age of Reason, the Age of Enlightenment, the time when men turned from a concentration on the life hereafter to an alert interest in earthly living; when the human mind worked confidently and with striking competence, when individual judgment denied dogmatic authority and grew vigorous. Above all, men were committed to the idea of human progress: the laws of nature would reveal the bounties of nature if man would gradually adapt himself and his institutions to these laws. Science and technology, offspring of these dynamic attitudes, drew closer together. Science, technology,

11

and art—in this century the giants were in music and literature—should be seen as different aspects of a violent ferment, man's new-found freedom to experiment and create. Whether the form it took was useful or not—whether it was expressed in cantatas, planets, or canals; in periodicals, chronometers, or politics; in essays, operas, gases, electricity, engines, orreries, gavottes, economics; in ideas or events—the exuberant impulse was common to all.

It became routine to experiment in fact as well as in ideas. Great men were active in a variety of enterprises. Those who were contemporary knew each other's work whether they lived in Great Britain, on the Continent, or in the New World; they thought of themselves as the Literati, and by an intricate chain of personal communications—it was an age of letter writing—acquainted their confrères with the new, the important. There was an awareness of the need to collect, to systematize, to synthesize, to instruct and enlighten men; wedded to this was a belief in progress and perfectibility. These spreading beliefs fused and produced, as its monument to the Age of Humanism, the French *Encyclopédie ou Dictionnaire Raisonné des Sciences, des Arts et des Métiers.* Its twenty-one volumes of text were published by 1765—to which later were added six volumes of plates and two of tables.

As eighteenth century enlightenment evolved from Newton, so its political liberalism flowed from the Glorious Revolution of 1688 and John Locke. In England the beheading of one king and the forced abdication of another had expressed popular dissatisfaction with the theory of the "divine rights" of kings. Locke justified the Revolution philosophically, and his arguments, his very phrases, still animate democratic theory. Using the heavy artillery of essay and treatise, he defended individual liberty from attack by pope or king even as he raked the ramparts where religious persecution and literary censorship lay entrenched. Where other political thinkers arrived step by logical step at an extreme, impractical conclusion, Locke used common sense to balance logic and theory with the urgency of existing facts. To him, the will of a people was sovereign; government was an instrumentality created by men to secure certain ends, to implement a social contract; and should a government act improperly in its role as trustee, then the contract was voided and revolution was a legitimate way of restoring the popular will.

An England politically insistent on tolerance and individual liberty (a vigorous rising middle class, conscious of its growing power and wealth, was impatient of restrictive authority), a people who had accorded Newton a national hero's burial in Westminster Abbey— such was the England to which Voltaire came on a visit in 1726. Voltaire became a symbol of the age; both were aristocratic in taste and tone, expression and background. Intellectually neither original nor truly creative, Voltaire was alert, critical, multifaceted, enormously articulate, and productive. Emotionally he was committed to reasonableness, a disgust with injustice because it is a crime against the individual; but he did not understand nor care about the miseries of the millions. Locke and Voltaire provided the atmosphere for the goals and word-weapons of Adams and Jefferson, of Rousseau and Condorcet. The revolutions in America and France were very different in spirit—the one essentially conservative, the other in the end so wildly radical. But they were alike in this, that it was when they moved out of the countinghouses and salons into the streets and assemblies that they gave tenacity and territory to the ideas forged by Milton, Harrington, and Locke, by Montesquieu, Voltaire, and Diderot.

The *Encyclopédie* is a monument. Here first were stated the principles of the physiocratic school of political economists. A compact cluster of influential landowners, irked by the crippling regulations of guild and government, created a comprehensive theory of free trade. Their immediate aim was to secure an unhampered flow of agricultural produce—*laissez faire, laissez passer*, was their slogan—but they quickly attracted to themselves men whose property interests were in nascent industrial and commercial enterprises. Together they by-passed the pitfall of carping at details and projected a complete system that, as they believed, expressed a natural order in society. They declared that this natural order, regulated by and responsive to natural laws, had been damaged by the blundering intervention of governments.

The history of the eighteenth century is dominated by the grand design and varied details of Anglo-French commercial and territorial wars. To wrest control of the rich sugar-producing islands of the Caribbean; to win the Spanish *asiento,* the exclusive right to profit from the African slaves delivered yearly to the plantations of the New World; to have dominion over North America, including Canada and the valley of the Mississippi, and command its annual harvest of fish and furs and tobacco, its virgin forests that provided vital naval stores; to conquer India and drain its vast reservoir of accumulated gold and silver; to govern world trade by binding its ever widening parts into an intricate contrived pattern—for this, and nothing less than this, England and France struggled. And within each national system trade was prescribed, administered, controlled. Freedom of trade was thus no longer the cry of a particular segment of society which felt frustrated by specific regulations; freedom to trade was transformed into a noble general principle. Thenceforth it attracted recruits. Because it channeled different needs and formless dissatisfactions, it spread across narrow national lines to tie in sympathy, in firm adherence, in obstinate defiance, men who shared a common creed.

This revolution in economic theory can be discerned in the *Encyclopédie*. There are portents that minor manufacturing interests might soon be made strong by the miracle of steam power and machinery. These budding industries knew that a world—not just an empire, great though it might be—awaited their wares, and they were sensible of the fact that restrictions were ill suited to their purpose. Boulton, who carried Watt's steam engine into successful production, said, in 1769: "It would not be worth my while to make for three counties only, but I find it very worth my while to make for all the world." Free trade likewise fitted the needs of New England traders who, during the years when England and France had faced each other in battle, had tasted the profits to be had by catering directly to the West Indian plantations—French, Spanish, and English. With the signing of peace in 1763, these traders were reluctant to return to their former position within the British colonial system. They resented being excluded from the West Indian market; they would not submit to a system that barred their products and ships from profitable ports. Nor could the colonial merchants accept as their proper duty "to be immediately dependent on their original parent and to make their interest subservient thereunto."

Geography and new enterprise promised these dissidents that they had not long to wait. In 1776, only thirteen years after Great Britain had her colonial and commercial supremacy acknowledged by the Peace of Paris, spokesmen for an emerging economy that sought "not to shake or plunder property, but to protect it," stated their case: philosophically, Adam Smith documented its needs and blessed it in *The Wealth of Nations;* politically, Jefferson sounded the call to battle in the *Declaration of Independence.*

Of a wholly different order is the story of mechanical ideas and inventions. Between idea and machine, specific problem and functioning answer, engineer and mechanic—where to peg a date? Between patent and guarded process, mechanic and promoter, between hand and purse—where to give credit for priority? Trying new techniques, men in small scattered shops experimented for decades, seeking to transform raw materials—coal, iron ore, clay, cotton—into goods that would satisfy the boundless needs of men. And over it all was the basic cry for power, a prime mover, that would be more dependable than water or wind, stronger than beast or man. And so the Industrial Revolution gathered momentum and seemed to burst upon a simple world. It was a revolution that broke no political ties, severed no allegiances; it revolutionized industry and thereby changed the rhythm of work and life.

To understand the magnitude and pace of this revolution, turn to the *Encyclopédie,* which stands like a museum wherein are to be found antique theories, outmoded machines, obsolete methods. Combustion is explained in terms of phlogiston, an element of negative weight; gases "are still entirely unknown quantities"; modern chemistry had not yet been born. In this museum machines are made of wood with but few metal parts; only firearms and precision instruments—clocks, watches, marine instruments—used brass and iron. Machines for knitting stockings and weaving ribbons existed, and the flying shuttle had been invented; carding, spinning, and weaving were otherwise much as they had been for hundreds of years. Bleaching, an important textile process, was still a primitive duet of sour milk and sun. Lathes of all kinds were known, but they were essentially devices for turning ornamental forms in wood, while in the heavy metal trades the file was the supreme tool used to achieve precision. Of the prime movers, the Italian turret windmill, developed about the time Columbus left Genoa for Spain, was the last important innovation.

The *Encyclopédie* appeared on the eve of profound technological changes. The statement that "a machine consists of craftsmanship and invention, rather than of strength and solidity of materials," clearly expresses the values placed on the work of their greatest technicians. This definition derives more from Jacques de Vaucanson's mechanical duck, which fed and digested its food, than from his sustained work on the ribbon loom and his decisive improvement of the drawloom action. Similarly, the writing boy that, by concealed machinery, moved his hands and fingers to form letters brought more fame to Pierre-Jacquet Droz than the pendulum he made out of two metals of uneven expansibility, which remained regular because it was unaffected by temperature changes. (It was this which made him the founder of the Swiss watch industry.) Not that the exquisite toys were more valued than useful inventions—the *Encyclopédie* gave space and prominence to inventions and industrial processes; the definition reflects that period's underlying attitude toward mechanical inventions.

Helmholtz has characterized how this differed from what followed: "The object, therefore, which the inventive genius of the past century [eighteenth] placed before it with the fullest earnestness, and not as a price of amusement merely, was boldly chosen, and was followed up with an expenditure of sagacity which has contributed not a little to enrich the mechanical experience which a later time knew how to take advantage of. We no longer seek to build machines which shall fulfill the thousand services required of *one* man, but desire, on the contrary, that a machine shall perform *one* service, and shall occupy in doing it the place of a thousand men." That is, invention no longer sought to build mechanisms which represented a whole system of acts, but instead concentrated on specialized function.

Steam power, iron, and textile machinery gave new meaning to the word *machine;* together they characterize the new era, the Industrial Revolution.

As this century has seen the variety of skills and materials required to resolve aeronautical problems, so the first half of the eighteenth century witnessed the successful construction of navigational instruments that reduced astronomy and physics to forms simple enough to be commonly used in guiding ships across the oceans. The sextant and the chronometer made clear the growing interdependence of science and technology. Newton, it is true, had answered questions raised by navigators since the time of Columbus and explained the mysterious movements of earth and sky; but the needs of navigators still pressed for solution. The demand was no longer for answers; it was for instruments.

Even before Newton's day, men knew how to find latitude and longitude; but what was still not known was how to make a good quadrant, how to construct a dependable, seagoing clock. Newton knew of these needs, for among his papers, unrealized and forgotten, he had tossed a completed sketch for a sextant. It was a sketch, not a sextant. Thirty-three years passed before two master craftsmen—John Hadley of London and Thomas Godfrey, a Philadelphia glazier and friend of Franklin—independently satisfied the need and constructed sextants out of brass and wood (1731). Meanwhile, a clock-maker, John Harrison, worked thirty years to perfect four chronometers (necessary to establish longitude), and then another fifteen years suing a reluctant Board of Longitude (it had been formed to encourage just such work) for the £20,000 prize it had offered. Only thus were the primary needs of a society of merchant sailors fulfilled.

The second half of the century focused on a new problem: the production of a cheap and dependable prime mover. Thomas Newcomen had made an effective start as early as 1712. Considering the kinds of tools and iron then available, his engine was a miracle of skill; it embodied no new scientific principles but ingeniously combined those that were simple and familiar. Newcomen's engine was a glorified suction pump. His atmospheric engine was designed to pump water out of deep coal mines and keep them from flooding, it was relatively safe and fairly effective, but its voracious appetite limited its use. To harness a power greater than atmospheric pressure, to make an efficient engine, meant that scientists and technologists had to pass outside the limits of theoretical mechanics and explore the unknown territory of thermodynamics. This reflects the change from a merchant age, in which trade dominated, to the new economy of industry, whose chief concern was production. In its turn, industry made demands on the whole society.

Out of clock and watch-maker shops came a noteworthy number of master craftsmen. In these artisans skill and science were happily wedded. Some started as apprentices; some began elsewhere as simple weavers and only realized their inborn talents when they gravitated to these shops where the work satisfied at once their intellectual capacities and their manual adroitness. Some learned by trial and error, while others solved problems after long, acute, and original analysis. However arrived at, their contributions were brilliant. It was the mathematical-instrument makers who incorporated known scientific principles in many kinds of tools, and this implementation, in turn, led to the formulation of new principles. The terms within which they worked were those of accuracy, and played a decisive role in establishing the quantitative basis of modern research and industry. For they understood that precision is an ideal; it manifests itself as a dynamic process to be pursued, and this pursuit in itself forms an integral part of research. Precision is a goal; measurement is a means.

Among these instrument makers, some names occur again and again. John Graham, watchmaker and inventor, financed out of his own private funds Harrison's first chronometer; he made the zenith sector with which the Astronomer Royal, Bradley, discovered aberration of light and the nutation of the earth's axis. The Dollonds—the father, John, the son, Peter—whose genius expressed itself in astronomy and optics, constructed the standard heliometer and contributed to the invention of achromatic lenses which restored confidence in the refractory telescope. There were Jesse Ramsden and John Ellicott, who devised pyrometers to measure the thermal expansion of metals, and recorded for use and study spectacularly minute changes; and the versatile John Smeaton, best remembered for his plan for building the Eddystone Lighthouse that outlived the rock on which it was built. It is among these men that James Watt (1736–1819) belongs—men who combine the intellectual grasp of the scientist with the manual creativity of the mechanic.

The story of Watt's discovery of the steam condenser has been told many times—that dramatic moment of solution as he himself recalled it: "I had gone for a walk on a fine Sabbath afternoon. I had entered the Green and passed the old washing house. I was thinking of the engine at the time. I had gone as far as the herd's house when the idea came into my mind that as steam was an elastic body it would rush into a vacuum and if a connection were made between the cylinder and an exhausting vessel, it might there be condensed without cooling the cylinder. . . . I had not walked farther than the Golf-House when the whole thing was arranged in my mind."

Just two years before that afternoon, Watt had had his first contact with a Newcomen engine; only then had he been introduced to the whole problem of steam power. The year was 1763. He had been called on to repair a model of the engine that belonged to the University of Glasgow, which he served as instrument maker. It was easy enough to get the model to work, but Watt was appalled at the hopeless waste of steam, of fuel. He talked the matter over with Dr. Joseph Black, who, at that time, was engaged in experiments that led to his formulation of latent heat (that is, the amount of heat involved when a substance changes its form—when water turns into steam or, conversely, into ice). From Black, Watt understood the heart of the problem: in the Newcomen engine the jet of water chilled the cylinder as it condensed the steam, and thus much steam was used just to reheat the cylinder. But it was two years before the idea of a separate condenser flashed into Watt's mind. A few days later he had contrived a test model, using a surgeon's large brass syringe for the steam cylinder and piston; it worked beautifully. Here, in principle, was the engine that would replace the hundreds of inefficient Newcomen pumps; here was the answer for which the coal and iron masters had been pressing. It only remained for Watt to make an engine, a full-scale working engine.

That simple step lay beyond his power. Precision tools for large and heavy work had not yet been invented—he found it impossible to make something as simple as a cylinder two feet long and six inches in diameter. He could not find mechanics who could follow his specifications; the cost of tools and materials became too much for him. At this point Dr. Black introduced him to John Roebuck, a pioneer large-scale manufacturer, whose Carron Ironworks were the first of their kind in Scotland. For Roebuck, Watt's engine had become a necessity; his Newcomen pumps were disastrously inadequate, the coal mines that fed his great ironworks were seriously threatened. Roebuck paid off the debts that Watt had incurred, and together they took out the patent of 1769.

They expected to be able to produce Watt's engine by using a boring machine that John Smeaton, the outstanding engineer of that day, had designed for the manufacture of cannon at the Carron Ironworks; but although it made satisfactory cannon it did not give a true cylinder. The piston could not be made tight, though it was wrapped "around with cork, oiled rags, tow, old hats, paper, and other things . . . still there were open spaces left, sufficient to let the air in and the steam out." Smeaton frankly acknowledged to the Society of Engineers that "neither the tools nor workmen existed that could manufacture so complex a machine with sufficient precision." Even Roebuck's resources of materials and skill and money were unavailing; they were unable to make the engine. His coal pits remained flooded, he was submerged in debt; in 1774 he sold his share of the patent. Watt left Scotland taking the ill-fated model he had tried to construct, and went to Soho, Birmingham, where a new partner, Matthew Boulton, was waiting.

Boulton and Watt! They made engines to satisfy a steam-mad world. The first, commercially built, was made in 1777 for the ironmaster John Wilkinson. And this was proper, for it was Wilkinson who had hit upon the answer to the problem presented by the manufacture of a cylinder, the answer that neither Watt nor Smeaton had found: he made the first metal-cutting tool able to perform large work with tolerable accuracy. By his contribution he ended the search that had led from Newcomen to Watt, from the atmospheric engine to the steam engine; his solution was possible because during the same long decades immense advances had been made in the coal and iron industries.

The first giant steps in the new order of production were made by Watt, Wilkinson, and others like them. Not only did they open new avenues of industry, but the story of their success touched the imagination of the poor man and the worker. Surely never before had men of enterprise and intelligence and native worth passed so swiftly from poverty to riches, from obscurity to fame.

The details of the peace that concluded the American Revolution traveled no faster than did the notices of Boulton and Watt's new patents granted the year before (1782) for the double-acting and rotative engines. By this the engine's strength was no longer confined to the raising of a pump rod; now it could turn a factory wheel, soon it would turn a carriage wheel. For, as Jefferson described the engine to friends at home, anything was possible now that a peck and a half of coal performed as much work as a horse in a day.

An epoch, a society, a nation were newly born. Of the revolution in industry, the social implications spread faster and reached further than did the machines on which it was predicated. To many young Americans the new order was a call for preparation.

Such a one was Eli Whitney.

His progenitors included precision-instrument mechanics like Watt, Graham, Bird, the Dollonds, and Ramsden; inventors of industrial tools—Smeaton and Wilkinson, Bramah and Maudslay, Bentham and Brunel; industrialists like the Darbys, Arkwright, Wedgwood, and Boulton. In this same sense a line of descent runs straight from Whitney to Henry Ford, from mass production of muskets to mass-produced automobiles. Whitney was what is today called an engineer—but at a time when that ancient word had not yet received its modern definition. He was a contemporary of other American inventors—Oliver Evans, Thomas Blanchard, and Robert Fulton.

But more than those of any of his contemporaries, his inventions changed forever the economy of his country.

The Village Schoolmaster

I GAVE a phil. Lect. Examd & admitted a Freshman." Thus the Reverend Ezra Stiles, president
of Yale, summed up a day's activity in his diary. The importance of
the day lay elsewhere: "G. Wash. inaugurated & proclaimed at N
York." The date was April 30, 1789. The freshman was Eli Whitney.
He had had his twenty-third birthday the previous December and
was, with one exception, the oldest member of the freshman class.

What the slow process of Whitney's awareness of his own capabilities was, how the hidden ferment of his hopes took form and
direction, cannot be traced. At one moment in his sister's recollections he is busy with his chores and special undertakings on his
father's farm; then, of a sudden, there is mention of his firm resolve
to undergo years of schooling to prepare himself for Yale. He confided to no diaries, and only the wildest surmise would presume to
retrace the lost outlines of a unique personality, maturing in another
age and a different society.

The known facts are few and bare of details. It was in the autumn
of 1783—the Revolution was over, peace had been signed—that
Whitney, close to eighteen, announced his intention of studying
for college. He was not sucked into the cyclone of Shays' Rebellion
that three years later ripped through Worcester County. His nature
did not respond to what to him seemed bitter and excitable, rash and
improvident. A college education was the one road that would lead
out of Westborough.

Today he would have driven straight for an institute of technology. Ideas as ideas played no part in his world. Speculative thinking, excursions into the current writings on psychological and social

problems, reading for curiosity's sake, did not detain him. His letters to his lifelong friend Josiah Stebbins explained what he had done or what he planned; they detailed the uneasy state of his health; bemoaned the long hard hours of work, the endless business trips, the lack of time for casual, friendly visiting; occasionally they revealed his moods and demands on life; they always included some light, graceful reference to his unattached heart, to town trivia.

"Brother Eli was I think nineteen before I heard him say anything about having a liberal education. It was some months before he could obtain Fathers consent that he might go to Leicester [Academy]. He went to Leicester early in the spring and if I mistake not he was twenty years old the December before. About this time Eli began to teach school with good success. He taught three winters before he went to New Haven. . . . While he was at Leicester he made an engagement with one of the schollars to try which would be foremost in their studies at the end of the next quarter. When the vacation commenced instead of coming home he went to Mendon to study with Mr. Alexander, was there nearly four weeks before we knew where he was. He applied himself so intensely to his studies that it brought on the Hypo and he wrote wishing Father to send one of the boys to bring him home. He staid at home one week and then went to Leicester. At this time in addition to his other studies he was striving to find something which would produce perpetual motion. . . . When he was nearly fit for colledge he engaged some of his friends to intercede with Father concerning his education. The Preceptor told Father he did not acquire the languages with as much ease as some did but he was an excellent schollar and ought by all means to go to colledge. Our Step mother was determined to do all that was in her power to prevent Father from giving his consent. . . . From the commencement to the close of his education he had trials to encounter which few would be able to surmount."

Was it the thousand dollars his stepmother knew would be spent that was at the core of her opposition? That thousand dollars, if he got it, would pay for his years at college—he still had to provide for the years of preparation. By accident he found the path that led circuitously and leisurely to New Haven. The neighboring town of Grafton advertised for a schoolmaster. The next day he went there on a horse borrowed from his father, was accepted by the selectmen, and returned home to announce triumphantly that he had been hired and was to get $7 a month and his board. Many years later he remembered his father's astonishment at his presumption in supposing himself qualified to teach. Why, he needed to go to school himself! Whitney agreed, but assured his father that if he worked hard during the three weeks before school opened, he would do very well. A calm competence won his point. He was vindicated when at the end of the year he was hired for the following winter. The money he had earned paid his tuition for the summer term at the Leicester Academy.

The scholastic level of the new academies that mushroomed into life after the Revolution was not high. They lacked resources but not ambitions. Manifestations of the lofty feeling for democratic, secular education that swept the new nation, they were pitifully cramped by the limited resources of trained men and money available. Leicester, opened in June, 1784, by Ebenezer Crafts, a Yale graduate, began with three pupils. (It is most likely that he influenced Whitney to go to Yale rather than to Harvard, which was but half the distance from his home.) Ten years later the enrollment had grown, but it was still so poor that the principal and associate preceptor shared a bed in a small chamber over the Latin schoolroom. Stiles remarked that the "spirit for Academy making is vigorous. In this State are already erected [13] Academies. The Method is this, a House 40 feet long, 20 wide & one story high is built by subscription for one sometimes two Preceptors, who unite in teaching a *Latin & English School*—subjoyning Rehearsals, Dialogues, & Maps: a few may learn a little Geometry."

Teacher and pupil, Whitney alternated with the seasons, always studying, always learning, gaining assurance. From the ambitious, audacious beginner who was but three weeks ahead of his pupils to the aspiring freshman examined by Stiles, the steps can be measured as they rise. Among his papers he kept documents attesting his right to teach school. The first, dated Grafton, 1785 (the places in which he taught were less than a day's ride from home), notes that the selectmen approve him to be "a Suitable person to keep a Reading and writing School as it appears that he is qualified therefor."

How circumspect is the wording—for as yet he had not proved himself; but he satisfied the gentlemen and kept their school the following winter (1786). In January, 1787, the selectmen of Westborough recommend him "to be a Person suitably qualified to instruct a public school . . . for the purpose of teaching Children and Youth to read and write, and instructing them in Arithmetick." No longer need caution temper their approbation—and to his other teaching qualifications, arithmetic has been added.

That summer he returned to Leicester Academy. He had not engaged himself to teach the coming fall term; he stated the reason in a letter to his friend Josiah Stebbins, written that September: "I am for the most part desolate and pensive. . . . I meant to have entered N.H.C. [New Haven College—Yale] this fall but the want of Money stops the Mare." So the following October found him teaching at Paxton, whose selectman described him as "a Person endowed with, and possess'd of every Qualification and accomplishment requisite for a School-Master. And . . . do Recommend, Approbate and Authorize him to keep a public School for the purpose of teaching children & Youth to read and write & instructing them in the rules of Arithmetic." Hopkinston echoed this unstinting recommendation the following year (1788), and at the same time the Reverend Benjamin Conklin of Leicester advised that "Eli Whitney is a person of good Sober life & conversation and well qualified to keep a Grammar School—having acquired a good acquaintance with the Latin & Greek Languages, & also with the English Grammar—at Leicester Academy."

Teacher or pupil, the life was arduous, the hours long, the work unremitting. Rote was the only method known to educators; the rod was the constant corrective. The young men and women teaching country schools shared a commonplace experience, and the schools themselves were of a pattern. The scene and the content were always the same. A small one-room schoolhouse, its design as crude and standardized as a six-year child's drawing; the interior finished with lath and plaster; a modicum of light provided by two or three windows; the New England cold kept partially at bay by a huge fireplace, where usually a blaze had been started before class began. A wooden shelf, set about three feet high, was nailed around three sides of the room and served as a desk. Under it were back-less benches where thirty or forty boys and girls sat, their feet dangling above the icy floor. This bleak abode was the temple of the three R's.

Textbooks were few; slates did not exist, and the paper was dark and coarse—but was still preferred to birchbark, which occasionally was used. For reading, Benjamin Harris's *New England Primer* was widely known, but the Bible and the Psalter were basic and universal. Spelling came into the curriculum after Noah Webster published his *Speller* in 1783, and spelling bees were as festive and popular and exciting as are track meets today. Arithmetic limped along without a real textbook, and most children were content to stop when they had mastered the intricacies of long division; only a few, the most gifted, were introduced to "vulgar" fractions. Nicholas Pike's *New and Complete System of Arithmetic*, published in 1788, answered an important need; it included algebra, trigonometry, logarithms and conic sections. It also listed the dimensions and tonnage of Noah's Ark! Endorsed by college presidents and professors, it was blessed by George Washington himself; its sale, a patriotic promotion, was urged so that it "would save much money in the country, which would otherwise be sent to Europe."

Writing, an everyday name for the fine art of penmanship, was pursued with patience and artistic fervor. The style—the florid letters embellished with coils and curves and streaked with the rhythmic densities of upstroke and downstroke, swept along into a flowing line—matched the ornate rhetoric of the day. Pupils were advised that the essential equipment for writing consisted of "a pen-knife, quills, paper, good and free ink, likewise a flat ruler for sureness; and a round one for dispatch; with a leden Plummet or Pencil to rule lines; also gum sandrich powder with a little cotton dipped therein; which rub gently over the paper to make it bear the ink better."

In the teaching of writing, Whitney deviated from prescribed routines in only one detail. But this small deviation has a specially charged meaning. It was his sister, herself a teacher, who appreciated its pedagogical usefulness and saw how it presaged the future. "He kept a large quill cane," Elizabeth recorded, "in complete shape of a writing pen, *for a pattern for his pupils to copy and enjoin'd them to make their own pens."* (Italics ours.) Here is Whitney's own mark; his understanding that the success of a mechanical operation rests on the quality of the tools used—a well cut quill was the first step in good writing; his perception that if each pen conformed to a perfect model a uniform standard could be achieved and maintained by every pupil; his experience that had taught him how by repetitive copying of the model even the most unskilled would in time become adept.

Nothing in Whitney's haphazard entries made while teaching at Hopkinston reveals the teacher. They indicate that he had his share of disobedient students and difficult parents and that for having kept school there for seven weeks and four days the selectmen paid him $7 in cash and gave their note—dated a fortnight ahead—for £2 10s. (Congress had recently changed the currency to dollars and cents from British pounds and shillings and pence; it took time for the new units to become acclimated.) Brief notations suggest the ceremony that graced his last afternoon as teacher. He had invited the parents. "We had a Spelling Match, Red &c &c— After pronouncing a benediction &c &c I bade farewell. It was rather a moving scene—not an Eye in House but was moisten'd."

A few days later, having raised enough money by subscription to continue school another month, the selectmen asked Whitney to return. "But my circumstances being that I could not keep it [school] even to oblige—gave them an answer in the negative—non aliud." The Latin phrase, so casually used, is both a clue to his next step and proof that he was ready to take it.

The previous July, unexpectedly, there had been a crisis in Whitney's efforts to secure his father's consent. A crisis and an understanding. He had gone home "in order to arrange his affairs," wrote Elizabeth. "Our people were engaged in getting hay. One very warm day Eli was at work among the hay when by a sudden change in the weather he took a violent cold and was seized with pain in his limbs all night and the next day. . . . on the shin bone of one leg a small puff was seen and soon became swoln. Eli was so much more comfortable in three or four days that he rode out to visit me—I was at this time a mile or two from home teaching a school—and by this means he renewed his cold." His leg infection got rapidly worse, "after some weeks it was opened—the bone scraped . . . symptoms were unfavorable. His countenance wore the appearance of a person in deep consumption. . . . I believe it was six or seven weeks we were afeared he would study no more. My being absent the first part of his illness, nursing devolved on Hannah [the silly stepsister]. This with the ill humor of our Step mother was very trying to him and he was some times grossly neglected. One instance I will mention."

And then, without again resorting to adjectives, Elizabeth gives the full mean measure of their stepmother. Eli was still very weak and still in bed. "He felt the need of some refreshment. Directions were left for him to take medicine once an hour. . . . he knocked and knocked again, became weary. . . . All this time no one was in the house but our Step mother and her daughters Hannah and Nancy. After being alone five hours and a half, he heard Father come home. He knocked. Father went to his chamber. He told Father how he had been neglected and said he could not endure it." Those last words she must have remembered as they came straight out of her brother's heart. "Father gave them a close lecture and commanded them to do better for the futer."

Elizabeth dismissed her school early; she had been told to come home to nurse her brother so that he might be strong and fit to start college.

After all this, it seems almost unnatural that Eli would write in every letter addressed to his father, "Please give my Duty to Mama —my compliments to my Brothers and Sisters [he placed Hannah and Nancy side by side with his own Elizabeth]," or, "My respects to Mama." Yet such words were expected and natural in the world in which he grew up. In those days the family was patriarchal in size and authority; it took its form and received its sanction from the Old Testament. Eli understood the problem his father had faced: he knew how well-nigh impossible it was for a man with four young children and a sizable farm to carry on successfully without a wife. The father's second marriage to a woman slightly older—he was but thirty-nine and she forty-two—with a large brood of her own, was dictated by motives far different from those that prompted his marriage to Elizabeth Fay, the neighbor's daughter with whom he had grown up. Now choice and courtship were not involved; this was a partnership. The measure of Eli's love for his father made it possible for Eli to accept his stepmother and, by showing her respect, to give his father the love he felt.

On March 4, 1789, he started from home early in the morning for "Durham in Connecticut—rode in the sligh with my Father—we arrived at Capt. Hitchcock's in Brookfield in the evening of the Same Day where we stay'd over Night. The Slighing being poor he returned back and left me to wait for the stage—payd all expense—left me the Dollars and bid me good by." The triumphant meaning of the last phrase is clear: at the very last moment, when the time had come for Whitney to present himself for examination, his father had given his promise—and dollars—to pay the college expenses.

Whitney had never been farther than a long day's ride from Westborough, for all his schooling and teaching, until he said goodbye to his father. He waited at Captain Hitchcock's tavern—most innkeepers seem to have been officers in the Revolutionary Army—for the stage that was to carry him to Durham and, after a stay there, to New Haven. The ride he was to take carried him much farther than those towns, it carried him to college and, later, to friendship with the great and important in all states along the seaboard. He said goodbye to the life and horizons of the village and to his family and friends; for though he returned there once a year, he returned as a visitor.

Behind him also was the teaching he had done to pay his tuition at Leicester Academy; for the next years he would be a student, dependent on his father for his college fees. He had learned all that Leicester could teach him; it was a beginning, adequate but elementary.

Whitney was one of the few who had learned a little geometry, but evidently this little did not satisfy him. Before going to Yale, he spent a short term at Durham with the Reverend Elizur Goodrich, one of the country's outstanding mathematicians. A member of Yale Corporation, Goodrich had tied Stiles for the college presidency in 1777 and had withdrawn in favor of Stiles. They remained close friends. Goodrich was esteemed by Stiles to be "an excellent and great scholar, one of the greatest of American Literati," a man whose outstanding attainments in diverse fields entitled him to fill "the double office of Prof. of Divinity & Prof. of Mathematics. . . . I think his indifferent Elocution prevented his choice."

Elocution, as Stiles used the word, meant a facile, effective oral communication. Stiles's own inaugural address, delivered in Latin with great animation, was remembered by Chancellor Kent as "a short but brilliant sketch of the entire circle of the arts and sciences." Goodrich lacked the gift of free and easy words—the gift that brings kudos and the reward of high office to its possessor. Whitney himself was not a man who spoke glibly. He spoke well—a simple, persuasive manner, a well reasoned argument—when he had something to say and knew whereof he spoke. He did not need to be dazzled by brilliant speeches to know the quality of Goodrich's mind, and it is certain that Goodrich sensed his pupil's solid native intelligence; intellectually and humanly they understood each other, and Goodrich's son, Elizur, Jr., and Whitney, who were of an age, became lifelong friends.

Half the academic year was past when Whitney appeared for his entrance examination. It was long and thorough—it lasted, as was customary, from nine in the morning till past two in the afternoon. Stiles, "both a living polyglott and a living encyclopedia," probed to see if Whitney had been well schooled in Latin and Greek. Eli had to read, translate, and parse passages picked at random from the classics and demonstrate his ability to write true Latin (*non aliud*, as Whitney might have said himself!); he must show his mastery of English grammar and his familiarity with "vulgar" arithmetic; he must produce evidence of "a blameless life and conversation."

As important as the examination and his recommendations was the fact that Whitney had had some preparation under two men for whom Stiles had high regard. Any pupil whom Goodrich would allow to present himself at such a late date must be well qualified, and Whitney's previous work with the Reverend Caleb Alexander of Mendon—with whom Stiles often visited—also spoke in his favor. (Alexander became an outstanding educator, wrote Latin, Greek, and English grammars, and was instrumental in founding Hamilton College.) Stiles also appreciated Whitney's age, and knew how much an additional year's delay would mean. Whitney was admitted, one of forty-three men in the freshman class.

For this moment he had worked and studied five long years. Walking past the dormitories and churches, the shops and houses, he could sense something of the urbanity and culture that made New Haven delightful and different from anything he had known. The physical aspects were soon seen and judged; the intangibles would disclose themselves much later—his great fortune in having Stiles as his intellectual guide, the enduring friendships he was to make at Yale, friendships that would serve him well at decisive moments in his career.

Had Whitney remained the sturdy farmer, his special gifts might have died for want of a chance. His college degree made it impossible to dismiss him as a clever mechanic—the word "engineer" had not yet received status—and his Yale education was invariably mentioned in the introductions he carried from influential friends to important personages. Not being a minister, lawyer, politician, or merchant, unwilling to be placed in a category that disparaged his vision and slighted his capabilities, Whitney created his own classification and dressed it in commanding apparel.

IV   *The Yale Years*

NEW HAVEN in 1785 unanimously conferred the freedom of the city on "ten French Personages at Paris." Among them were the Duc de la Rochefoucauld, the eminent lawyer Target, and the Marquis de Condorcet. Three years later Condorcet wrote his *Lettres d'un Bourgeois de New-Heaven.* This was no claim to celestial citizenship, nor a plea for Utopia—it was a case of bad spelling.

The happy temper of New Haven was noted by many travelers. Though its population was under four thousand, it was not a small town, remote and provincial. Its harbor was filled with ships of shallow draft that poked into every trading inlet along the coast; packets sailed weekly to New York, and passage could be had for $2.50. Trade carried enterprising New Haven men to Spanish ports and Chinese cities, to the Canadian wilderness and far-off Batavia— the horizons of New Haven were as wide as its commerce. Lying between New York and Boston, just where the roads forked to Hartford and New London, the town entertained many distinguished visitors. Jefferson passed through to his post as American ambassador to France; Franklin received an honorary degree from Yale; Washington stopped on his tour of the eastern states; John Adams, newly elected Vice President, was escorted into town by a cavalcade of chaises, and presented with the freedom of the city.

Settled in the heart of the town, the college attracted bright, ambitious young men from every state; their diverse backgrounds gave the town a national flavor as their studies and interests brought worlds removed in time and space into daily conversation. The rich curriculum seeped out into community activities and gave them an intellectual piquancy. In New Haven the seasons were underscored by the ceremonies and rituals, the semesters and vacations, of the college calendar. A cordial town, it was always ready for the unexpected. The unusual mixture of carnival and college, of science, patriotism, and religion, has been wonderfully preserved in the great diary of Ezra Stiles.

"A spherical air Balloon, eleven feet in Diam, was let off from Chapel Street in this City. It took fire in its ascent, and being converted into a great Pyramid of flame at it greatest height, exhibited a grand & pleasant object to the Spectators, who had only to regret that the same spectacle was not shown in the night. It was decorated with the figure of an Angel flying, in one hand bearing a Trumpet, & with the other displaying the flag of the United States, and the motto Nil Intentatum nostri liquere was affixed to it in seven different languages—viz Latin, Greek, Hebrew, Chaldee, Arabic, French & German—& I think in English." Such a population had every right to expect great learning from their ministers and teachers.

In those days Nature itself put on marvels almost as fantastic. Benjamin Silliman, whose name is synonymous with the early teaching of science, remembered that when he was a student (1795) the sky would be filled with "flocks of pigeons which screen the sun's light and darken the air; [they] fly continuously hour after hour, their number being beyond estimation, and when they alight for the night by their weight break down the branches of large forest trees, strew the ground with the ruins and fill the air with the sound of their cooing, and their various notes and the rustling of their wings sounding like thunder. . . . I once saw when in college a flight of pigeons passing over New Haven so dense and continuous for many hours . . . [that] as I stood in the gallery of the steeple of the chapel, I could almost seize them by their feet as they brushed along by the buildings, apparently fearless of men."

A modern, looking at New Haven as Whitney first saw it, would be prepared for most of the physical differences—the compactness of the little city, the houses wherein a man lived and carried on his business, the absence of paved sidewalks and streets, of sewers, running water, and street lights. Only the Green, that seems to have been rolled out of the great forest, would cause astonishment and dismay. In those days it was half level, half sloping, cluttered with tombstones and naked of trees. It was not until 1796 that James Hillhouse gave the Green its present beauty; he plowed it level, girdled it with elms, and removed the burial grounds to the northeast corner of town. A casual visitor of Whitney's time, Henry Wansey, described New Haven as a "very neat pleasant town . . . [that] has a large area or market place in the centre, one hundred yards square. Three wide streets, parallel to each other lead from it on each of the four sides. There are four churches of the Presbyterian persuasion, one Episcopalian chapel, and a Methodist meeting. Many handsome well-looking houses, though chiefly built of wood, and separated by a court or garden from its neighbour; a very sandy soil, the situation low and flat. The society of the town is particularly agreeable and pleasant; many men of liberal education residing there . . . Pierpoint Edwards, Mr. Hillhouse. . . . I went over to College, which stands in the market place." Wansey's shrewd eye noted that the best houses in the state belonged to lawyers—surely a loud invitation to the most ambitious to enter the law.

Yale, as Whitney knew it, consisted of five buildings along the West side of the Green: the hundred-foot three-story severe, barrack-like dormitory, Connecticut Hall, built in 1752; the president's house and the house for the professor of divinity; the chapel, which later as the Atheneum sheltered in two upper rooms the library and the museum containing the scientific equipment, or "philosophical apparatus"; and the dining hall and kitchen, new but dingy, and already badly in need of repairs.

Around the buildings ran "a close fence of panneled boards, painted red and relieved by cross strips of white." This fence enclosed the college square, which was filled with a "grotesque group, generally of undesirable establishments, among which was a barn, a barber's shop, several coarse taverns or boarding houses, a poorhouse and a house of correction, and the public jail with its prison yard; the jail being used alike for criminals, for maniacs and debtors. Being very near the college, the moans of the innocent prisoners, the curses of the felons, and the shrill screams and wild laughter of the insane were sometimes mingled with the sacred songs and with the voice of prayer, rising from the academic edifices."

The library had about 2,700 volumes—about the size of John Adams's private collection—but almost a third of the books were obsolete, having been given by Dean Berkeley in 1733; the rest were in deplorable condition. But the library could boast that its copy of the *Principia* had been presented by Sir Isaac Newton himself. The charge for use of the books varied from nine cents a month for a folio to a penny for a pamphlet; it was double for all books which were "recited."

For the museum Stiles had purchased several important items—a three-foot telescope, a micrometer, and an orrery—which arrived from England during Whitney's sophomore year. They took their place beside an air pump, a whirling table, an electrical machine, a quadrant, a theodolite, the mechanical powers, a spouting fountain, and a collection of miscellaneous articles. Such instruments, as Silliman recalled them, "were sufficient to excite our wonder and procure some reputation for the College, especially in pneumatics, mechanics and electricity." "Mechanical powers" include those fundamental mechanical contrivances based on the principles of the lever or the inclined plane. To the first belong the lever, the wheel and axle, cord and pulley, and toothed wheels; to the latter, the inclined plane, the wedge, and the screw. Visitors came to see these marvels and have them explained. Especially popular were the "miscellaneous articles," which included Indian helmets curiously woven with feathers, two large mammoth "teeth," twenty-two inches in diameter, that had been found along the Ohio River, beautifully spotted South American snake-skins eighteen feet long, an Indian calumet, a young alligator preserved in spirits, weapons and fishing gear from Nootka Sound, bark cloth from Tahiti, several pieces of asbestos found in the neighborhood, and other oddities gathered from all over the world.

To Whitney the library and the museum were banquet tables spread with new and nourishing foods on which his special talents fed. One of the items he always treasured was the *Catalogue of Books in the Library of Yale-College* in which is inscribed, "The Authority of the College induced by the esteem and regard which they have for Mr. Eli Whitney, Junior Sophister, present this valuable pamphlet for the trifling consideration of nine pence lawful money."

This was written and signed by Ezra Stiles, Praeses, to which were added the signatures of the tutors Ebenezer Fitch, Amos Bassett, and Ebenezer Gay. The copy would indicate that Whitney had already been marked as unusual and that he had been noteworthy in his use of the library.

Veneration and solemn awe gripped the Yale students at the mere sight of the Reverend Ezra Stiles. Silliman recalled that "no matter whether in rain or snow, in winter's cold or in hot sunbeams . . . we always approached the presidential presence *uncovered*, and with a distinct and guarded reverence . . . which ill accorded, however, with the peculiarly kind and cordial feelings of one of the mildest and best of men." These emotions are shared by any modern who visits him day after day in the volumes of his *Diary*. His portrait with its white full-bottomed wig and black clerical frock bears the uniform minted look of New England divines of that period. It is not his face that attracts the reader, nor his manner—that special blend of the worldly man who is at once polite and aloof, hospitable and formal, instructive and charming, rarely personal, and always quick to garb his emotions in quiet dress. It is with his mind, his ranging, avid curiosity, that admiration comes. It is with his spacious interests, his continuous peregrinations, his prodigious correspondence, that admiration yields to wonder.

Stiles is not a man to live with easily, in spite of an engaging manner and an entertaining speech. He is too active, too energetic, too unrelenting in his intellectual pursuits. Yet he is human. His daughters, Betsy, Polly, and Ruthy, and his seafaring son Isaac, wander in and out of the pages in an aura of parental solicitude. He had hesitated to accept the presidency because "a hundred and fifty or 180 Young Gentlemen students, is a bundle of Wild Fire not easily controlled and governed—and at best the Diadem of a president is a Crown of Thorns." He was a cleric, head of a denominational college, yet he appointed Josiah Meigs, the first layman to enter the Yale faculty, to the professorship of mathematics and natural philosophy. This might have been expected of a clergyman who could record: "Good Friday. Reading Cavallo on Electricity." A member of the American Philosophical Society, he was friendly with the great in America: he corresponded with Franklin on electricity and faith;

Rittenhouse immediately informed him of Herschel's discovery of the planet Uranus; and Jefferson received for Stiles, as for Franklin and Madison, the volumes of the *Encyclopédie* as they appeared.

Temperamentally, Stiles had no sympathy for the mass hysteria produced by revivalists; his contempt for the famous Reverend Joseph Bellamy was based on a considered opinion that the latter "had not arrived to the first Eminence for real Erudition. His numerous noisy Writings have blazed their day, & one Generation will put them to sleep." Stiles used the word "erudition" with authority. Meigs lists his linguistic attainments: "He had a thorough knowledge of the Hebrew, Greek and Latin languages," and had made great progress "in the knowledge of the Samaritan, Chaldee, Syriac, and Arabic. On the Persic and Coptic he bestowed some attention. The French he read with facility." A man of many parts, he had noble standards; he was a stern humanitarian who tried to lift the yokes fastened by ignorance and intolerance, by greed and superstition, by blind orthodoxy and savage guilt.

Ezra Stiles was a finished product of the eighteenth century, its enlightenment and humanism; he also reflected the tolerance and elegance of the wealthy Newport trading community. In his person he summed up the erudition and ethics of his day and world; he was the funnel through which the newest ideas and most noteworthy work being done in Europe and America found its way into Whitney's mind and gave body and authority to his way of thinking.

There is something essentially modern about the demands Whitney made on a college education. In part—and most acutely realized—college was a social gesture. He aimed to learn there the language of the gentry, to become acquainted with the cultural baggage to which casual reference is made in polite conversation, and to gain the social ease conferred by such familiarity. He conformed eagerly in the telling details of dress and deportment, and cultivated an elegant handwriting. This nice attention to externals was retained all his life; his letters to his nephews reveal the man who has labored consciously to better himself. In larger part, he went to college to learn facts systematically grouped into scientific disciplines that have practical applicability. He thought he was preparing himself for a lawyer's career, but he offered that information tentatively, without enthusiasm; for still unknown to himself, his ambitions and his talents were preparing themselves for another future.

Of Whitney's student activities a few scattered references remain. Soon after his admission he was "scribe" for the Linonian Society, which, with the other academic society, the Brothers in Unity, was open to all students. These were essentially book-buying clubs, and members had access to the library of each; they also had meetings at which "dramatical Exhibitions," orations, disputations, and other entertainments took place. Membership was open to all; but to belong to the Phi Beta Kappa was a matter of election by the society, and a measure of a student's popularity. In those days Phi Beta Kappa, the oldest of the Greek-letter societies, was merely a social fraternity; it had not yet become the non-secret group selected for scholarship. Whitney was elected on November 28th and initiated on December 8, 1791.

The following year Stiles asked Whitney to pronounce the public "Funeral Oration upon his classmate Grant, who died in Georgia. . . . He was the fourth that has died out of that Class." Stiles found "the Oration was well delivered." *The Oration on the Death of Mr. Robert Grant, Member of the Senior Class in Yale-College, Connecticut, Who died on the fourth of April 1792, Aetat. XXIII, by Eli Whitney, A Classmate of the Deceased,* was published at the request of the class to whom it was affectionately inscribed. It is Whitney's only published writing; its overblown, pious phrases and rhetorical pastillage reveal nothing about Whitney, except to show that he had mastered that idiom of oratory and was considered a leader in his class.

Money, a desperate need for money, is the theme that fills Whitney's letters during his stay at Yale. "I am, Sir," he writes his father, "in the most streightened circumstances. Depending on your sending me some money, long ago I made engagements which ought, long since to have been fulfilled, & must be fulfilled immediately. . . . I was determined to come home if I did not hear from you, before, but those to whom I am indebted say they cannot & will not wait till then. . . . I am now preparing for examination and it will lay me under great disadvantage to come home this spring. . . . I have succeeded very well in my studies, & meet with no other difficulties but the want of money, which indeed is very great. But I conclude that my Father will do everything for me that lies in his power."

And his father did. Not only did he send him money—"I have deposited the sum of twenty-five pounds to be forwarded the first Safe Conveyance"—but he tried to help him save every possible expense: "I want you should Send Back by the Same man a letter wheather you Shall com hom at Commencement [that was for the long six weeks' vacation] and wheather you want I Should com up and fich you a horse or what you think will be Cheapest or the best way to do." The father was harassed by the pressure to raise funds. "You wrote me you are in want of money—I Cant Send any at present. . . . I wish you to write and let me know how littel money you can do with. I have Laid out to have Sum money by the first of September for you, but you must do with as little as you can between now and then." He was apprehensive and skeptical about additional outlays: "As to your profession my advice is to look forward and count the Cost before you plan on bilding and Consider your Surcomstances for I shall not be able to help you much after you are through College."

The father's misgivings about his son's college venture found still another outlet—he had qualms lest his son subscribe to the current "infidelity and atheism which were then piously proclaimed," a lapse which the leading clergymen blamed on the French Revolution. "Godless atheist" was the indiscriminate charge hurled at those who questioned the existing order and defended the right of the French people to have their own revolution. "You say in Your letter," his father cautioned Whitney, "that among the Clarge their is a grate many Hypocrites. We must not, whatever our Ocupation is, excuse our Selvs and have no religon at all because others mak a bad Use of it—but we ought to Esteem it the higher."

To farmers who lived comfortably but to whom cash was scarce, the college expenses were high. They were figured on a basis of four ten-week periods. The necessary items alone totaled $130 to $140 a year, and bills had to be paid within a fortnight; otherwise, interest charges were added. Instruction was $33, to which were added classroom charges of $2.40 for "ordinary repairs and contingencies," $1.30 for wood to heat the recitation rooms, and about $10 for the use of books and stationery. The living costs included $5 for a room in Connecticut Hall, $3 for sweeping up, making the beds, and general damages (broken windows, torn bedding), $8 for light and fuel (candles and wood), and another $5 for the use of bed and bedding. (The pupils bought their own chairs, mirror, washbasin, andirons, and bellows—New Haven always had a brisk trade in secondhand furnishings.) Board in the Commons cost $1.60 a week, and laundry might run as high as $3 a quarter; the treasurer's bill was about $50 and class taxes another $5. These were the fixed sums that had to be met; to these were added: Linonian or Brothers in Unity Society dues; traveling expenses, pocket money, commencement expenses, and a minimum expenditure for clothes. College men were expected to dress well. A wardrobe must include a pair of pantaloons made of mixed cotton and wool, linsey-woolsey, very fashionable, cheap, and well adapted to the season ($8); shoes ($2), and a waistcoat and a pair of cambric handkerchiefs ($5).

To meet these expenses, Whitney had the $1,000 promised him by his father—not in a lump sum, but when he could spare the cash; the remainder he tried to earn "by his own industry and ingenuity." A friend who knew him at this period remembers how "he received a dollar from many young men who had more money and less industry than himself for coloring the outlines and divisions in the maps of Guthry's Geography (the Geog'y then studied in College). At the close of the College term those Geographies which were thus colored commanded a higher price than others." Unable to bridge the entire spread between income and outgo, Whitney "still had pecuniary embarrassments to struggle with after paying the College bills with the last remittance made by his Father. He gave *Notes* for his debts in the town and reserved the remainder to enable him to go to South Carolina to engage in the duties of Private Tutor in a gentleman's family with a salary of Eighty guineas a year."

It is not difficult to present a fairly accurate financial schedule of Whitney's college education; what is difficult is to see where he found enough time for the extracurricular work that brought in the needed dollars. The day's activities were long and the hours rigidly allocated. In winter the wakening bell sounded at five-thirty, in spring and summer a half-hour earlier. The students had to light their fires, run

downstairs to the pump (perhaps through the snow), wash, get
dressed, and be in the chapel by six for prayers. After an hour's service they recited prepared lessons and only at eight breakfasted on
toast, coffee and, generally, oyster stew. From nine to eleven they
studied in their rooms for the second recitation. Then came dinner
and after that a lone hour to relax—"playtime" it was called—more
study in their rooms for the third recitation period at four; evening
prayers, supper, and further study for the prebreakfast recitation.
All study in the rooms was closely supervised by the tutors, who
constantly made rounds to see that students were busy.

Strenuous as was the students' routine, that of the teaching staff was
heroic; the teaching load for about 125 students was borne by the
president, one professor, and three tutors. The last coached the students in Greek, Latin, and English grammar; the elements of "chronology and history"; geography, composition, and public speaking;
"syllogistic disputation"; and Vincent's *Explanation of the Catechism.*
Stiles himself carried the major lecturing assignment.

A few notations from the *Diary* haphazardly chosen during Whitney's student years give the preparation he received in science and
law. "Senior Class finished reciting Montesquieu's *Spirit of Laws.*
. . . A Latin Oration, a forensic Disputation whether Authors ought
to be invested with Copy Right? . . . Lecture on the 3 learned Professions [ministry, law, and medicine] . . . Lecture on Laws: 1.
Laws of Nature & Nations; 2. Jus Civile or ancient Roman Law, Pan-
dects [complete digests] Imperatorial Edicts, & Eccl. or Canon Law;
3. Laws of Englnd; Common Law, statutes, Courts of Westminster,
Reports; 4. Laws of the United States." Both the legal principles and
his training in debating were to be used by Whitney in his fight for
the patent rights of his cotton gin.

Science was systematically surveyed. "I gave a public lecture in
Chapel, beginning a Description of the Encyclopedia or Circle of the
Sciences. Beginning with Language or Philology . . . I delivered a
Philosophical Lecture upon the structure of the Eye & the Nature of
Vision . . . Lecture on Mathematics, particularly Arithmetic, Geom-
etry & Conic Sections . . . I gave a Lecture on the Astronomy of
Comets. . . . Lecture on Natural Philosophy—different kinds of at-
traction, Mechanical Powers, Laws of simple & compound motion,

Hydrostatics & Hydraulics, Central Forces, Optics, Electricity, Chemistry—especially Priestley's Expt. on fixt air, Impregnating water with it & thereby making artificial Spa water." (Carbonated water was a recent scientific accomplishment—Priestley thought it might cure scurvy.)

Whitney went home for the long vacation before graduation, and his sister remembers that "Father gave him money to pay his last bills. He gave [Father] his note of hand for the Bills and made use of the money to furnish himself for his future employment." Whitney faced special needs for commencement. He had to buy the proper clothes—a coat, a waistcoat, pantaloons and cotton shirt, slippers and silk stockings; he had to pay for his diploma and the parchment with its official blue silk ribbon; and he had to meet the class tax levied to pay for the commencement music, catalogue, and dinner. Always prudent, he had consulted President Stiles about work; he knew before he went home that he had secured a teaching position.

Commencement then was not part of the college term. It was held late in the summer vacation, when the close of harvest gave the rural state some leisure. In 1792 it was scheduled for the second Wednesday in September. Commencement was a brilliant drama, richly texted, built up out of separate acts and sideshows, presented with a profusion of prayers, processions, and solemn excitement. From the governor to the chorus of New Haven citizenry, from President Stiles to the youngest freshman, each had a role, with no line dividing actors from spectators.

On the Sunday prior to the Wednesday, the annual baccalaureate sermon was preached—an impressive service for an impressive audience that caught subtle allusions and followed involved theological argumentation whether given in English, Latin, or Greek. Early the following Tuesday afternoon the Phi Beta Kappa—Whitney among them—marched from the Court House to the Brick Church, where they listened to an oration; immediately afterward, picked students from each class delivered orations in English and Latin before a brilliant assemblage. That evening, Silliman remembers, "crowds of people assembled to view the illumination of the college windows and the dazzling pyrotechnics of mounting rockets and burning wheels, revolving with blazing coruscations, and fiery serpents flying through the air with comet trains, along the front line of the College yard." He recalls the forgotten prerogatives permitted different academic classes—the freshmen who previously "were not allowed to wear gowns nor to carry canes," now assumed their sophomoric rights and "ostentatiously paraded the College yard in close phalanx;" while the seniors walked singly, proudly, as befitted heroes, recognized by their "triangular hats, cocked in military style," the peculiar badge of the faculty.

To Whitney his commencement was a noble adieu to his sustained effort. To Stiles the commencement of 1792 was also significant. After protracted, delicate negotiations the State of Connecticut and Yale Corporation had reached an agreement: Yale was to have tax arrears of over $40,000 canceled; and for granting this pecuniary relief, as well as additional sums for a new building, designated members of the state government were made ex-officio members of the corporation. This commencement thus was not merely the traditional performance; it was the ushering in of a new régime, and had, as Stiles's program implies, a momentous excitement.

Special color graced the procession as State and Church marched side by side, pomp matching circumstance. The order of the procession had been meticulously arranged to assure that "due honor was accorded to each group." The column formed at nine in the morning and made its way from the Chapel to the Brick Meeting House, accompanied by a band of six musicians (imported from New York) with clarinets, French horns, and other instruments. The exercises included an anthem, an English oration, a forensic disputation, a Hebrew oration, an English dialogue, an English oration, a Greek dialogue, an English oration. A formal dinner was served in College Hall at which 140 were present. The afternoon was filled with "An English Oration by Mr. Tutor Basset on The great and happy Event of a Union of Civilians & Ecclesiastics in the Govt of the University, A Latin Oration on the same subject by the President, An English Oration by Mr. [Pierpont] Edwards, A Latin Valedictory Oration, Anthem & Musick." Prayer concluded the ceremonies, and at sunset the procession returned to the chapel. The great day was over.

It was when he returned to college for commencement that Whitney was told of a radical change that had to be made. He was not to go to New York; he was to go South.

The original teaching position had been too ephemeral for Elizabeth to remember rightly; what stayed in her memory was the final pressing need for money and the subsequent melancholy of unspoken farewells. Certainly she shared the anxieties which Whitney poured out in a letter to his brother Josiah, penned on September 25th, after he had agreed to go to South Carolina. "In four days I shall set out for South Carolina. . . . The climate is unhealthy and perhaps I shall lose my health and perhaps my life, but I hope to return to you again some time or other. Be a good Boy and do as you ought. . . . Long life, prosperity and happiness attend you for ever and ever Amen."

The following day, less dramatically, he wrote to his father: "I failed of the school, which I mentioned, in N. York. As soon as I arrived at New Haven the President told me that a Gentleman from S. Carolina had applied to him to recommend a suitable person for a Private Tutor in a family, that he had recommended me, that he thought it a good offer on the whole, I had better accept it. After mature consideration I have concluded to go. I shall go from here to N. York next Monday, from there I shall go to Savannah in Georgia, from there to the place of my destination, the name of which particular village I do not know. The climate of the Southern States is something unhealthy but I hope by temperance and Prudence to withstand it. If I should find my health declining, I shall return, if possible before it is too late. I shall live in a particular family where I am to have everything found me. I hope to save fifty Guineas Pr. Year besides my expenses, which is more than I can make in New England. If I should have good success I shall make something handsome, but I may have bad luck and loose all. The world is a Lottery in which many draw Blanks, one of which may fall to my share. . . . Going so great a distance is attended with many inconveniences and many advantages. I shall have the opportunity of seeing the Country, which is a consideration of some consequence. I can tell better when I get there how I shall succeed. Tho I by no means set out upon uncer-

ainties. I have agreed with Mr. P. Miller, a Gentleman from Connecticut, a man of reputation and abilities."

Why does self-pity streak wildly through one letter while the other
presents the same facts in reasonable words? They are dated a day
apart, yet nothing had intervened to cause the change. Events alone
could not explain the difference; events are precipitants that reveal
but do not explain the emotional chemistry. Whitney had achieved
his college education, and his rich talents lay unused, awaiting another goal. On Josiah, the brother from whose birth his mother had
never rallied, he fastened the anxiety the motherless boys shared, the
anxiety suddenly given power by the idea of Georgia. Georgia had
become to Whitney less a state than a graveyard. There his first Yale
tutor, Denison, and there just recently his close friend Grant, had
died. He did not stop to remember that both had left Yale mortally
ill and hopefully had traveled southward to a warmer climate.

His father, on the other hand, called forth his capacity for circumspect evaluation, for determination, for orderly, scheduled procedures; with his father were associated the realities of financial returns
and the obvious advantages of social connections. So much is clear.
What is not clear is Whitney's obvious failure to mention that "Mr.
P. Miller, a Gentleman from Connecticut," managed the estate of
the late General Nathanael Greene—a name needing no adjectives
of recommendation.

Mr. Miller had engaged Whitney, on behalf of a neighboring
South Carolinian planter, a Major Dupont, to tutor the Dupont chil-
dren. Young Whitney could travel to the South with Mr. Miller,
Mrs. Greene, and her family, whom he would meet in New York.

Mulberry Grove

WHITNEY's career immediately after graduation seems shadowed by the pathos of hopes vainly spent. He was almost twenty-eight, and for ten years had struggled for a college education. He had lifted himself out of Westborough and wrenched himself away from family, friends, and an habitual way of life—and now, like any youngster, he was irresolutely drifting into a teaching job. The prospect of being a tutor in a wealthy southern household did not attract him, but he had a living to make and hard times to face. "Col. Duer's failure for One Million Dollars or some high amount," the largest bankruptcy the country had as yet experienced, had precipitated a short, intense depression.

At the same time the prospect did not discourage him. Had he been really committed to the idea of studying law as the best way to realize his potentialities, his tenacity would have held him to that purpose. It was not the business slump that forced him into teaching, it was his own indecision; it was his way of marking time, of digesting what he had learned, of finding his own landmarks.

He boarded the New York packet with quiet resignation, and the trip lived up to his worst expectations. In later years, when he had made the journey many times, he must have remembered that initial voyage as a most bedevilled series of misadventures.

"I was very sea-sick after I left you on Tuesday," he wrote Stebbins from New York in the beginning of October, 1792. "At 2 oClock next morning our vessel ran on the rocks just below Hell-Gate. This I think was owing to the carelessness of our Capt. The tide was ebbing when we struck and at sunrise we were almost on our beam's end—at which time five of the passengers, including myself, went

46

on shore and procured a waggon to carry us to N. York, six miles from where we landed." A superstitious person might have seen in this mishap a warning, but Whitney sensed nothing ominous and walked straight into trouble. "Had been in the City but an hour or two," he continued, "before I met Sturges in the street and shook his hand, then perceived he was broke out full with the small-Pox. Saw several Stamford People, found it much less convenient and more expensive for me to take the infection at that Place, than I expected. After advising with Mr. Miller concluded to be enochulated here. . . . This is the fourth day since I was enoculated by Doct. Gogge-well who is famous here; he tells me it has taken tho' I feel no inconvenience from it yet."

The "Place" suggested by the "Stamford People" was probably one of the luxurious smallpox resorts. For a flat fee a person received inoculation and the proper medicaments—basilic powders and barley water acidulated with tamarinds—and, while waiting for the serum to work, the ladies and gentlemen enjoyed hunting, boating, and fishing, with dancing and singing in the evenings. It might have been Daniel Lee's elegant establishment on Ram Island or that on Duck Island run by John and Elisha Ely, who boasted they had not suffered a single loss in twenty-seven years. So fast had the treatment of smallpox progressed that efforts to control the scourge did not wait on Jenner's historic experiment with cowpox inoculation in 1796. Variolation (inoculating with serum obtained from a mildly infected human patient), though not as safe and simple as vaccination, had come into practice early in the eighteenth century. Gone were the days when the public had participated in pro- and anti-inoculation riots and men suspected of being carriers were tarred and feathered. Variolation became fashionable, a business of which it was said there were "millions in it."

Whitney, having decided against the Stamford establishment, was spending his time "partly in Mrs. Greene's family and the rest in viewing the City." He assured Stebbins, "I am more and more pleased with Mr. Miller and have reason to believe him one of the best of men." He might also have added that Mrs. Greene was the most understanding and generous of women. For in answer to a request from Whitney, now lost, she had directed Miller to promise either to advance him "the money for your passage, or become responsible for its payment after our arrival. So you will be able to proceed in the same packet with us."

When he finally, on October 17th, boarded the ship for Savannah, he had recovered from an extremely light case with "only a dozen pock and they will not all fill." Still fearful of "committing myself to the boisterous ocian," he exhorted Stebbins to pray that "God Almighty bless *you* and Land *me* safe in Georgia."

Nothing Whitney had studied at Yale would have prepared him for Catherine Greene. He had had friends: there was Josiah Stebbins—"from distant towns he and I first met as students at [Leicester] Academy"—to whom, down the years, he remained attached with loyal affection; there were his friends at Westborough, his companions at Yale, and his close association with New Haven families. Friendship, as Whitney knew it, was shaded by reserve; it had always been born of a community of interests that gradually developed an atmosphere of mutual trust and liking; it had been confined to men.

And now suddenly he met Catherine Greene, sociable, engaging, entertaining; a woman of the graceful, cosmopolitan world of Newport, Charleston, and Savannah. She possessed to a rare degree the instinct for friendship, given directly and without reservation to those she chose; and such was her witchery that the recipient returned it on her terms. She never thought to distinguish between love and friendship—it was enough that in both one gave one's heart. Her friendships moved quickly into intimacy. Gossips, measuring her by ordinary standards, interpreted her gift for familiarity in hackneyed physical terms; her friends valued the warm world she created and knew the artlessness of her gestures. The portrait of her now in the Telfair Academy, Savannah, shows quiet eyes set in a soft round face. Demure and middle-aged, it conveys none of the animation that breathes in her letters, none of the colorful aura through which she moved.

Catherine was born on Block Island in 1753 and reared in her aunt's fine home in Warwick. Rhode Island had been founded by men and women who would not surrender their spirits to pious conformity; singly or in small groups they had rejected the theocratic climate of Massachusetts. Their settlements, dedicated to religious tolerance, attracted others seeking asylum, and soon, side by side, Anabaptists, Jews, Quakers, and Episcopalians lived pleasantly together; without prejudice members of all beliefs rose to positions of importance.

As the colony grew rich, the colonists found that they had also reserved the right to enjoy the leisure wealth brought—the spirit had not been hobbled by guilt or crippled by sin; they had never subscribed to the Puritan idea that leisure was Satan's invention. The first learned society in America, the Literary and Philosophical Society, was started in Rhode Island in 1730, its members meeting regularly to discuss news and exchange ideas. Abraham Redwood, a mercantile Maecenas, gave generously to buy books in London, and organized a botanical garden—his own ship captains brought him seedlings and plants from all their ports of call. Interest in ideas grew, and Newport shared with Philadelphia a preoccupation with science and belles-lettres.

Wealth flowed into the colony, largely from trade on the high seas. Newport was the center of a lively lucrative commerce. Dozens of ships made fancy profits in the triangular traffic of rum, molasses, and slaves; other ships went north after whales; still others carried Rhode Island manufactures—rum and refined sugar, sperm oil and spermaceti candles, pig iron, hatchets, axes, hoes, plows, hammers, and shovels—to coastal settlements, to West Indian plantations, to foreign ports.

The aristocratic tone was introduced when, in the 1750s, wealthy planters from Charleston, Savannah, and the West Indies, who had close business ties with Newport merchants, came to set up summer residences. They brought their mastery of the lighter art of living, the gracious sociability of tea parties and corn-husking festivities, and the assemblies where minuets and reels were danced. Is it any wonder that Stiles, who for years had been the pride of Newport and had had charge of the Redwood Library, should see nothing amiss in allowing Yale students to take ballroom-dancing lessons? The people of Newport cultivated an elegance in manners, an extravagance in dress; for their patronage ships were stocked with luxuries from Europe and the East: fine silks, gossamer cottons, laces, porcelains, tea, sandalwood boxes, Turkish carpets, and Indian shawls. Men and women sitting to Robert Feke or Gilbert Stuart presented themselves in coats of brocade and scarlet, lace ruffles, high-heeled shoes with golden buckles; their hands seem to be fragile ornaments holding delicate fans and jeweled swords; solemnly their children clutch pet monkeys and parrots.

This was Catherine's world; it breathes in all her letters. Whatever the main burden of her letters—financial and legal crises, family dislocations, concerns of health—they always convey the bustle of conviviality, of chatter and music, of constant visiting, and of long, uncomfortable journeys made agreeable by friends and funds. "My house is full of company—all in high spirits and I have retired to Scribble nonsense to my friend. . . . I have just come from the Play and according to promis left the gay throng to sup while I devote myself [to answering you]. . . . Last evening I arrived safe here [Newport] we had the pleasure of the Company of Mrs and Mr Amory. . . . They came merely to be three days longer with us, and three days of real delight they have been; so stoped on the road to see everything that was curious, in short, devoted ourselves to pleasure."

In Jefferson's second administration, forced by the Embargo ("Smuggling goes on here [New York] like the duce almost every night vessels go out") to make the long trip south by land, Catherine bought a coach and hired a driver recommended for character as well as skill: "We are up early in the morning as to ride 15 miles before Breakfast—which we do in three houres. Our afternoon journey is accomplished with equal ease. . . . The Driver is everything I could wish. He certainly is at the *head* of his *Profession* as a driver and I have the notion to dub him Doctr. Why not? as well as Doctr of Music? . . . One of my Carriage Horses got lame the second day after I left Phila which detained us two days at Baltimore where we received every species of kind and friendly attention from the Holingsworth family, who we took letters to." Still later she wrote Whitney: "Come here and let me teach you by *My example*, how to enjoy the few fleeting years which any can calculate upon. . . . We are as gay as larks and really pass our time delightfully. Company enough

—you know we always have. . . . We have a party of Eighteen to eat turtle with us tomorrow. I wish you were the nineteenth."

From her first invitation to have him join her party, Catherine was to be Whitney's cicerone in genteel company. The education Whitney had received at Yale made him familiar with contemporary intellectual and scientific activity; it was Catherine who prepared him to feel at home in the great world. From Boston to Savannah, as the years extended the boundaries of her experience, she came to know nearly everyone worth knowing.

Catherine showed discernment when she chose her husband. Nathanael, though a distant cousin, did not belong to the gentry. His father, one of the local leaders in the Society of Friends, had a successful foundry and desired nothing more for his seven sons than that they operate the family forges and foundries profitably, live peacefully, honestly, simply, frugally, and abide with the Quaker teachings. Catherine described the six Greene brothers many years later, when they were in their sixties. They were "Just coming out of Their forge or Mill. . . . They are plain Country people with very good sense tho but little Education, live in the Most plentiful, but plain Manner and are celebrated for their hospitality. They are opulent (Nay Rich) but [work] just as hard as if they were poor and feel a kind of vanity in doing so."

All but Nathanael lived according to the father's precepts. A chance encounter with Stiles in a bookshop enlisted him as friend and mentor; and with only this informal guidance Nathanael Greene, by his own marked aptitude for study, acquired a good education, especially in mathematics and the sciences of his day. When the Revolution came, Greene was prepared—his campaigns are monuments to his brilliance and leadership; it took the war and his appointment by Washington as quartermaster general to reveal his unexpected genius for organization. Stiles, who followed closely his career, noted in 1777 that "Greene is the General whom Washington most relies upon in the whole Army—and I believe the Congress have their Eye upon him as a Successor to G. Wash. in Case of Accident—altho' both Schuyler, Lee & Putnam are before him."

Catherine was not just the wife of a great man; in her own way she earned fame and respect. She joined the general when the army went

into winter quarters. She was one of the devoted group that had
shared with Washington and his men the misery, cold, hunger, and
sense of abandonment at Valley Forge; the next year—the severest
of all the war winters—undaunted, she was with her husband at
Morristown, where her fourth child was born; she was with him
when, in that protracted anticlimax of the war, he besieged the British until they left Charleston. Of the twelve years of their marriage,
more than half were consumed by the war. Had she only endured
those grim experiences, she would have won the devotion of her husband's close friends; it was her lightness of spirit under such conditions that brought her the admiration of Washington, Lafayette, von
Steuben, Wayne, and Kosciusko, while the soldiers took consolation
from the knowledge that she was one with them during their black
days.

From the moment when he accepted Washington's appointment
to command the Southern armies, Greene stepped into trouble. Cornwallis's surrender at Yorktown (October, 1781) did not end the war
for him; not until a year later, in December, 1782, did Greene, at the
head of his victorious army, enter Charleston. His starved soldiers
plundered the food shops. "In this critical situation, I had but the
choice of difficulties; to turn the army loose upon the country, or take
the risk upon me of supporting the contractors. I chose the latter as
the least evil." Greene personally endorsed notes to obtain food and
clothing for his troops.

From that time on, the vast sums for which he had made himself
liable left him no peace. Heroically, Greene threw himself into his
last campaign—to salvage something for his family's protection. He
hurried back to Rhode Island, where again he started up the foundry
he had left when he marched off to war; he hurried to Princeton, where
Congress was meeting, and implored them, fruitlessly, to assume the
ruinous debts that rightfully were the nation's obligation. Meanwhile,
South Carolina had gratefully presented him with Boone's Barony, a
valuable confiscated estate. But even this handsome gift—it included
some slaves attached to the land and a grant of credit to enable
Greene to purchase additional slaves for the plantation—could not
save him.

Seventeen hundred and eighty-four was a terrible year. The bank-

ruptcy of the contractor who held his endorsed notes added intolerably to his burden. But, as if to help him parry the blow, the people
of Georgia, in March, 1785, having confiscated the estate of the Loy-
alist Lieutenant Governor, John Graham, deeded it to General
Greene. This was Mulberry Grove.

By name, Mulberry Grove recalled the hopeful labors of its
founder, who set out a mulberry nursery—one argument advanced
for establishing Georgia was that it might supply England with raw
silk—and was so successful that five years later he sold Oglethorpe
some six thousand trees. To Greene it presented problems. For ten
years it had been deserted, its great fields neglected; floods had wiped
out the drainage system that had converted swamp acreage into rich
rice fields. "We found the house," Greene wrote to a Newport friend,
"situation and outbuildings more convenient and pleasing than we
expected. The prospect is delightful, and the house magnificent. We
have a coach house and stables, a large out kitchen, and a poultry
house nearly 50 feet long and 20 wide, parted for different kinds of
poultry, with a pigeon house on the top, which will contain not less
than a thousand pigeons. Besides these are several other buildings
convenient for a family, and among the rest, a fine smoke-house. The
garden is in ruins, but there are still a great variety of shrubs and
flowers in it."

Such a property was well worth laboring over to restore, and
Greene, with his customary vigor, lost no time in erasing the signs of
neglect and getting the fields back to their former productivity. "We
are planting," he wrote some time later to his Newport friend. "We
have got upwards of sixty acres of corn planted, and expect to plant
one hundred and thirty of rice. The garden is delightful. The fruit
trees and flowering shrubs form a pleasing variety. We have green
peas almost fit to eat, and as fine lettuce as ever you saw. The mock-
ing birds surround us evening and morning. The weather is mild,
and the vegetable kingdom progressing to perfection. . . . We have
in the same orchard apples, pears, peaches, apricots, nectarines,
plums of different kinds, figs, pomegranates, and oranges. And we
have strawberries which measure three inches around. All these are
clever, but the want of our friends to enjoy them with us renders them
less interesting."

"Gen. Greene died of a *Coup du Soleil,* Stroke of the sun." Stiles noted the tragic event of June 19, 1786. "He walked about freely in his Rice-Grounds in the heat of the sun, to over-see his Negroes of which he had about 130." Those were the facts as communicated to him by the governor of Georgia; but the statement that Greene died of a sunstroke should be put down as an eighteenth century conceit. That a man whose greatest campaigns had been fought in the South, who had directed a mobile policy which had dislodged the British and who had then besieged them for a year until they had evacuated Charleston—that such a man now should be mortally stricken by the sun does small justice to Greene's vitality and intelligence. It is much more likely that he suffered a fatal heart attack. Worry, tension, a desperate drive to succeed before ruin should engulf him—these were enough to break a heart as hopeful as Greene's.

Less than a year before his death, Greene had engaged as tutor for his children a young protégé of Stiles, Phineas Miller. A year older than Whitney, he came from Middlefield, Connecticut; his family were prosperous enough to send him to Yale. Stiles mentions that he "Dismissed . . . Miller, a Sophimore," and that the following April he "Examined and readmitted Phineas Miller into the Sophimore Class. He was dismissed 15 Nov. last on account of illness." On September 20, 1785, "Sir Miller"—"Sir" was the title bestowed on Bachelors of Art, the equivalent of the Latin *Dominus*—as Stiles called him, was "offered £5 per month & Board at Barrington, but will prefer General Greene's offer of £3 Sterling & Board &c if the Gen. agrees." Miller might have chosen the general's offer to favor his delicate health by wintering in the South, or he might have gladly sacrificed the higher stipend to become associated with a man of Greene's standing. Miller accompanied the family when they took possession of their new home, Mulberry Grove.

No portrait of Miller exists. From the things he did, from the letters he wrote, a picture slowly takes form; not of his appearance—was he tall, was he thin?—but of the inner man. When General Greene died at forty-four, it was to Miller that Catherine Greene turned for help and counsel. It was Miller who over the next seventeen years struggled to untangle the debts that Greene had left behind him.

At once Miller's role was changed. He was part of the ménage. Friends poured in on Catherine, to mourn with her and pity the five little fatherless children—the oldest was barely eleven—and when the friends returned to their far-flung homes and the house was emptied of them, Catherine had only Miller to talk to, to worry with, to rely on for the day-to-day decisions required on a great plantation, to carry on the enormous correspondence demanded by Greene's affairs. He was no ordinary humble retainer. He was a college graduate and had been recommended by Stiles; and to serve the Greenes, whom he held in highest esteem, Stiles would have been most particular in his selection. Miller, as Stiles judged him, was cultivated, serious, conscientious, honorable, gentle. Time would add to those qualities constancy and integrity, but it was residence—permanence and continuity—that first gave Miller his unique position in the household of the late General Greene.

"I am now at Mulberry Grove with Mrs. Greene's family. I arrived here eight days ago—but let me begin at New York." Whitney was in good spirit. He whose world had hitherto been bounded by Westborough on the north and New Haven on the south poured out to Stebbins (November 1, 1792) the crowded impressions of his first great adventure. "The first two days after we left N. York, the wind being contrary, we did nothing more than beat out of the harbour. After that we had a better wind and in five days and half arrived at Savannah. We made what they call a five day's passage; for they count only from N. York lighthouse to Tibe lighthouse, which stands at the mouth of the river Savannah. The six first days after I left N. York I was very seasick indeed—eat nothing but what I puked up immediately—since that I have been in good health. Nothing happened on the passage worth relating. I will remark, however, that we were out of sight of land four days of the five and therefore I can give no account of the coast. . . .

"Most of the productions of nature here are entirely new to me—I could much easier enumerate those which are common in New England than those which are peculiar to this country—Oranges, Pomegranates, figgs, Olives &c all grow within ten rods of the place where

I now sit. There are several fruits which grow spontaneously in the fields that are quite agreeable—but as yet I am quite unacquainted with the production of the country.

"The town of Savannah did by no means equal my expectations—it stands on the river Savannah fifteen miles from the Ocean and is about two thirds as large as N. Haven—the houses are mostly of wood and not well built—the town is laid out in squares much like N. Haven and the streets are excessively sandy—the buildings in general appear very much weatherbeaten which I believe is owing to the great degree of moisture in the air. The river Savannah is rather more than half a mile wide at its mouth, it gradually decreases as far as I have ascended it—opposite the town it is not more than fifty rods wide and at this place, which is 12 miles above, not more than 20 rods—the tide rises about 35 miles up the river. The Country is low and the banks of the river are very little above the surface of the water, indeed the water o'er flows its banks, every tide, where the land is uncultivated but to what extent I am not able to say. I should have remarked that the town of Savannah stands on a sandy Bluff about thirty feet above the water in the river, which is said to be the highest land in this part of the country.

"Rice, corn and potatoes are the principal things which are cultivated as far as my observations have yet extended, all which are different in their species from those of New England—but stop! there is no rice in N. Eng. The most I know about the corn is that it is much whiter and makes good homine. The Potatoes are excellent—very sweet and mealy and of an enormous size. The cultivation of rice requires much more labour than I supposed before I saw the manner in which it is done. But I am teaching you that which I know nothing about myself so I believe I had better be Easy.

"I have spent my time very agreeably since I left N. Haven in the family of Mrs. Greene. I slept in Savannah one night after my arrival and the next day went to Mrs. Greene's Plantation. Tomorrow I expect to cross the river into Carolina and enter on the tutorship."

Nowhere in Whitney's long account is the word "cotton" mentioned.

On the same day, he wrote to his father, and then all letters for five and a half months stop. He communicated neither with his family nor friends. This silence is significant, as is the tone and content of his letters when he writes again. He is evasive, enigmatic, mystifying; he fills pages with generalities; the hints which stud his sentences could only have muddled the recipient. "It is so long since I have written to you that I fear you begin to be very anxious to hear from me." So, on April 11, 1793, he breaks the long silence in a letter to his father.

"I have the pleasure to inform you that I never enjoyed a better and more confirmed state of health, in any part of my life than since I arrived in this Country. This is certainly a very pleasant country in the winter and spring. Vegetation is as far advanced here as it is in the last of May in Massachusetts. I shall return to N. England sooner than I expected when I left it. I have been disappointed in the salary I expected and fear I shall return as poor as I came. I, however, do not repent coming here. I shall at least enlarge my acquaintance with men & things and gain some experience, which is the best kind of knowledge."

To Stebbins, on the same date, he restates the same facts and adds a little: "I must omit apologies of every kind and come immediately to the *point*. There was a misunderstanding between Mr. Miller and Maj. Dupont concerning the wages to be given to an *Instructor*. Instead of Eighty Guineas Pr. year, I found, on my arrival at Mr. Dupont's, that Forty was the most I could expect. . . . I wish you not to ask any questions, because you might ask some which I cannot answer. . . . I can give no good account of myself; Ergo I'll be silent. You know I always considered this a dam'd kind of world, and to say the truth, I have no great reason to change my opinion since I saw you. I find some, however, among the human species in this part of the world as well as N. England who are not unworthy, among whom Mr. Miller ranked. He has really treated me very much like a Gentleman. I have a great deal to say to you but must omit it all, till the Fates permit me again to ramble with you in the suburbs of N. Haven where you may expect to see me in June, at farthest. . . . I have not yet repented coming to this part of the U. States tho' perhaps I may. Fortune has stood with her back towards me ever since I have been here and when she turns around whether she will frown or smile is quite uncertain; but let the capricious Dame put on what appearance she pleases," Whitney will ever esteem his friend.

It was not disappointment in the arrangements at Major Dupont's that caused Whitney to remain at Mulberry Grove. The real reason? He dared not even mention it in a letter; the need for secrecy was too great. But his intense preoccupation with something momentous can be felt when, less than one month after his letter to Stebbins reporting the failure of his tutorship, he writes, "Dame fortune has turned about, and, for the first time, her Ladyship deigns to look upon me with a smiling face."

So starts his letter of May 1, 1793, to Stebbins. The upsurge of success races the need for silence through his sentences, turning sense into nonsense; he seems likely to burst with the news he dare not tell. "You must know, Brother Stebbins, I have become very expert in the Hocus-Pocus line. I already rank among the higher order of the conjurers. I have only two grades more to rise before I can be chief of all the Magicians, or Magi. My salary is now half a Guinea Pr. Day. I have a fair prospect of being advanced in about two weeks, when my salary will be doubled, and shall undoubtedly rise the other grade within six months; then my salary *is to be* five Guineas Pr. Day. My first business will be to pay all my honest debts and do as I please with the rest. I am very sorry that I have neither the time nor talents to give you either a geographical description or the natural history of the Country—the figg-tree puteth forth its figgs, the pomegranate its blossoms, Indian Corn its tassel and we have peas and Salad all winter. . . . I hear of wars and rumors of wars; but very little of the news of the Day. I have not seen a News Paper these three months. Lest you should be out of patience with my nonsense I will stop here." He writes no more from Georgia.

He arrived in New Haven during the first week of July. Three letters to his father from that place continue the story—the first two add a little to Whitney's state of mind and health. On July 22, 1793, he writes: "I am very anxious to hear from you, not having heard anything of your welfare since I left you in August last. . . . I have not as yet realized much property, but have the prospect of securing to myself a comfortable living. . . . I shall reside in this place during the summer in the course of which I shall if possible make you a short visit and give you a particular history of my life since I left you."

On August 5, 1793, he complains that "I have been a little out of health for ten days past, which I believe is owing to having over-heated my self in Philadelphia during the extreme hot weather in June. . . . I shall continue in this town, I believe till Oct when I think it is probable I shall return again to the Southward." This note, though it is carried as far as "to Northboro' by Mr. Trask a young Gentleman belonging to Cambridge College," still says nothing of moment.

Only when he received a letter from his father brought by a West-borough neighbor who promised to take one back to him, was Whitney confident that now he could entrust his idea to writing and feel safe that what he put on paper would not surrender its secret to pry-ing eyes. Moreover, his father's letter made an answer imperative.

"After my tenderest Regards to you"—thus the father began his note. He continued, his bare words urgent, solicitous: "The Grate Distance which You have been from us and the Unhealthy Climate hath made me Anxiously Consarned for Your welfare. . . . I have nothing Very Remarkable to inform You of but I would intreat of you not to Returne to the Sothard till You Come home for I want to See you very much and to Know what fortain You have had and the Biziness You have been in. We Rote to You while You was at the Sothard thow I suppose You Never Received the Letters."

Whitney's answer (the third letter to his father, dated September 11, 1793) raises the curtain on his place in history: "I went from N. York with the family of the late Major General Greene to Georgia. I went immediately with the family to their Plantation about twelve miles from Savannah with an expectation of spending four or five days and then proceed into Carolina to take the school as I have mentioned in former letters. During this time I heard much said of extreme difficulty of ginning Cotton, that is, separating it from its seed. There were a number of very respectable Gentlemen at Mrs. Greene's who all agreed that if a machine could be invented which would clean the Cotton with expedition, it would be a great thing both to the Country and to the inventor."

Instantly upon his arrival in the South, Whitney's talents were drafted. Within a few days he had found a way whereby the short-staple, the green-seed, the upland cotton—call it by any of its names —cousin to the showy hibiscus and marshmallow, the hollyhock, the mucilaginous gumbo, could be freed from its seeds. His invention, addressed to cleaning the woolly plant, carried the South to wealth and vast dominion; it gave to the world the fiber whose threads, as Faulkner has said, were "frail as truth and impalpable as equators yet cable-strong to bind for life them who made the cotton to the land their sweat fell on."

The Great Invention

Among the college debates that Whitney wrote are the perennial favorites: "Ought Capital Punishment ever be inflicted," "Does the Mind always Think," and "Is a Savage State preferable to a Civilized"; but subjects of topical interest are also included: "Ought Religious Tests be required of Civil Officers," "Is Privateering Justifiable," and, particularly, "Ought the U States develop Manufactures," and "Does the National Security depend on fostering Domestic Industries." In preparing his argument on domestic manufactures—at different times he argued both pro and con—Whitney's immediate reference was to Lord Sheffield's *Observations on the Commerce of the American States with Europe and the West Indies.*

Lord Sheffield's book had appeared in 1783, almost with national independence. A disturbing book that quickly ran into six printings, it aimed to prove that political freedom must spell economic ruin, since the United States now lay outside the Navigation System, "the guardian of the prosperity of Britain." The British Empire, Sheffield asserted, should close up the wound occasioned by the loss of the thirteen colonies and, self-sufficient, reduce her trade with America to the minimum. The American States, he argued with a certain morbid satisfaction, faced a hopeless future: they lacked an adequate labor supply; they lacked textile fibers to satisfy their needs; they lacked machinery such as England had and, therefore, he predicted, America could never establish extensive manufactures.

One of Whitney's arguments must have been written after December, 1791; it contains the essence of Hamilton's *Report on Manufactures,* a document that pointed the way to meet Lord Sheffield's terrible truths. The great *Report,* communicated to the House of Representatives, was widely read; Hamilton said nothing new when he stated that "the defect of hands constitutes the greatest obstacle to success." To effect "an increase in hands, an accession of strength," he suggested water-powered machinery tended chiefly by women and children—a method marvelously productive in the cotton manufactories of Great Britain. Such machinery would increase the labor supply, since it makes women "more useful, and the [children] more early useful."

Hamilton, with his copy of Adam Smith's book before him, made it clear that Sheffield was predicating the future in terms of a static present, and countered with a prophecy of economic freedom to match the political freedom—to be won as the latter had been won, after time and great effort. The labor shortage would be overcome, for there was "in the genius of the people of this country, a peculiar aptitude for mechanical improvements."

The new United States, like the separate colonies earlier, faced a shortage in textile fibers; each colony had a record of legislation, premiums, prescriptions, bounties—bounties more numerous and important than for any other raw materials—to increase the cultivation of flax, hemp, wool, silk, and cotton. And yet America had always depended on imports to satisfy her full needs. Flax was the fiber best established—"Spinning of flax is the general employment in private families in the evening"—and flaxseed was a sizable export item, but the finest linen cloth came from abroad. Wool was unprofitable and unpopular (farmers keeping just enough sheep to satisfy their own needs) until Colonel David Humphreys, the American minister to Spain, sent home some merino sheep in 1801.

Silk, which seemed so easy of cultivation and was so elegant a fabric, exceeded flax in its demands for patient, skillful, cheap labor—a factor lacking in America. Yet vigorous efforts were made to promote silkworms in colonial America. Stiles investigated, recorded, and promoted silk culture and manufacture in Connecticut. Silkworms could be raised in the north, and as early as 1734 Connecticut had offered bounties on sewing silk, silk stockings, and silk stuff. When fifty years later another bounty included raw silk and mulberry trees, the response was immediate.

While still a student, Whitney saw hundreds of mulberry trees being hopefully planted along New Haven streets. Stiles, whose *Diary* treats economic needs and national problems in the language of local enterprises, mentions them: "The Spirit for raising Silk worms is great in this town . . . & some other places in Connecticut. Mr. Aspinwal has it is judged one hundred thousand worms. I visited them yesterday." Or: "I rode round town to visit the Silkworms, the most of which are cocooned. Cocoons taking down & reeling. I found *twenty-three Families* within this City, which raised this season from five to seventy thousand worms. . . . Last year & this I have distributed Mulberry Seeds chiefly in this State, some up Mohawk R., & Vermont Towns on L. Champlain." (Every Mulberry Street in towns along the Atlantic seaboard is a memento of this widespread activity.) He adds up the number of nurseries and notes their swift increase—94 in 1789, 267 in 1790. More significantly, he records that in 1791 Mr. Aspinwal "has succeeded in N York in his silk Culture, having obtained from the Assembly of that State an Act promising a Praemium of three Dollars per hundred Mulberry Trees growing and in good State at the End of Three years after setting out."

Silk was not the only textile fiber to which the people of Connecticut paid serious attention. Tantalizing reports of the British textile machinery had reached America, but precise information was lacking. Cotton was the fiber fed into these machines; cotton imported from the West Indies, Surinam, Brazil, Cayenne; long-staple cotton, easily cleansed of its black seeds, poured out in a river of yard goods. Hargreaves, Crompton, and Arkwright, the giants who led the unparalleled progress of cotton manufacture, were known; but their machines, their methods were closely guarded secrets. Though New Englanders could not grow cotton, they were eager to emulate old England's prosperity, and immediately after the Revolution attempts were made to establish cotton manufactories. States gave public aid, and societies were formed to encourage this industrial art; it was a period of experimentation, of failures, of limited success. Independently, Americans could not achieve the advances made in techniques, in machinery, in organization, which gave the British industry its commanding lead.

Stiles's attention to this manufacturing gives a partial measure of the skill and capital concentrated in the local factories and the interest they aroused. "Visited the Cotton Manufactury newly erected [June, 1794] in West Rock two miles from Town. Saw the carding machine compleat and working and also two Jennies going for spinning cotton. About half a dozen Jennies finished from fourty to Eighty Threads. The Manufacturing House about half as big as new College, 100 feet long & four stories." (Perhaps Whitney visited such a factory, as he passed through Worcester on his way home.) These jenny mills run by hand or horse power were not the mighty Arkwright warp-spinning mills geared to water power. In these mills cotton was only spun into weft; the warps still required the strength of flax, and the cloths so woven were heavy coarse denims and ducks; in patterns, texture, and finish they were vastly inferior to the British all-cotton textiles bought by Americans.

The American cotton industry began in 1789, only four years before Whitney's momentous letter to his father, when Samuel Slater, with twenty years' experience in Arkwright and Strutt's mill, slipped away from home, eluded vigilant British authorities, and sailed for America. To Moses Brown in Rhode Island he brought his training in practical mechanics learned from working on the machines themselves; he implemented this knowledge with skilled fingers that, bit by bit, from memory and according to principle, duplicated the machines that had been perfected by the British master craftsmen. With Slater's arrival a complicated skill slowly perfected in Europe was successfully transplanted to America. News of the event spread in a matter of months, and Hamilton, with pride, referred to it in his *Report.* "The Manufactory at Providence has the merit of being the first in introducing into the United States the celebrated cotton mill which not only furnishes materials for the manufactory itself, but for the supply of private families, for household manufactures."

To obtain cotton for his mill, Moses Brown paid an impost of three cents a pound on the fine long-staple black-seed cotton. True, there was some cotton grown in the southern states, but in the interior it was the green-seed cotton, grown as a garden plant or, if cultivated for house use, doomed by its tenacious seeds to be woven into the coarsest goods. A small amount of black-seed cotton, newly being grown along the coasts of South Carolina and Georgia, was available; but it was almost a different fiber, and more prized than silk. Moses Brown brusquely dismissed the cheaper southern-grown green-seed cotton: "The unripe, short and dusty part being so enveloped with that which would be good, *if separated properly at first, so spoils the whole as to discourage the use of it in machines.*" Yet it was to this very fiber that Hamilton had paid attention. He urged cotton cultivation because it was peculiarly adapted to machines. And because it promised to grow abundantly in the southern states —"an additional and very cogent inducement to [its] vigorous pursuit"—its quality, he believed, could be in time "carried by a more experienced culture to much greater perfection."

Even before the news of Slater's accomplishment at Moses Brown's mill, some southern planters were aroused to the need to produce a staple the mills could use. In 1789 a member from South Carolina stated in the House of Representatives that southern farmers intended to take up the cultivation of cotton, but their success, he added, depended on their procuring good seed. It was still hoped to find a long-fiber cotton that would grow in the interior. English travelers of that day, riding through the empty southern states, remarked that "the staple of America at present consists of Land;" they were impressed with "the appearance everywhere of a vast outline, with much to fill up." Something would rush into this vacuum.

Southern agriculture till then had produced rice and indigo, turpentine, tobacco, and corn. Vast plantations were still largely wilderness. The great fortunes of the South were yet to be made. Tobacco had not only exhausted the planters' soil, its market was glutted; rice and indigo brought no profit; the price of slaves had dropped, inflicting a severe loss in capital; sea-island cotton was promising but severely handicapped because it was limited to a small region; the green-seed cotton alone adapted itself to the variety of conditions imposed by the vast hinterland. Only that crop could lift the South out of its depression, make the capital investment in slaves profitable, and bring rich returns on the world market. Was not England hungry for the staple? She could not get enough for her new machines. One can almost see the eager, serious, worried planters sitting around Catherine Greene's table, sipping port and Madeira, talking always of what was uppermost in their minds: A method to clean the green-seed cotton quickly and properly was all that stood between them and wealth.

From the moment he arrived at Mulberry Grove, Whitney heard much of this. He had never seen the cotton plant before; he examined its boll carefully, remarking that the seed was "covered with a kind of green coat resembling velvet." He tugged at the fiber, trying to separate it from the seeds.

Only a few days after reaching Mulberry Grove (Whitney was sketching in the significant details in the long letter he wrote to his father on September 11, 1793), he "involuntarily happened to be thinking on the subject and struck out a plan of a Machine in my mind, which I communicated to Miller. . . . He was pleased with the Plan and said that if I would pursue it and try and experiment to see if it would answer, he would be at the whole expense, I should lose nothing but my time, and if I succeeded we should share the profits. Previous to this I found I was like to be disappointed in my school, that is, instead of a hundred, I found I could get only fifty Guineas a Year.* I however held the refusal of the school untill I tried some experiments. In about ten Days I made a little model, for which I was offered, if I would give up all right and title to it, a Hundred Guineas—. I concluded to relinquish my school and turn my attention to perfecting this Machine. I made one before I came away [June 1, 1793] which required the labour of one man to turn it and with which one man will clean ten times as much cotton as he can in any other way before known and also clean it much better than in the usual mode. This machine may be turned by water or with a horse, with the greatest ease, and one man and a horse will do more than fifty men with the old machines. It makes the labour fifty times less, without throwing any class of People out of business."

The old machines, to which Whitney referred, were roller gins, similar to the ancient, primitive Indian charka, whence they derived, the selfsame gins pictured and described in the *Encyclopédie*. In appearance they resembled a clothes-wringer, their two rollers coming into close contact, and set in motion by a single crank. Friction alone was sufficient to disengage the long fibers of the sea-island

* And yet Whitney himself in another letter mentions eighty and forty guineas as the sum.

cotton from its smooth black seeds, aptly called "bald-headed seeds"; the rollers were fluted, and fine grooves running lengthwise caught the lint but did not admit the seeds. But the frictional power of the roller gin, whether a single unit or a multiple variation, was powerless to detach the cotton from the seed of the upland variety: its fiber was too short and adhered too firmly to its green seeds—it seemed to grow out of the seed as wool does from a sheep's back.

"I returned to the Northward for the purposes of having a machine made on a large scale and obtaining a Patent for the invention. I went to Philadelphia soon after I arrived, made myself acquainted with the steps necessary to obtain a Patent, took several of the steps and the Secretary of State, Mr. Jefferson, agreed to send the Patent to me as soon as it could be made out—so that I apprehend no difficulty in obtaining the Patent. Since I have been here I have employed several workmen in making machines and as soon as my business is so that I can leave it for a few days, I shall come to Westboro' . . . I am certain I can obtain a Patent in England. . . . How advantageous this business will eventually prove to me, I cannot say. Tis generally said by those who know anything about it, that I shall make a Fortune by it. I have no expectations that I shall make an independent fortune by it, but think I had better pursue it than any other business into which I can enter.

"Something which cannot be foreseen may frustrate my expectations and defeat my Plan; but I am now so sure of success that ten thousand dollars, if I saw the money counted out to me, would not tempt me to give up my right and relinquish the object." His words announce that he had come into a world that had meaning for him; his drifting had stopped; his feet had felt a path, and he would follow it where his talents and the needs of his society led.

He then repeated the importance of continued caution, underlining words: "I wish you, Sir, not to show this letter nor communicate anything of its contents to any body except My Brothers & Sister; *enjoining* it on them to keep the whole a *profound secret.* Mr. Robbinson came into town yesterday and goes out tomorrow, this has been such a bustling time that I have not had the opportunity to say six words to him. I have told him nothing of my business—perhaps he will hear something about it from somebody else in town—but only two or three of my friends know what I am about tho' there are many surmises in town—if Mr. Robinson says anything about it, you can tell him I wrote you concerning it but wished not to have it mentioned." This was not the admonition of an unduly secretive man; caution was necessary until the issuance of the patent.

Obtaining the patent was not a single act to be finished in a day. From June 20, 1793, when Whitney first addressed himself to the Secretary of State, until the patent was granted and signed by President Washington on March 14, 1794, a series of requirements was to be met, each of which took time. November 6, 1793, the date on which the patent was officially acknowledged to have commenced, terminated the months of imperative secrecy.

The summer and fall of 1793 were a period of arduous toil for Whitney; for while taking the series of steps necessary to gain his patent, he had to equip and man his workshop in New Haven, where he first produced his patent model, and then make ready to manufacture his full-sized gins. To retrace the legal and business intricacies is like assembling a jigsaw puzzle where, though sizable pieces are missing, the pattern can be ascertained. The letters Whitney wrote to Miller and Catherine have disappeared; disastrous fires—one in Whitney's workshop in 1795 that destroyed his papers, and another in the United States Patent Office in 1836 that consumed the original model and drawings—add to the magnitude of the loss. But fortunately, from existing papers, ledgers, preliminary drafts in copybooks, letterbooks, letters, and legal documents, enough of the picture can be reassembled for its design to emerge clearly.

Before Whitney left Mulberry Grove on May 27, 1793, he had agreed with Miller that if he could make a machine that would work like the model, "the profits and advantages arising therefrom, as well as all privileges and emoluments to be derived from patenting, making, vending, and working the same, should be mutually and equally shared between them." For this half-interest Miller financed the preliminary expenses.

That he might have an exact record of all sums disbursed, Whitney kept a little "Expence Book." The entries cover the ten months from his departure from Georgia in June, 1793, to April 15, 1794, when he booked passage back; phrased in dollars and days, it is almost a diary of his activities during that first busy preliminary year. June is filled with movement. On the tenth he pays $36.25 for "Passage and Freight from Savannah to New York"; on the fourteenth he engages "Passage in the Stage from NYork to Philadelphia" ($4.00), and spends another dollar for "Expenses on the Road to Philad."; on the eighteenth he buys the *Laws of Congress* for thirty-three cents. With this to guide him—the original Patent Act of 1790 had just been substantially changed by the Act of February 21, 1793—Whitney paid the required fee of $30 and accompanied it with a letter to "The Honorable Thomas Jefferson Esquire Secretary of State for the United States of America," who was empowered to receive all patent applications:

"The Petition of Eli Whitney of the County of Worcester and Commonwealth of Massachusetts, humbly showeth: That having invented a Machine for the Purpose of ginning Cotton, he is desirous of obtaining an exclusive Property in the same. Concerning which invention, Petitioner alledges as follows (viz) first.

"That it is entirely new & constructed in a different manner and upon different principles from any other Cotton Ginn or Machine heretofore known or used for that purpose.

"2nd. That with the Ginn, if turned with horses or by water, two persons will clean as much cotton in one day, as a hundred persons could cleane in the same time with the ginns now in common use.

"3rd. That the Cotton which is cleaned in his Ginn contains fewer broken seeds and impurities, and is said to be more valuable than Cotton, which is cleaned in the usual way—

"Your Petitioner, therefore, Prays your Honor to Grant him the sd. Whitney a Patent for the sd Invention or Improvement, and that your Honour cause Letters Patent to be made out, in the name of the United States, granting to him your sd. Petitioner, his heirs, Administrators & assigns, for the term of fourteen years the length of time stipulated by the Act the full and exclusive right & liberty of making, constructing, using and vending to others to be used, the sd. Invention or Improvement."

The next day, the twenty-first, he paid $3 for "5 Days Board at No. 5 Fourth St.," and took the stage to New York, where he paid $12.75 "to Mr. Anthony for Boarding 2 weeks & 3 days." He spent his time shopping for available materials and hired a horse to ride out to the "cotton-works at Turtle Bay." On July 8th he paid $4.50 "For Passage, freight &c from NYork to N. Haven." Stebbins must certainly have been on hand when his packet landed to hear, as they strolled happily together, the tremendous secret Whitney had not dared put into writing.

The "Expence Book" is also invaluable as a guide to the simple tools and mechanical techniques of that time. Vividly it presents a workshop where most of the tools today considered indispensable are absent; where the mechanic relied on a saw, hammer, chisels and reamers, and files of different shapes and textures; where cutting pliers, pincers, and knives, beeswax and rosin for lubrication, glue, varnish, emery, and sandpaper completed his inventory. The ancient arts of brass casting and iron forging were carried on with skill; but screws were still cut out by hand, individually. So basic a machine as the lathe had to be assembled part by part: "Screw for Lathe" and "Pin for lathe screw," the rails and gudgeon, "1 side of leather for Bands, Irons for the treddle of the lathe, 1 Turning Wheel," and "Axis & crank for turning wheel"—item by item they were bought and fitted together. He designed a special turning tool; though the price for making it is noted, its design is not mentioned. This lathe, made for work on wood, was operated by the mechanic, though it could be powered by water or a pair of stout oxen.

Primitive as was this level, it was still beyond the resources of the South, for it was to secure suitable supplies and competent skills that Whitney had been forced to return to New Haven, where he could be certain of creating the model and manufacturing the gins. While in New York he had bought equipment not easily found in smaller towns —"7 Polishing files, 2 Pair Cutting pliers, 1 Do. spring Compasses, 2 Do. Pliers"—and to Nicholas van Antwerp he gave $20 for "96 lbs. Iron Wire." Artisans, in those days, relied on imports for the little wire they needed. Usually it came from France, where men who made uniforms resplendent with gold embroidery had learned to draw metal into fine threads. There wire drawing had developed into an art; in America it was an exacting skill, rarely practiced. But in Whitney's gin, wire of a required fineness was essential; that he still had to draw the wire to suit him is evidenced by his buying "timber for

Expenses July — 1793		98	33
July 2	Amount brought forward	98	33
	To Nich. Holm receipt for 96 lb ware wire	20	10
	For washing clothe	1	0
July 8	New House		
	For ... freight & ... New York to St Mary's	4	50
11	Sawing boards & ...	0	75
	...	1	0
17	Sawing ... to make cypher...	2	26
	For timber to make cypher...	1	13
20	Carting ... timber to ... wharf	1	75
29	... for bottle	1	25
	... for ...	0	50
	...	0	9
August 2	... for ...	0	10
	...	0	13
	... timber the ...	0	70
	2½ Days work of ...	0	25
	...	0	50
	...	0	25
		134	00

Expences — August 1793		134	88
Aug.	Amount brought forward	134	88
3	Beef wool	0	8
	... of ... for ...	2	34
5	...	0	17
8	2 ...	0	25
	1 ½ ...	0	20
	...	0	25
	...	0	13½
8	1 lb Nails	0	50
	...	0	11
9	...	0	45
	...	0	25
	...	1	25
10	...	4	00
	... for ...	1	25
16	...	0	50
	...	2	0
17	...	0	25
	...	0	25
	...	3	64
	...	0	25
		159	06½

PAGES FROM THE LITTLE "EXPENCE BOOK."

Drawing-wire Block, Hooks for wire work, 1 Pint of Whale oil to draw wire," and the expenditure of twelve and a half cents "for making wire plate."

The items give a fuller picture of this initial manufacturing. For the shop he bought a "Brass Key" and a broom; to present his specifications for the patent properly, he supplied himself with fine hair pencils, sheets of fish skin, "a Drawing Board and drawing square"; he experimented with different kinds of wood—white pine boards, birch planks, "sundry pieces of timber," mahogany and lignum vitae. For special tasks he paid fifty cents to "Mr. Brown for sawing half day; J. Smith for forging a pair of gudgeons—$2.00; Mr. Houghton for putting Cylinders together &c—$7.50; $5.00 for Brass Castings; Mrs. Wales for Board and Lodgings from 10 Oct. to the 7th of Nov.— $5.50." Items, prices, dates are carefully noted. When, in August, he mentioned to his father that he had been ill, his book confirms this by several purchases of "1 oz. Sal Ammoniack." Summer passed, and as the days got cold and dark he regularly bought rum, candles, and firewood.

By the middle of October he was certain enough of the excellence of his model and his ability to translate it into a full-size working machine; he took the next important step to secure his patent. Now he was willing to entrust his drawings with their accompanying description to the mail; his covering letter to Jefferson is dated New Haven, October 15, 1793:

"It was my intention to have lodged in the Office of State a description of my machine for ginning Cotton, immediately after presenting my petition for an exclusive property in the same; but ill health unfortunately prevented me from completing the description until about the time of the breaking out of the malignant fever in Philadelphia." Early in August, 1793, the dreaded pest, yellow fever, made its terrible appearance in Philadelphia and raged with violence and unprecedented mortality. Stiles took from Mathew Carey's report the frightening figures of the calamity that began in August and lasted until the middle of November—4,000 deaths and some 17,000 who fled the city. He added that the capital was "supposed usually to contain 50 Thousand souls but I judge about 35 or 40 Thousand." The disaster, Whitney wrote, "so interrupted communication and deranged business of every kind, that I thought it best not to send my description till the disorder had in some measure subsided. But as the sickness, which I hoped would be of short continuance, still prevails, and as I am unwilling to delay any longer, I herewith enclose and forward it, together with a short description designed to form the schedule annexed to the Patent.

"It has been my endeavor to give a precise idea of every part of the machine, and if I have failed in elegance, I hope I have not been deficient in point of accuracy. If I should be entitled to an exclusive privilege, may I ask the favour of you, Sir, to inform me when I may come forward with my model and receive my patent."

Accuracy was not Whitney's only concern. As he had been cautious about maintaining secrecy, so he was careful that his patent rights did not depend on the existence of just one statement. And so, though the description he sent along with his letter to Jefferson was lost in the Patent Office fire, he had among his papers two additional copies, each written in a bound paper copybook. One, lengthy, detailed and explanatory, has his affidavit affixed to it. Before Elizur Goodrich, his friend, the son of his tutor, and now alderman of New Haven and notary public, on October 28, 1793, Whitney "made solemn Oath . . . that he is the true Inventor and discoverer of the Machine for ginning Cotton . . . [and] that a machine of similar construction hath never before been known or used." The drawings, to which reference is made, are missing.

The other, a condensed version, might be a first draft of the abbreviated description sent to Jefferson. It is untidily written, with deletions and corrections; yet Whitney himself had labeled it "The True Copy," dated it "Phl. 8 March 94"—he was there to receive the official patent—and secured what seems to be unofficial recognition of its importance, for, in another's handwriting, this identifying sentence is added parenthetically: "The schedule is written on parchment which is separate from the Patent and connected with the Patent by a ribbon the ends of which are brought under the seal." *

This short description made his approach to the problem of ginning the green-seed cotton quite clear. Instead of the fluted rollers of the existing gins, Whitney's machine had a revolving cylinder and a sta-

* See Appendix A.

tionary breastwork. The cylinder bristled with hundreds of short sharp wire hooks set at a studied angle and in such ordered arrangement that in effect they formed closely set circular saws separated from each other only by a narrow disc; opposing this was the breastwork whose finely spaced grooves corresponded with each line of hooks and whose function, like that of a fork, was to hold back the seed while the cotton, impaled on the wire hooks, flowed through. (The shortest description, and the most graphic, was that current among the boys of Augusta, who tersely reduced the new invention to its essential features: it "had teeth which worked thro' slats and a brush.") Whitney's brief summary—preserved in his writing in the "true copy"—shows how his machine literally tore the cotton from its velvety seeds, the brush whisking the fiber away from the teeth while the seeds fell into a hopper.

Jefferson's answer quickly disposed of the official routines involved in securing the patent: "Your favour of October 15th inclosing a drawing of your cotton gin was received on the 6th inst," he wrote from his home in Germantown, November 16, 1793. All through the dreadful months of the plague, Jefferson had daily visited his office in Philadelphia, and it was probably because he wished to shorten the time spent in the stricken city that an official communication was answered from his residence. "The only requisite of the law now remaining uncomplied with is the forwarding a model, which being received your patent may be made out & delivered to your order immediately."

The letter continues with questions that are less characteristic of his personality than of the region whence he came, and the planter economy of which he was so distinguished a member. For he was always a Virginia planter, rooted in, and committed to, the society which had formed him. In the decades since the Stamp Act he had shared in the militancy that had rejected British manufactures and created a preference for domestic goods. The Revolution had seriously disrupted the southern economy in the flow of exports; those states geared to the raising of rice and tobacco for export were so gravely affected that they were forced to supply their own wants by homespun industries. Jenny mills and manufactories sprang up in the South as well as the North. While their methods and products were the same, those in the South were primarily oversized plantation loom houses where, under the watchful eye of skilled supervisors, slaves spun and wove the coarse heavy materials that clothed them. Southern household manufacture of textiles was a necessary part of the plantation system, and it is this that prompted Jefferson's queries.* He wrote:

"As the state of Virginia, of which I am, carries on household manufactures of cotton to a great extent, as I also do myself, and one of our great embarrassments is the cleaning of the cotton of the seed, I feel a considerable interest in the success of your invention for family use. Permit me therefore to ask information from you on these points, has the machine been thoroughly tried in the ginning of cotton, or is it as yet but a machine in theory? What quantity of cotton has it cleaned on an average of several days, & worked by hand, & by how many hands? What will be the cost of one of them made to be worked by hand? favorable answers to these questions would induce me to engage one of them to be forwarded to Richmond for me." And then, he adds a postscript: "Is this the machine advertised the last year by Pearce at the Paterson manufactory?"

In his most elegant penmanship, Whitney, on November 24, 1793, replied and added a few more facts to the meager outline given to his father:

"It is about a year since I first turned my attention to constructing this machine, at which time I was in the State of Georgia. Within about ten days after my first conception of the plan, I made a small, though imperfect model. Experiments with this encouraged me to make one on a large scale. But the extreme difficulty of procuring workmen and proper materials in Georgia, prevented my completing the larger one, untill some time in April last. This though much larger than my first attempt, is not above one third so large as the Machines

---

* The plantation system resisted the introduction of English machinery and the imitation of the English factory system, the characteristics of the early New England textile manufacture. In 1809, when northern cotton manufactories were establishing industry on a par with agriculture and commerce, Jefferson discussed the advisability of promoting the sale of spinning machines in Virginia: "I must inform you we have no large manufactories in Virginia. This state tho without any comparison manufacturing more clothing than any other in the union, does it all in private families, each for its own use & no more,—no homespun is ever to be bought scarcely in our stores."

may be made, with convenience. The cylinder is only two feet two inches in length and six inches in diameter. It is turned by hand and requires the strength of one man to keep it in constant motion.

"It is the stated task of one negro to clean fifty Wt. (I mean fifty pounds after it is separated from the seed) of the greenseed cotton pr. Day. This task he usually completes by one oClock in the afternoon. He is paid so much Pr. lb. for all he cleans over and above his task, and for ten or fifteen Days successively he had cleaned from sixty to Eighty Wt. Pr. Day and left work every day before sunset. The machine cleaned fifteen hundred weight in about four weeks, which cotton was examined in N. York [which explains why he drove out from New York to the cotton factory at Turtle Bay], the quality declared good and sold in the market at the highest price. . . . I have not had much experience in cleaning the Blackseed cotton. I only know that it will clean this kind considerably faster than it will the green seeded, but how much I cannot say. After the workmen are acquainted with the business, I should judge, the *real* expence of one, which will clean a hundred Wt. Pr. Day, would not exceed the price of ten of those in common use.

"I shall have another person concerned with me in carrying on the business. . . . We have not yet determined at what price we shall sell the machines, it will however be so low as to induce the Purchaser to give them a preference to any other. We are now erecting one on a large scale, to be turned by horses, for our own use [at Mulberry Grove] and I do not think it will be in our power to make any for sale this winter.

"This, sir, is not the machine advertised by Pearce at the Patterson Manufactory. [Jefferson's postscript was being answered fully and positively.] I never saw a machine of any kind whatever for ginning cotton, untill several months after I invented this. . . . Some time last spring, I saw it mentioned in a Savannah News-Paper that Mr. Pearce of New Jersey had invented a machine for ginning cotton—but there was no mention made of the construction. I have since understood that his improvement was only a multiplication of the small rollers used in the common gins. This is everything I know concerning the machine to which I suppose you allude."

Whitney wanted it understood that his machine was not just another variant of the roller gin; his invention was the first to propose a new principle.

From his sojourn in the South, Whitney was acquainted with the importance of plantation manufactures. Not only was this a market where he and Miller would sell their gins, this was a market that could use special attachments to expedite home industries. His way of thinking, in terms of continuous processing to facilitate and increase production, can be seen in his answer to Jefferson's question about the gin's applicability to "family use."

"I think the machine is well calculated for family use. It may be made on a very small scale and yet perform in proportion to its size. I believe one might be made within the compass of two cubic feet, that would cleanse all the cotton which any one family manufactures for its own use. The machine itself does considerable towards carding the cotton, and I have no doubt [here is the hallmark of Whitney's acute perception of technical possibilities] but by leaving out the clearer and adding three or four cylinders with card-teeth, it would deliver the cotton completely prepared for spinning." Having thus indicated the versatility of his gin, Whitney closes his long letter: "It is my intention to come to Philadelphia within a few weeks and bring the model myself." From the model, Jefferson will be able "to form a more perfect idea of the machine."

But the weeks passed. The model he had been so certain of finishing still presented problems in construction: "I make very little progress in my preparations for the Southward," he wrote to Stebbins a few days before Christmas. A month had passed, a month of mishap and vain labor: "One of my best Cylinders have failed—I mean one of the pierced ones—but I lament the misfortune less since (I think) I have found a remedy for the general evil. I am convinced that it is impossible to procure any wood which will not spring if the wires are driven into it after the manner I have heretofore used. I now drive them across the grain of the wood, that is, the flat point of the wire, the edge of which went parallel with the grain is now driven across the grain so that it cuts its way and does not strain the timber." This change, with his reasons for revising his method of fixing the wire in the cylinder, is clearly explained; unfortunately he merely alludes to the special machine he devised "for cutting wire, on the plan which

I mentioned to you." How this was built, the principle on which it worked, is never stated. He only adds that "it answers very well, cuts equally on both sides, feeds itself and goes remarkably easy."

It is likely that his boyhood experience in manufacturing nails now stood him in good stead, for nail making was a pioneering step in mechanically producing uniform metal objects. It is quite possible that while he was still at college he heard about the new machinery that automatically cut the wire for card teeth, bent it according to specification, and set it into its leather backing. What is so extraordinary is that Whitney, without a lengthy apprenticeship in practical shop routine, intuitively approached the problem of producing cotton gins by analyzing the various processes into those elementary operations that could be easily performed by machinery. Whether he invented his wire-cutting machine or adapted another's invention to his special needs is of far less significance than that from the very first he tooled his shop in industrial, not handicraft, terms. In Whitney's case there is no sharp transition from one method of production to another; his initial attempt, though small and limited, has a modern quality—all his work was an improvement, an extension, an intensification of this basic pattern.

Finally, in February, having solved the cylinder construction, he finished his model—the last requirement for the formal issuance of his patent. Before he left for Philadelphia, he showed it to Stiles, for had not Stiles introduced him to Catherine Greene and Phineas Miller, the two friends who dominated the background of his signal achievement? "Mr. Whitney brot to my house & showed us his Machine, by him invented for cleaning Cotton of its seeds," Stiles records for February 22, 1794. "He shewed us the model which he has finished to lodge at Philadelphia in the Secretary of States Office, when he takes out his patent. This miniature model is perfect & will clean about a dozen pounds a day, or about 40 lbs. before cleaning. He has completed six large ones, Barrel perhaps five feet long to carry to Georgia. In one of these I saw about a *dozen pounds* of Cotton with seeds cleaned by one person in about twenty minutes, from which was delivered about *three pounds* of Cotton purely cleansed of seed. It will clean 100 cwt. a day. A curious & very ingenious piece of mechanism."

When he arrived at the seat of government in March, Whitney did not have the pleasure of demonstrating the actual working of the cotton gin to Jefferson, who had resigned and left for Monticello. But he undoubtedly showed it to Oliver Wolcott, Comptroller of the Treasury, who was known to be "strongly interested in the inventions of this country." Whitney's old tutor, Elizur Goodrich, gave him a letter of introduction. Wolcott, as a Yale graduate (1778), respected the opinion of the formidable mathematician, who personally recommended "Mr. Eli Whitney, a young gentleman [but five years Wolcott's junior] who has occasionally resided in my family for some time past." Then Goodrich, respected for his guarded words and discerning, discriminating mind, evaluated Whitney's qualities— qualities which his invention disclosed. Whitney, he wrote, "sustained a very fair reputation in the academic studies and is perhaps inferior to none in an acquaintance with the mechanic powers, and those of the branches of natural philosophy which are applicable to the manufactures and commerce of our country. To theory he happily unites talents to reduce it to practice; a circumstance which is rarely found in our young men of collegiate education. Surpassing the exactest workmen of my acquaintance in wood, brass, and iron, he is his own master workman in these respective branches, and resorts to himself to reduce his theories to experiment and practice."

Not a cloud marred Whitney's triumph as he proved the worth of his invention and received official recognition. The letter he wrote to his father on March 30, 1794, on his return to New Haven, shows that his debut on the world stage was all that he could have wished.

"It is with no small satisfaction that I have it in my power to inform you I am in good health. I have just returned from Philadelphia. My business there was to lodge a Model of my machine and receive a Patent for it. I accomplished everything agreeable to my wishes. I had the satisfaction to hear it declared by a number of the first men in America that my machine is the most perfect & the most valuable invention that has ever appeared in this Country. I have received my Patent. I have also obtained a passport from the Secretary of State to go into foreign Countries & also a particular letter of introduction from Mr. Randolph, Sect. of State, to Mr. Pinkney Minister Plenipotentiary for the U.S. at the Court of London.

"I have long been doting on making you a visit before I left New England again and have been waiting for an opportunity when I could leave my business, but having been detained a fortnight longer in Philadelphia than I expected, I find it impossible for me to come to Massachusetts before I go to Georgia. I must therefore desire you to come and see me before I leave this Place. I think the Roads are so much settled that it will not be a tedious journey. I expect to go directly from Georgia to England and it is uncertain when I shall return. I wish very much to see you before I go. But should I come to Westboro' now I must neglect my business so much as to lose several Hundred Dollars. If you come I shall be able to show you my machine. I have six of them nearly complete which I expect to carry to the Southward with me. I shall leave this place for Georgia in about twelve or fourteen days at farthest. I shall pay the Postage of this letter and desire the Postmaster to send it forward immediately. If it should so happen that you cannot come yourself, I wish Benjamin or Josiah or both to come—it will be a clever jorney for them & give them an opportunity of seeing the country. I am extremely sorry I cannot come and see all my friends, but as I have a fair prospect of making a handsome property and as I am so much in need of it, I think I ought not to neglect the opportunity. Though I have as yet expended much more money than the profits of the machine have been heretofore, and am at present a little pressed for money, I am by no means in the least discouraged. And I shall probably gain some honour as well as profit by the Invention. It was said by one of the most respectable Gentlemen in N. Haven that he would rather be the author of the invention than to be prime minister of England. But I mean not to be elated by my success so much as to be vain.

"I have a fair character and am in good Credit, as far as I am acquainted with myself.

> "My Respects to Mama & love to Brothers & Sisters
> "Hoping to see you here in a few Days I subscribe
> "myself your most obᵗ. & most
> "Affectionate Son

> > "ELI WHITNEY

"Mr. Eli Whitney"

VII Cotton and
The Industrial Revolution

NEVER did an American invention meet a more urgent need than Whitney's. Never was one hailed with more instant, widespread rejoicing. Its appearance could have been predicted with reasonable accuracy: the gin to clean the green-seed cotton could not have been invented before 1786, and its invention could not have been delayed long after. For the progress of the British cotton-textile industry was not confused nor capricious; it had its own order of development in which the production of raw cotton was the last of the imperative solutions.

A short-spaced series of inventions created the British cotton-textile industry, inventions that discarded skills unchanged since ancient days for processes of linked steps in which no skill was needed; inventions that made it profitable to bring the raw stuff across the Atlantic to Liverpool and thence distribute finished goods halfway round the world in India and China; inventions that drew families from the village and crowded them into slums, that transformed the farm laborer into a town worker, that denied the spinner his dexterity and the weaver his art, replacing them both with children just old enough to tend the simple wants of a machine. A vast literature documents how the great mass of the people lived through those momentous decades. Of a sudden new mountain ranges were lifted up, old landmarks wiped out. The change was abrupt, bewildering, harsh; the rhythm of work was torn loose from the seasons; its motions were new, monotonous, impersonal, without obvious meaning. A nation was quickly broken to industrial harness.

Today it is sometimes assumed that the words "Industrial Revolution" describe the shift from man power to steam power, that Watt's inventions overshadowed all others; whereas those who lived at that time knew that before there was a revolution in the prime mover, there had been one in production. In 1785, before engines were turning factory wheels, Arkwright's counsel, while arguing his client's patent rights, declared that the most useful discoveries had been made "by ingenious mechanics, conversant in the practises in use in their time, and practically acquainted with the subject-matter of their discoveries."

The machines constructed by the great mechanic-inventors did not add to the processes by which the vegetable wool was converted into cloth; these had been inherent in the seemingly simplest skill. The inventor reduced each action of the artisan's hands into its component parts, analyzed their function, and reproduced the function mechanically—the sum and sequence of separate acts giving an equivalent result. Baines in 1835 wrote lyrically of wonders still considered new: "It is by iron fingers, teeth, and wheels, moving with exhaustless energy and devouring speed, that the cotton is opened, cleaned, spread, carded, drawn, roved, spun, wound, warped, dressed, and woven. The various machines are proportioned to each other in regard to their capability of work . . . all are moving at once —the operations chasing each other; and all derive their motions from the mighty engine, which . . . toils through the day with the strength of perhaps a hundred horses . . . each workman performing, or rather superintending, as much work as could have been done by *two or three* hundred men sixty years ago."

"Sixty years ago"—his words hurry back to the decisive decade when a succession of inventions changed the very face of Britain. Already the period prior had been relegated to old wives' tales— when the manufacture of cotton goods in England was on the same simple level as in India, and all textile techniques, save for the introduction of the fulling mill and the Italian silk-reeling process, persisted as they had been in the days of Constantine. True, the genius of John Kay had revealed itself significantly in weaving. His fly shuttle, for which he was granted a patent in 1733, immeasurably lightened the weaver's task and doubled his production. Ignored by the woolen weavers, his invention was appropriated by the weavers of cotton cloths. Soon the yarn they required taxed the cotton spinners beyond their capacity. The one-thread wheel turning from morning till night in thousands of cottages could not keep pace with the demand created by the weaver's shuttle; men thought on how to improve spinning methods that they might augment the supply, for yearly yarn grew scarcer as more and more weavers adopted Kay's fly shuttle. The improvements in weaving necessitated improvements in spinning.

Silk spinning had been done on machines in Italy since late in the thirteenth century, but the secret technique had been so closely guarded that not until the eighteenth century was it introduced into England. But even then the devices used to spin silk yarn could not be adapted to wool, flax, or cotton; silk needs only to be doubled and twisted, the drawing-out process is not a prerequisite. The principle of spinning by rollers was first thought out by Lewis Paul, the son of a Huguenot refugee, and John Wyatt; the patent issued to them in 1738 clearly presents the basic idea: "The wool or cotton being prepared, one end of the roving is put between a pair of rollers, which by their motion draw in the cotton to be spun, and a suction of other rollers moving proportionately faster than the first draws the roving into any degree of fineness which may be required." Their concept was sound, and the mill they erected at Birmingham for the manufacture of yarn was decidedly modern—the rollers were operated by "power from a capstan with two asses"; notwithstanding, their venture failed. Spinning continued to be the bottleneck in the textile industry until Hargreaves, Arkwright, and Crompton righted the balance and provided yarn enough to feed the looms.

James Hargreaves, by trade a weaver and carpenter, by ability a man of original talent, is said literally to have stumbled on the germ of his invention. He noticed—how often competence has revealed itself as the capacity to notice—that when a spinning wheel was overturned, its spindle, now upright, continued to revolve even as its wheel continued to turn. For three years he worked to give form to the idea, and by about 1764 had perfected it; he named it, for his wife or daughter, the spinning jenny. (It was not patented until June, 1770.) In his original jenny, eight bobbins stood side by side in a row with an equal number of spindles in another. It increased production eightfold—within very short order a jenny would have a hundred spindles; but the jenny was robbed of some of its efficiency because its action was discontinuous. The machine was so simple that a child could operate it, and thus young children made their pitiful entry early in the textile industry.

Even as Hargreaves was bringing out his spindled jenny, Richard Arkwright—he was knighted Sir Richard before he died—was patenting his throstle, or, as it came to be known when harnessed to water power, the water frame (1769). How much of this machine Arkwright stole from Thomas Highs, a mechanic, how much he adopted from Wyatt and Paul's roller invention, is almost of less moment than that he brought their ideas to perfection and introduced them successfully. Neither mechanic nor inventor, Arkwright was by trade a barber; in part his genius lay in his quick unerring ability to sense what was needed, to get others to make it, and to combine separate parts into a functioning whole. Not the first to organize machines in factories, he was the first to make factories pay and to establish the factory system as the characteristic economic unit in the textile industry.* Other men might have been ingenious enough to find a way to spin cotton yarns strong enough for warps, but it was Arkwright who was smart enough to get Parliament to revoke its strenuous laws prohibiting the use of pure, unmixed cotton cloth. (The Act, passed in 1736, was framed to protect the woolen industry against the importation of Indian cottons.)

Kay, Hargreaves, and Crompton worked alone and died in poverty, but Arkwright confidently secured the backing of bankers, enlisted the technical advice of Strutt, the knitting-machine maker, and, when his patents were overthrown, showed his rivals that he needed no patent to secure him his preeminence. Carlyle savagely referred

* The factory system invited as many bizarre, ingenious ideas as any of man's inventions. There was, for instance, a Mr. Hatton of Dumferline, Scotland, who announced about 1820 that he had "kept *two mice* constantly employed in spinning sewing thread, by means of a machine similar to the tread mills. Each of the little animals spins every day from 100 to 120 threads, in performing which they have to move about ten and a half miles. The expense of maintaining each mouse is a half-penny for five weeks, & comparing this, with the quantity of the work done, it appears that each mouse earns about six shillings sterling per annum. Mr. Hatton proposes to hire an old edifice 100 feet long and 50 feet wide, in which he may employ 10,000 mice machines. If this enterprise should succeed, it is estimated that the annual gain will be about £2,300 sterling, clear of all expense & interest."

to him as "the bag-cheeked, pot-bellied barber," and seemed to describing "his fat, vulgar face, his goggling, heavy-lidded Arkwright's contemporaries begrudgingly acknowledged his capabilities but deplored his mind that was as coarse as it was bold and active. But the picture of the illiterate millionaire has a wistful air —he stole from his own scant sleeping hours to study spelling and grammar and improve his handwriting. Arkwright was the prototype of the captains of the new industries. Strong-willed and ruthless, ignorant of everything save their own ambitions and capacity for power, these men were in the strictest sense self-made; a bleak childhood deprived them of the cultured standards of their society, and taught them only the stark, mundane essentials required to keep alive.

Arkwright's invention did not conflict with Hargreaves': the water frame could spin strong warps, but it could not make fine threads; the jenny's finer, more fragile threads were ideal for filling. That these machines should have arrived on the scene simultaneously is remarkable; it is almost miraculous that an independent synthesis of the two should shortly have developed a third machine that borrowed from both and practically superseded both. Samuel Crompton's mule—so nicknamed because it was a cross between the water frame and the jenny—was finished in 1779. (It was never patented.) Its distinguishing feature—its spindles placed on a movable carriage —was an ingenious arrangement which permitted the roving to be stretched gently and evenly to make a yarn fine and strong.

Crompton was the very opposite of Arkwright. Ill at ease with himself and the world, he could not have found a more suitable place to live and work than his patched-up rooms in the decaying tenement that had been carved out of a former mansion, Hall-in-the-Wood. To Mantoux his portrait suggested "the features of Bonaparte in his younger days with the expression of a Methodist preacher," but Crompton was pathologically shy; his only reaction was to regret the fuss that prevented his enjoying "his little invention to himself in his garret."

Alas, for Crompton! The very existence of the machine he had called into being would make it impossible for spinners and weavers to remain isolated and independent in their garrets and cottages. A machine so complex was too expensive for workmen to own; a machine that could be enlarged to accommodate a multiplication of spindles would soon have burst their small houses asunder. Sixty years later Baines described a single factory room, containing a few massive mechanized mules whose "several thousand spindles may be seen . . . revolving with inconceivable rapidity, with no hand to urge their progress or guide their operations—drawing out, twisting, and winding up as many thousand threads." Crompton's mule carried cotton manufacture to a perfection it had not otherwise been able to attain. Inevitably, it strained the supplies of raw cotton to fill the whirling spindles.

In Whitney's day no one knew how fabulous a future awaited raw cotton. A plant that provides clothing, shelter, and even food, it is grown in sixty countries; somewhere in the world, every day in the year, cotton is being planted and picked. The boll contains, in addition to the textile fiber, the seeds—two-thirds of its weight—and the cotton linters, the short fuzz that adheres to the seed after the cotton has been ginned. Originally only the fiber was used; today the seeds and linters are no longer waste products. Cottonseed is rich in oil; it is transformed into vegetable shortenings, oleomargarine, and salad dressings, face creams, soaps, and automobile greases; its crushed hulls are an ingredient in the manufacture of plastics; its pressed kernels furnish fertilizer for other crops, and hulls and kernels, ground together, are an important food for livestock. The linters, removed in the cottonseed-oil processing, are even more mutable: chemistry gives them dozens of disguises—as rayon, as photographic and movie film, shatter-proof glass, plastics, writing paper, liquid cement, varnishes and lacquers, dynamite.

Subtract cotton in all its forms from the world as it is; strike out the thousand-odd widespread uses to which cotton has lent itself, and the answer will reveal modern man's dependence on this valuable staple; it will also make worth remembering when and how cotton as a textile became a giant serving England's economy.

Cotton is the cheapest, most plentiful, most versatile, and whitest of textile fibers, and a thread of cotton is stronger than an iron wire drawn out to the same diameter. Cotton can be washed and boiled and sterilized and starched; a pound of cotton can be spun into a thread so fine it will reach more than 150 miles, or twisted into a coarse cord of but a few hundred yards; it can be woven into textiles delicate and sheer, or those sufficiently tough to wear down metal surfaces, into cool fabrics or fabrics quilted to retain heat; its softness makes it ideal for clothing, and its durability and stamina give it industrial importance. It has been called "white gold." With steel and oil it is one of the titans of the present-day world; yet on the earliest horizons of history it was already known that cotton could be spun, woven, and dyed.

India is the home of its cultivation, and the processes devised by the ancient Hindus have not been changed: the machine has increased production astronomically even as it has sought to approximate the fineness, softness, and strength achieved by the unrivaled skill of those master craftsmen who used only primitive tools. Baines, a sober historian, writes lyrically of the "incredible perfection" of the sheer muslins that "might be thought the work of fairies, or of insects, rather than of men." In India the raising of cotton was as universal as the growing of food; every woman spent part of her time spinning, and in each village weavers furnished the cloth locally needed. After the cotton was picked, it was separated from its seeds by a rude roller gin, the charkha, turned by women. Then it was bowed, or teased, to cleanse it of dirt and knots.

Directly after, without carding, it was spun by women whose learned, marvelously acute touch produced yarns finer and more tenacious than any a machine could make. Reeled and arranged for the warp beam, the yarn went to the weaver, who, having sized the warp threads with starch, set up his rudimentary loom—as in Guzerat—under the "shade of tamarind and mango trees," and wove cloths so incredibly transparent that Baines agreed that their being called "webs of woven wind" was less poetic license than it was truly descriptive.

Each kind of cloth, specific for texture, weave, or patterning, celebrated the region of its birth; its distinctive manufacture was perfected over the centuries as its style was carefully transmitted from father to son. Bengal was famous for exquisite Dacca muslins, the Coromandel coast for chintzes and calicoes (that most American of words comes almost unchanged from the great city of Calicut) brilliantly dyed and printed; Surat, the port whence baftas, dhotis, puli-cats—strong cheap goods—were shipped, became a generic word for coarse cloths as Madras did for ginghams and patterned weaves; Raioxary and Baroche specialized in the dazzling art of bleaching "because of the large meadows and plenty of lemons that grow there-abouts, for they are never so white as they should be till dipped in lemonwater."

Herodotus first wrote about it for Europeans. His word "tree-wool" —*Baum-wolle* is the German for cotton—was enough to give birth to a mythical zoophyte, the "vegetable lamb," a strange kind of fruit "much resembling a sheep, having head, feet and tail. Its skin is cov-ered with down, very white and as soft as silk. It grows upon a low stalk, about two and a half feet high, some higher, and is supported just at the navel. The head hangs down as if it pastured or fed on the grass."

Qutun, whence the English word derives, was the name used by the Arab traders who imported the cloth into Italy and Spain, and it was from the Moors that England probably first bought cotton. The Wardrobe Act of 1212 mentions "twelve pence as the price of a pound of cotton for stuffing the acton of King John"—the acton was a quilted tunic worn under armor to prevent chafing. Soon cotton found a steady use as candlewicks, and from that time on, in in-creasing amounts, it was imported from Italy and the Levant. But cotton, even as late as the middle of the eighteenth century, was a minor auxiliary fiber of little commercial consequence.

For England, as for all Europe, wool, since the Stone Age, had been the staple yarn, and after the Norman Conquest Flemish weav-ers supplied a large part of England's needs, since, as it was bitterly said, the English had known no better what to do with their wool than the sheep that wore it. From a country that imported both raw wool and all but the crudest cloths, England in the time and under the leadership of Edward III (1327–1377) took the first step that was to secure for her the monopoly of this valuable commodity. Agents of the king went among Flemish workers urging advantages for them if they would move to England; about seventy families, bringing their trades and their tools, were dispersed throughout the land; gradually these and later arrivals established the mystery, as a skilled trade was called, of fine weaving. A time came when "English" was synonymous with the best in woolens and worsteds. Wool became "the flower and the strength, the revenue and blood" of the kingdom; England came of age knowing that her woolens were like gold, a commodity of exchange always needed, accepted everywhere. On this rested her monopoly that, like a talisman, outweighed the gold and silver treasure of Spain and multiplied faster than did the wealth made by the great trading fleet of Holland.

Manchester was a thriving town devoted to the weaving of woolens; but in 1641 the London merchant Lewis Roberts already noted that "neither doth the industry rest here." His *Treasury of Trafficke,* or a *Discourse of Forraigne Trade,* makes the first definite mention of its cotton manufacture. "They buy Cotton Wooll in *London,* that comes first from *Cyprus,* and *Smyrna,* and at home worke the same into Fustians, Vermillions, Dymities, and other such stuffes; and then return it to London, where the same is vented and sold." Manchester and cotton had not come together accidentally. Climate was a factor: an unpleasant dampness rolling in from the Irish Sea provided the moisture needed to keep cotton fibers supple as they were being processed, and the local farmers found it congenial to spend their time making yarn or cloth, only working outdoors during the short harvest season. Because English spinners could not make cotton strong enough for warps (until the spinning machines were invented), English weavers strung linen warps and only used cotton for fill; this limited them to the manufacture of heavy weaves which did not compete with the elegant domestic woolens nor with the fashionable calicoes and muslins imported from India. Cotton advanced slowly: no Hindu craftsmen were lured to England to establish there their inherited skills and techniques.

It was an infant industry—perhaps a lusty infant, but one that scarcely gave intimations of its future giant size. Defoe, in his tour of Great Britain (1727) had noted how Manchester had "extended in a surprising manner, being almost double to what it was a few years ago," and explained that "the grand manufacture which has so much raised this town is that of cotton in all its varieties." Yet despite this impressive expansion and activity, the cotton industry forty years later was still so negligible a factor in the national economy that neither cotton spinners nor weavers were represented in the procession of trades that marked Manchester's celebration of the coronation of George III (1763). How different was the coronation procession of George IV in 1820! On that occasion the cotton magnates were accorded places of honor and preferment. They walked slowly, importantly, conscious of their power. Cotton was now king, and Manchester, the heart of the new empire, was Cottonopolis.

Thus it was explicitly acknowledged that cotton, the newest of the fibers to be manufactured in Britain, had preempted the place of the first, wool. The woolen industry had a long-established tradition; techniques and practices had become as sacred as the standards they had maintained. Over the centuries the woolen manufacture had neither to worry about supplies of raw wool nor compete with superior foreign-made cloths. It was secure. It rejected any innovation, any deviation from the prescribed rituals. The woolen weavers had not disregarded Kay's fly shuttle out of stupidity; the demands on them were for a faithful performance of customary practices, not for inventions. The mechanics working in cotton manufacture were not smarter nor more flexible; it was simply that they were in a new, growing industry whose arteries had not hardened with investments and habits. It was their good fortune that they were free to create their entire plant within a relatively short period and at a later, more technically advanced time.

"Cotton, cotton, cotton was become almost the universal material for employment"; a vast change had swept over Lancashire as cotton replaced wool. This booming, determined, accelerating industry made the large-scale production of raw cotton inevitable. And those who had seen the upsurge of fruitful inventions that, following their own laws of progression solved the problems of production, strength, and fineness of yarn, doubted not that an adequate supply of raw cotton would be forthcoming. *When* was the only question asked.

Whitney, like most Americans, received from Hamilton's *Report* his first concrete knowledge of the textile machines that had been invented during the long war years and the troubled decade that had anticipated hostilities. In December, 1791, the Secretary of the Treasury, assured that Slater's efforts had succeeded, had proudly announced that the Arkwright machines had crossed the Atlantic and were already operating in Rhode Island. The *Report* also made the southern planters acutely aware of the vast amounts of cotton annually required by the British millowners, and of the potential worth of cotton as a crop in their own economy.

Statistics printed in newspapers reinforced the meaning of generalized statements and gave a measure of the magnitude of British raw cotton needs: in seven years (1783 to 1790) cotton imports had climbed from 9,000,000 pounds to 28,000,000. These amounts must have seemed fantastic to the Southern planters, for in 1791 their total cotton crop amounted to less than 190,000 pounds, and the exports but a few hundred bags. Extreme as the figures appeared, they would be trifling compared with the cotton-consumption figures soon to be reached and the percentage which the South would contribute. When in 1812 Whitney petitioned Congress to extend his patent rights in the gin, of the 63,000,000 pounds imported by England, close to half was grown and ginned in the southern states. In 1825, the year of Whitney's death, the United States had raised three-quarters of the 228,000,000 pounds imported by Great Britain! (The cotton raised in the South far exceeded these amounts; the figures do not include the cotton used domestically.) These figures tell the dramatic shift in British dependence on the American South for her raw cotton; conversely, they imply that the powerful British cotton-textile manufacturers accorded a dominant position to the leaders of southern agriculture, and sustained them in their unshakable belief in their economy—the crop, the method of cultivation, the necessity for slave labor.

It is a striking fact that the answer to the planter's hopes came as speedily as it did. With but a brief preamble, Whitney invented the gin designed to clean the only kind of cotton that could be grown in the interior; his invention made possible the crop that paced the growing production of the powered machines.

VIII

Will the Planters Pay?

From the very first, Miller and Whitney's business was circled by pitfalls. To know simply that they did not realize their great expectations is not enough—Tolstoi begins his tragic story of Anna Karenina with the observation that "happy families are all alike; every unhappy family is unhappy in its own way." So an examination of the sad, worrisome welter of detail that filled the short life of the partnership makes clear the devastating mistake on which their business was predicated; it also gives insight into that society. Then the gin becomes, not a machine with an unusual name, but the wonderful and useful creation of a particular person; and Miller & Whitney is no longer a business partnership, but two men—Miller and Whitney—united by respect and affection and a common cause.

Together they fought a series of protracted, shifting encounters, grappled with credit stringencies and legal loopholes, contended against the Georgia planters and farmers, who were resentful and covetous, straitened and accustomed to direct action; together they patiently dispelled the uncertainties and suspicions of the powerful British spinners. During their lifetimes they had a partial success. The final thundering triumph of the cotton gin reduced them to anonymity; by fostering southern cotton cultivation, the forces they evoked were too mighty, too removed in time and complexity, to be tied to the memory of their ginning business. Because the cotton gin shaped the South as it is today, it is well to turn a high-powered microscope on that first fruitful moment.

Miller & Whitney was formed to exploit a patent, and a patent had become an unstable fulcrum on which it was hoped to balance pri-

vate right and public good. It has been cynically noted that a patent
does not protect, it merely gives its owner the right to sue. Since a
patent is concerned with an intangible property—a technological
idea—its ultimate strength as a legal instrument rests, paradoxically,
more on the social climate than on statutory provisions.

Its ancestry goes back to the exclusive privilege, or monopoly,
granted court favorites by the king; in England the abuses that attached themselves to these privileges were pruned during the reign
of James I by the Statute of Monopolies (1623). At that time the
ambivalence of the institution was recognized and its elements
separated into the socially useful and the politically offensive. No
longer was a patent a royal gift arbitrarily bestowed; it became a
right open to anyone who satisfied stated routine requirements. Only
new inventions of proven worth were to be rewarded with favorable
privileges; the protection granted a patentee was limited in time to
a definite period. Historically, a patent has always had to fight for
its privileges: from Spitsbergen to China the trading companies—
monopolies operating under a royal charter—were plagued by inter-
lopers just as later trespassers infringed on the right of those who
lawfully held patents.

In the United States the first patent bill (1790) defined as its subject matter "any useful art, manufacture, engine, machine, or device,
or any instrument thereon not before known or used"; it created
a board, composed of three cabinet members, to grant a patent "if
they shall deem the invention or discovery sufficiently useful and
important," and it set the patent's duration at fourteen years. In 1793
these provisions were substantially changed. The board was discon-
tinued, and instead the Secretary of State was empowered to issue
a patent to anyone who paid the application fee and presented working drawings and a model. Thus an administrative right to evaluate
deteriorated into a clerical function that merely recorded anything
properly submitted; the Executive branch of the government, as licensing agent, was relieved of the responsibility for sifting priority
and settling technological principles. It was under this amended
act of February 21, 1793, that Whitney obtained his patent.

Who in the United States before Miller & Whitney had tried to
create a new kind of business—and one of considerable magnitude?

Until that time most of the forms of economic activity, like the tools and the skilled workmen who used them, came from Europe or preserved European practices. The notable creative thought in America had been directed into political channels—Franklin is not remembered primarily for his electrical experiments nor Jefferson for his plough. What had Miller & Whitney to take as an example, as they detailed the nature of their business? Today, they could choose whether they would manufacture or license the manufacture of gins for sale to individuals, rent gins to planters, set up ginneries and charge for cleaning the cotton, or buy the cotton, clean it, and sell it to the mills. In those days, when trading was synonymous with business, they could have thought only in trading terms. The size of their undertaking might have suggested the structure of the great land companies that profitably opened the trans-Allegheny country to settlers; but even though the partners knew that they were offering planters the means of exploiting the upland country (how vast a cotton empire, no one could have imagined) their patent did not convey the same property rights as a land grant. The gin, like a mill, a forge, a furnace, processed raw material; but while these catered to limited local markets, demanded capital to start and considerable skill to run, the gin cost little to make, no skill to operate, and was designed for a rapidly expanding world market. (Almost from the first, efforts were made to sell the gin rights outside the United States; as far as can be judged, these efforts all failed.) The partners might have considered the strictly legal aspects of their patent and equated them with those of a franchise for a turnpike, a bridge, a canal, or a ferry, where tolls were allowed to reward the promoters' initiative and compensate them for expenditures. This idea came to them later, almost as an afterthought.

What had they to learn from other inventors? Could they be guided by the example of Joseph Jenks (Jenckes), one of the earliest American mechanics and one of the very few to be granted a patent (1646) in colonial Massachusetts? He gave the scythe its modern shape; true, he perfected an agricultural tool, but his invention did not give dominion to a crop. Or could they profit by the experience of Oliver Evans, the self-taught, brilliant engineer whom, perhaps, Whitney had met when in Philadelphia? His recently acquired patent

(1790) revolutionized flour milling, for in his machinery were embodied and utilized modern techniques for the movement of materials during processing. Evans was even then making trips throughout the central states trying vainly to find a millowner who would accept his machinery as a gift in return for acting as his agent. Perhaps the apathy of the millowners who clung to their established work patterns even when confronted with money-saving, time-saving, labor-saving devices impelled Miller & Whitney to feel they must arouse interest in their machine.

The possibilities they had reviewed were those that presented themselves at that time; no other. They had tied their fortunes and their futures to promoting a "jaunty devise," as Thomas Hobbes, in the heyday of a mercantile economy, would have called Whitney's invention. They were guided in their decisions by the traditions of an economy where enterprise was secured by a monopoly; but the business they launched served the textile industry, the industry that in men's minds was equated with the vigorous, victorious new order where enterprise sought to be free.

At that moment of triumph, in that year of discovery, when models were being built and plans projected and a wholly new business shaped, who could have said whether the invention needed promotion or protection? Certainly Whitney, Miller, and Catherine Greene must have weighed the question and felt satisfied with the solution they reached: the machine Whitney had put together was shown to friendly, influential visitors but withheld from public view. This compromise originated from their worry that the gins might lack enough cotton to process; it blinded them to a greater danger—the appetite of planters starving for want of a marketable crop.

The first notice of Whitney's invention to the community at large appeared on March 6, 1794, in the *Gazette of the State of Georgia:*

"The subscriber will engage to gin, in a manner equal to picking by hand, any quantity of the green seed cotton, on the following terms: viz. for every five pounds delivered him in the seed he will return one pound of clean cotton for the market.

"For the encouragement of cotton planters he will also mention that ginning machines to clean the green seed cotton on the above

terms will actually be erected in different parts of the country before
the harvest of the ensuing crop.

"Phineas Miller
"Mulberry Grove near Savannah, March 1, 1794."

The date is important; it attests to the partner's feeling the need
for quick action. For Miller rushed into print before Whitney had
received the formal patent, before they had signed their partnership
papers. Whitney sold a half-interest in his patent rights to Miller
on June 21, 1794, for $1,000, and they then signed their copartnership
agreement. Their haste to advertise may have been due to their desire to notify the planters to be ready for the April planting; it may
have been a reassurance given the planters that no matter how large
their crop, it would be cleaned of its seed. The partners remembered
the frenzied laments of but a year and a half earlier, when Whitney
had first come to the South and "the culture of the Green seed cotton
had then just commenced as a crop in the upper country, & two or
three Million pounds of this article in the seed, had been raised &
picked in from the field, but for want of a suitable Gin but a small
part of it had been prepared for the Market." Finally—and this was
not incidental—they were serving notice that the commission appointed by the State of Georgia to secure the invention of just such a
machine need look no further.

The terms offered by the partners are revealing. They show the
nature of the structure of the completely new enterprise of which
Whitney's invention was the keystone. They were not offering the
gin for sale. They knew, on the one hand, that they could not manufacture enough machines to satisfy the market were every planter
to want one and, on the other hand, that few of the men who would
turn to the growing of cotton had the price of a gin—one of Whitney's elaborately finished machines would have had to sell at from
$400 to $500. Prudence suggested their solution: the advantages of
a business that confined itself to processing the cotton for the planters, the fee to be paid in cotton, not cash. Yet the terms also make
clear that their monopoly was to be complete, their charges high.

Their actual calculations do not exist, but their method can be
surmised. Experiments had given them the ratio of cleaned cotton

to uncleaned cotton—the weight of the former was one-third the weight of the latter, seeds and field débris accounting for the difference. In setting up their system of charges, they used five pounds of uncleaned cotton as the unit which yielded one and two-thirds pounds of cleaned cotton. Of this they returned one pound to the owner and retained for themselves two-thirds of a pound. From this gross profit they covered their manufacturing and shipping expenses plus an annual prorating of the cost of the gin to be paid off during the term of their patent; it also included installing, operating, and maintaining their ginneries, sums expended for the purchase of water sites, and the erection of elaborate gear and buildings. To this was added their labor costs—in each ginnery allowance had to be made for feeding the white overseer, who was "to receive & deliver the Cotton, repair the gins & superintend their work, paying for the labour of the Negroes who are required to attend the gins & Bag the cotton at the rate of two shillings per day for the men & one shilling & sixpence for the women." The hiring of slaves from masters was common practice. Miller, writing to a planter, closed a letter with the remark that it had been mentioned "that you might be induced to hire out some Negro fellows. If a hundred dollars per annum or upwards would procure them, I would make such a proposal."

An integral part of the business, announced at the very beginning, was setting up establishments in "different parts of the country." While Whitney was in Connecticut getting the machines made, Miller had been traveling through the upper country, examining the localities where cotton cultivation was displacing everything else, and choosing sites accessible to the growers so as to reduce the heavy costs of overland transportation. Miller was responsible for managing these installations.

There is a clear statement of how energetically Miller had erected ginneries around Augusta, where the cotton cultivation centered. Writing Whitney just two years after they had started, he listed and commented on the extent of their operations. Already the size of their enterprise is impressive; there are also hints that trouble was in the offing. At Mulberry Grove "five gins in good order which will clean out 500 wt. per day & pretty well supplied; this is a good draught for eight lean cattle"; at the ginnery at Augusta, "ten gins well put up—and water plenty, which will clean when they have employment 800 wt per day but are three fourths of the time idle"; the ginnery near Washington has "four gins now in order (two more erecting), clean about 400 wt per day & have been employed the greatest part of the winter"; the ginnery near Petersburg "had only cleaned out six thousand wt when the fresh [spring flood] over set the gin house, they are just now re-erecting it"; the ginnery at Golphinton still worked their two gins "with horses but the water machine is to be put up this coming summer—he [Major Shields] cleans his cotton with more attention than any one of the persons engaged with us"; the four gins in their Waynesborough plant clean "as much as five hundred wt per day when there is water—but this is the greater part of the time very deficient—this establishment as soon as our funds admit must be removed"; at Louisville (Georgia) two gins would be in work by the middle of that month to process the "fifty thousand wt of cotton on hand—Waynesborough has about the same quantity"; the ginnery being set up at Beaufort, South Carolina, promises to "work very well & will clean about 300 wt of black seed per day and has the promise of about thirty thousand weight to clean."

And this was but the beginning: "Application had lately been made for another establishment at the mouth of the Eddito [Edisto] River, which will most probably be accepted. I have in view also to erect in the upper part of this state about two others during the summer & perhaps three in the upper parts of Carolina. This degree of extension will answer pretty well to meet the ensuing crop of cotton."

The partners minutely considered the internal organization of their enterprise. Meticulous keeping of all kinds of records was routine; but that they would schedule the many separate elements—the cleaning, packing, baling, shipping, every step of which was new—submit each particular process to experiment, and standardize the preferred technique, is arrestingly modern. (Scientific management is the term now used for such studied methods; its great exponent, Frederick Winslow Taylor [1856–1915], instituted elaborate research methods to establish manufacturing techniques.) Viewing the critical first years through their business letters, one sees the cotton gin less as a single creative act than the initial, crucial impulse from which flowed a succession of minor inventions, clever innovations, and skills. Many valid ideas were stillborn, and some died for lack of funds: there were the carding attachment Whitney had suggested to Jefferson to expedite household cotton manufactures and the projected mills "of suitable construction" to extract cottonseed oil. It was appreciated from the start that the seeds might "also turn to some little value." * Those ideas intimately related to their business were instantly put to use, such as a bagging machine Whitney perfected when he was at Mulberry Grove assembling and testing the first gins. Miller was enchanted with the contraption: "The saving of labor will exceed my expectations," since with the bagging machine "three hands will perform all the labor of ginning & bagging six hundred weight per day." In a slave economy, the work done by prime field hands, as they were called, had to maintain a population of less productive slaves—the very young, the old, the sick, the maimed. This consideration in estimating labor costs is reflected in Miller's advising a planter that "two boys, or one old or lame hand and a boy can conveniently attend two [gins]." The machine reduced operating charges to one strong, able-bodied man trained to pack the clean cotton properly.

The bagging machine made it more likely that the packing would be done properly—an important consideration, for they had been told that the cotton "will both sell better and be transported with more care when it is packed hard." Miller, instructing the manager of the Golphinton ginnery, makes the thoroughness of the partners' investigations very clear: "First then after your bag is well sewed with twine, let a strong hoop be put over the mouth and being turned over basted on with twine. Then let the bag be well wet and

* How farsighted the partners were in their thrifty ideas to extract the oil from cottonseed can be seen from the remarks made by Professor Denison Olmsted thirty years later (1824). Writing in the *American Journal of Science and Arts,* he deplored the fact that no use had been found for "the vast quantity of cotton seed [that] is annually accumulated, forming a useless and in many instances, an offensive and noxious pile around the cotton gins." Only limited, imperfect efforts were made to extract oil, even though "nearly three fourths of the entire cotton crop consists of seed." Considering any aspect of cotton cultivation—rapid soil exhaustion, agricultural methods, labor, and so forth—one is appalled at the blatant, unrelieved waste.

continue to keep it so while packing by a loose mop, of cloth or cotton, and let the packer continually beat down the cotton round the edge of the bag with a pestle as heavy as can be worked with convenience—the upper end to be fitted to the hand & the lower end a little flatted & rounded at the same time as to force the cotton down like a wedge. A packer can in this way pack a bag made of five yards of cloth in a day with care, and such a bag ought to weigh from 260 to 320 lbs. according to the hand employed."

Baling and bagging were only less important than ginning. The partners methodically investigated each. What was the best kind of bagging in which to ship the cleaned cotton? They specified that the bagging cloth should average about one and one-third pounds per yard and contain a "web of an improved quality." There are suggestions that Miller invested money in a bagging factory started by a Newport friend, Christopher Fowler; it is certain that despite loans, specifications, pleading, visits, and lawsuits, Miller & Whitney never obtained what they had contracted for and that they finally relied on the superior European-made cloth or an adequate substitute woven in Massachusetts.

Their insistence on quality was based on sound business reasons. Miller itemized for Fowler the increased costs incurred when "an inferior quality of cotton bagging in packing Cotton for the European Market" was used, since "a bag of cotton containing five yards of Cloth will pay [in freight] about ten Dollars, it being perfectly immaterial whether the bag holds three hundred weight or but two hundred. The space it occupies on the ship is the same." Loosely packed cotton not only cost more to ship, it did not travel as well as the tightly packed fiber.

Then again, the question might center on the size of the storeroom to be built at a ginnery. How were they to reckon when no two installations were alike in size and capacity and it was uncertain how much cotton the growers would bring in? Yet, despite intangibles and variables, the partners could suggest a simple, basic unit of measurement: "For the store-room you can judge as well as we," they wrote their manager at Petersburg, "only take into consideration that a Cubic foot of building will contain about twelve pounds of Cotton in seed and if well trod together, about fifteen."

The same neat estimating went into packing the gins themselves to insure their safety on their long journey from the factory in New Haven to their final destination in the South: "The Machines themselves weigh 315 lbs. each, and two of them are packed for transportation in three boxes whose weight [when empty] is 200 lbs. So that two Machines when ready to be carried on waggons weigh 830 lbs." And, lest this seem unduly arbitrary, it was explained that the gins "having been packed up in Boxes two together at the Northward, cannot be repacked in a different form without great inconvenience. I have therefore sent two machines, with a view that the other may remain until it shall be wanted by yourself."

Miller painstakingly pointed out that packing and handling had not been the only considerations—two gins were a more efficient operation than one; especially where the purchaser had mentioned that he intended using horsepower: "The strength of one horse is fully competent to carry two [gins]." Continuing in the same expository vein, he adds: "If there is a stream of water in your Neighborhood, it is by far the most eligible force which can be applied to Ginning cotton. You will then require a simple water wheel at eight to ten feet in diameter with a drum of the same size and on the same shaft which will turn the Ginns." He reassured the gentleman who erected the first ginnery in the upper country of South Carolina that his outlay in money and effort to install the gins in a satisfactory manner will be repaid: "A good set of gear work, properly made to work two of these machines will last with care and slight repairs, I presume, nine years which will reduce the expence to a small amount on the very large crops which you are able to make."

From the business letters of Miller & Whitney, it is hard to say whether their didactic tone reflects Miller's nature—he corresponded for the firm—or whether each step in the installation and operation was a new lesson, carefully presented with full explanations, to new pupils. No matter to whom written, on practical subjects they only suggest, they are never curt; they never issue peremptory orders, but honor their managers with their reasons and conclusions. "The size or form of the water wheel is not very material, as we have found by much experience that the gins work best with bands which go around a Barrel . . . for a Barrel of about 4 feet diameter lying horizontally and turned about 40 times per minute will be sufficiently fast for the purpose. . . . The length of the Barrel may be about fifteen feet and may best be placed under the floor where the gins are at work by which means it will be entirely out of the way. . . . With respect to the size of the building, twenty by thirty feet will be of sufficient extent to work the Machines; such a building ought to have about six panes of glass . . . [and] stand with the side towards the water wheel as the drum must work under the floor."

Objections raised by a millwright, who disagreed with specifications they had proposed, were tactfully answered. "The opinion offered in our letter to you was the result of the best theoretic calculations we could make. And altho a certain degree of experience is requisite for forming a mature judgment in the construction of all kinds of water works, yet the general principles of the force & pressure of water remaining always the same, knowledge of these principles may perhaps alone be depended on for work on so Small a scale as the one in contemplation." After this polite preamble, their objective is stated: "We wish the Gins to be turned at the rate of at least twice per second & to be able to turn them as fast as twice & a half in that time, if there should not appear to be too much heat generated by so great a friction."

To mechanic or customer, manager, broker, lawyer, the letters show the same amiable breeding. To all they are courteous. A manager whose careless ginning and packing had cost them two bags of cotton was mildly rebuked; their strongest expressions, shock and disappointment, were directed to another manager who had been caught in an act of unmitigated knavery. The long sentences flow on and on; nothing disrupts the cadence of the full rounded phrases, amenities expressive of a more leisurely age. Correspondence had not yet been whittled down to the new business order.

The letter books contain lengthy letters faithfully, painstakingly copied out in longhand; dry letters spiced with the minutiae of the moment which still hold an unobtrusive, authentic flavor; letters which, even when they cry out at the events that seem about to overwhelm the firm, give forth an aroma of hope. Both Miller and Whitney were fighters—not aggressive, but determined; they faced the problems that gradually, it seems inevitably, took shape.

The first sentence of the first letter (May 11, 1794) is almost lyric. Miller proclaims the end of their worries: "Mr. Whitney has arrived with the Cotton ginning machines, & the one which has been put together discovers them to be much superior to the description I had given you." Whitney had returned to Mulberry Grove, his patent secured, the machines manufactured for the first ginneries. During the next busy weeks a stream of impatient visitors came to see the wonderful invention; everywhere it was discussed, but still only friends were admitted to the building where the gins were being installed. Continued caution was necessary, for already they had been warned that their property was being threatened. A few days after the partnership had been formed, the new firm addressed itself to Edmund Randolph, Secretary of State, advising him that "application will be made at your office for patenting some intended improvements on the machine for ginning cotton," and asking "that action be deferred untill we have sufficient time to shew the infringement which is therein attempted." Their tone is still one of calm confidence; they appear to feel that they have but to advise and ask and their rights will be safeguarded.

Certainly no misgivings could have been sensed in 1794, when Whitney's "greatest apprehensions" were that "we shall not be able to get machines made as fast as we shall want them. We have now Eight hundred Thousand weight of Cotton on hand & the next crop will begin to come in very soon. It will require machines enough to clean 5 or 6 thousand Wt. of clean cotton per Day, to satisfy the demands for next Year, I mean for the crop which comes in this fall. And I expect the crop will be double another year." Whitney was elated at the prospect of the first year's business, and eager to have the gins ready to handle the greater crop promised for the next year. He had planned to stay only a short time in Georgia, but "was taken sick with the Georgia fever [probably malaria] about the middle of June & confined to my bed ten or twelve days, but had got quite well before I left. . . . My machinery was in operation before I came from Georgia."

It was August before he could get back to his small workroom, and he arrived in New Haven to find the "town much alarmed with the sickness." Stiles, who watched the epidemic gain momentum, remarked that "there seem to be two disorders 1. The scarlet fever & ulcerous sore Throat which raged here last winter and tho much abated, yet extant. 2. The yellow fever brot in by a Vessel here about 15 or 16 June last, which has been lurking about ever since & now proved dreadful. . . . More mortal than the Small Pox, tho' less contagious." Some of Whitney's workmen took ill, and panic gripped New Haven. All communications with the stricken town were stopped; the absence of letters from Whitney caused Miller "not a little anxiety," and slowed down his ambitious schedule.

His fears for Whitney's safety—"Our Eli Whitney, notwithstanding his own personal danger still remains at New Haven"—were matched only by his fears that they might not be ready for the season close at hand. Thus, while he reassured his managers that they might expect the new gins in time for the autumn harvest, he exhorted Whitney: "Do not let a deficiency of money, do not let anything hinder the speedy construction of the gins. The people of the country are almost running mad for them, and much can be said to justify their importunity. When the present crop is harvested, there will be a real property of at least fifty thousand, yes of a hundred thousand dollars lying useless unless we can enable the owners to bring it to market. Pray remember that we must have fifty to one hundred gins between this and another fall, if there are any workmen in New England, or in the Middle States to make them. In two years we will begin to take long steps up hill, in the business of patent ginning, fortune favoring."

There was little need for Miller to add pressure to Whitney's own awareness of the urgency to produce the machines. On the trip home he must have planned how best to manufacture quickly a large number of gins; by late fall many ideas had taken shape. "I have been so busy that I could hardly find time to write," but write to his father he did, and for all his activity, he sounded serene. "The approach of winter obliges me to improve every moment in preparing for it. My Barn 26 feet by 20 is raised and I expect will be covered and finished in the course of next week. I have been laying in materials and I have a prospect of my business going on well this winter." The success that seemed within sight allowed him to be generous, for generosity was part of his nature; from the first harvest of cotton then being cleaned on his machine he arranged to have a bag sent to his father—"as much as you will want for your own use, to which you shall be perfectly wellcome."

Happily, auspiciously, 1794 drew to a close. Miller had succeeded in securing loans to finance their manufacturing and operating expenses; he rejoiced to have obtained sums at a reasonable interest rate of 8 per cent. Another year or two of hard work, a steady expansion, a profit that would soon begin to increase handsomely—Whitney faced the coming year with trust.

Miller & Whitney's credit situation was a thing patterned by that age and tailored by that region. The firm was started when the national coinage began to be minted and the first Bank of the United States was but a few years old. In those days barter prevailed, and an accumulation of capital was usually in kind, not cash; money was scarce, large personal fortunes were exceptional, and credit was designed for long-term commercial enterprises or to carry farmers from crop to crop. Extended in the expectation of profits, credit was not yet invested in industry to secure interest. Miller's solutions to his problems are a forcible reminder that the Revolutionary War left the South poor; and the passing years had seen it grow poorer as plantations that relied on tobacco, rice, and indigo found these crops less and less profitable. Mulberry Grove—when Whitney visited there—was a grandiose ghost of the wealth its rice fields had once purchased, a wealth that neither Greene's genius nor Miller's zealous devotion could revive. The antebellum South, as it has come to be remembered, had not yet been born. It came and flowered with cotton.

The financial structure of Miller & Whitney owed its resilience and stamina to the credit it could command by using the Greene estate. That it was pledged for substantial sums was Catherine's contribution to the enterprise, for without her full approval as executrix Miller could never have hazarded the estate. Her faith in the patent, in the partnership, expressed itself in such tangible terms that Whitney never forgot it. Years later he assumed a $5,000 mortgage to relieve Catherine of "embarrassments, perplexities & misfortune." In addition to the Greene estate, Miller had—as far as can be reconstructed—an assortment of assets with which to work.

A large part of his commitments and expenditures were to be met by money he expected to receive—money paid for Miller & Whitney's share of the ginned fiber, money from cottonseed sold to planters. Some cash he had, and both he and Whitney could personally raise a little more. It was in the hope of quickly making a large cash profit that Miller participated heavily in the Yazoo Land purchase.

"Fraud" is the word that usually follows Yazoo. It summarizes the landgrab—a deal pushed through the Georgia legislature by a handful of influential, wealthy men; its magnitude—some thirty-five million acres in what is now Alabama and Mississippi; its secrecy—the sale price was set at a cent and a half an acre when the grantees already had assurances that blocks of their land companies' shares would be taken up by northern purchasers at a considerable advance; its arrant partiality—hundreds of applicants for shares at par received nothing. In Georgia, in December of 1794, every one was bewitched by the Yazoo; Miller offered, by way of apology, the excuse that "the purchase about to be made of the western territory of this state has so entirely engrossed the public attention as to leave it very difficult to transact any other business." When the corrupt facts spelled out their story, the disillusioned outcry of a defrauded citizenry was so loud, so general, so continuous, that in February of 1796 a new governor signed a rescinding act; the sale was revoked; and as if to exorcise an evil deed, the records of the transaction were publicly burned in an official ceremony.

The Yazoo Land débacle—one in a series of frenzies recurrent in American economy, frenzies of which Clark, in his scholarly study of manufactures in the United States, said tersely, poetically, "Unoccupied land drank up liquid capital as thirstily as a desert"—preempted funds in the North, as well as the South, that might otherwise have been tapped for loans by Miller & Whitney. His gamble cost Miller his available cash; it added costly suits filed in Connecticut to collect from reneging buyers. Whitney early appreciated how unfortunate the Yazoo flyer might prove. Even before the sale was revoked by the Georgia legislature, he sounded a warning. "Money is growing extremely scarce in this State [Connecticut]—ten times so much as when you were here. Speculation is at a stand. . . . It is a conceeded Maxim that it is altogether uncertain whether a Land-Speculator is worth anything or not. And the money-lenders are very shy of a man who is concerned in the buying. . . . Josiah Wooster, for instance, (Who is worth more money than when he is engaged in speculation) cannot hire money so low by six per Cent *per* Ann. as he could before he engaged in speculation. And it makes that difference in his getting his notes discounted." Whitney was not passing judgment on gambling; he was convinced of the hurt being done the firm by Miller's diverting cash and energy into Yazoo stock manipulation.

To the charge of having been imprudent, Miller conceded that perhaps he had been, but only in having placed "so much confidence in the punctuality of the People of Connecticut & to engage in the land purchase to an extent that I cannot pay for." And then, as if weighing his mistake and his motive, he continued in an acrid tone: "It also may be considered as imprudent to pledge so much money as we have done in the construction of the cotton gins before the successfull use of them was rendered certain. But if my disposition has heretofore been too ardent, I think it has become pretty well cooled down." At the time Miller was excusing himself, nothing but excuses were left him; he was inextricably caught in the consequences of that venture.

The partners were insensitive to local opinion; neither appreciated that the greatest harm done their business by Miller's Yazoo involvement was that his connection was commonly known. His name was linked to the original sale, and it was widely said that he had disposed of shares at an enormous profit to Connecticut merchants. What was more natural than that the hate and opprobrium generated in the great number of frustrated would-be buyers powered their opposition to Miller & Whitney's exclusive privilege; their success in having the land sale rescinded emboldened the rank and file of Georgia farmers to attack his ginnery venture and persevere in trying to have the patent rights set aside.

Ill fortune sometimes uses an event, not as a causative agent, but as a touchstone to reveal unsuspected, unplumbed potentials. Such was the disaster which now struck the new firm. Whitney's shop in

New Haven caught fire and was completely consumed. The flames for a few moments illuminated other elements. Seventeen ninety-five was an ugly year; it had still uglier sisters.

"I wrote you from New York but a few Days since at which time I was quite out of health," Whitney's letter of March 22, 1795, to his father begins. In that earlier note he mentioned that his work was so well organized as to be able to satisfy Miller's demand for gins; that he was in New York on business—to arrange for the "Continuance of the loan on the same Terms (Viz) at one per cent per month"—and that there he had suffered an attack of malaria, a recurrence of the sickness contracted the previous summer at Mulberry Grove. Then, bluntly, he tells his father how, still weak, he had returned to his busy workshop. "But alas, how is the scene changed! When I returned from N. York I found my property all in ashes! My shop, all my tools, material, and work equal to twenty finished cotton machines all gone—

"The manner in which it took fire is altogether unaccountable. It caught fire when the workmen were gone to breakfast. The shop was swept as clean as any dwelling house the evening before—there was not a hat-crown full of fire in both chimneys—and not a bucket full of chips or shavings in all the building. The hearths were swept the last thing before the shop was left. The most probable conjecture that I can make is that it took from the broom. From the account I have collected since my return, I am convinced that it was not more than ten or fifteen minutes at most after the workmen had left the shop before they returned and found the shop so completely on fire that it was impossible to save the least article of it. It burned with amazing violence and it was with difficulty that the new building which I set up last fall was saved. You have probably seen some account of my misfortune in the News Paper where the damage is estimated at Three Thousand Dollars. But I would freely pay ten thousand dollars, if I had the money, to have it restored— Indeed, three thousand pounds would by no means make good my loss.

"For more than two years I have spared no pains nor exersion to systimatise and arrange my business in a proper manner. This object I had just accomplished. [The workshop itself had been running but eight months.] It was the purchase of many a toilsome Day

nd sleepless night. But my prospects are all blasted and my labour
ost. I do not, however, dispair and hope I shall not sink under my
misfortune. I shall reestablish the business as soon as possible, but
t must be a long time before I can repair my loss." All his tools—
cunningly devised, especially made—all had to be made again.

The fire occurred on March 11. Stiles, noting that "Yesterday
Morning VIII h. Mr. Whitney's Work Shop consumed," lists the
oss in money and gins, and adds sadly, "& all the Tools which no
man can make but Mr. Whitney, the inventor, & which he has been
two years in the makings." Three days after the disaster, Whitney
wrote of it to Miller. His summary adds no new details of what they
had suffered: "All the machinery and every tool we had are gone;
17 machines were almost finished and many others in great forwardness"; but he did indicate how far he had been able to work
out his method of production: "two years and a half spent in col-
ecting the tools, constructing and making the several machines that
were used for different purposes in the shop." Obviously, Whitney
had been creating a way to produce gins quickly, in quantity, fairly
standard in size and weight—a necessity dictated by his crating and
packing arrangement.

Stunned by the tragedy, weakened by his recent illness, he could
only feel how complete was his loss. Nothing remained. But he
would learn that the time, the energy, the thinking that had gone
into constructing special tools and machinery had not been destroyed; that once having thoroughly explored and resolved each
technique he had but to rebuild his factory to resume production
in short order. He would learn from this catastrophe that in his
method of manufacturing time was not a constant factor: although
he had been two years making some twenty gins he would not be
two years making another twenty.

Seven months later, with a certain quiet triumph, he could tell his
father, "My Business goes on quite successfully. We have shipped
twenty six machines since the fire. . . . I fear I shall not be able
to find time to Visit you this autumn. My Business increases so fast
that I find no leisure." Henceforth, a new way of calculating production schedules was fixed in Whitney's consciousness.

When Miller received Whitney's news, he thought of the talent and care his partner had lavished on the shop, and rushed to assure him: "I will devote all my time, all my thoughts, all my exertions and all the money I can earn or borrow to encompass and complete the business we have undertaken. . . . It shall never be said we have lost an object which a little perseverence could have attained. I think, indeed, it will be very extraordinary, if two young men, in the prime of life, with some share of ingenuity, with a little knowl edge of the world, a great deal of industry, and a considerable amount of property should not be able to sustain such a stroke of misfortune as this, heavy as it is." A few weeks later, when Miller experienced difficulty in raising money to rebuild the shop, he sug gested that Whitney try to secure a loan locally, but cautioned him that he "use great care to avoid giving an idea that we are in a *desperate situation* to induce us to borrow money. To people who are deficient in understanding, this precaution will be extremely neces sary: men of sense can easily distinguish between the prospect of large gains and the approaches of bankruptcy. Such is the disposition of man, that while we keep afloat there will not be wanting those who will appear willing to assist us; but once let us be given over and they will immediately desert us." In the handling of the Greene estate, Miller had long ago learned the value of appearances.

His capacity for circumspection was not dislocated even by the letter Whitney wrote to him directly after the fire. When, without adding or changing a word, Miller published it in the *Georgia Gazette,* he must have felt that the whole truth openly stated would serve Miller & Whitney better than that rumors gain entry into men's minds; he wanted the Georgia cotton growers to learn from Whitney of his loss—Whitney's words would command their sympathy. Also, he wanted to convince the planters that this was not the end of Miller & Whitney. "I cannot yet determine what plan to pursue in resuming our business," Whitney had said in closing his letter, "but shall omit no exertion to have it reestablished as soon as possible." Thus Miller was announcing in unmistakable words that he and Whitney were still in the cotton-ginning business.

IX

The Battle for the Patent

THREE months before the fire, Miller had been advised by his Golphinton manager that some rudely made gins were being surreptitiously used, and had decided to "defer for a few months the necessary attention to such intruders." Now, after the fire, the trespassers could no longer be ignored; they had grown in number, in boldness; and when Miller & Whitney were suddenly deprived of their factory, the planters were possessed of a valid excuse for extending the use of illegal, locally made gins. Their activity threatened to siphon the cotton crop away from the established ginneries and end the plan to open additional ones. It threatened the very life of Miller & Whitney.

Miller began to feel that they had made a fatal mistake in demonstrating Whitney's original machine even to friends and that their decision to stimulate business before they were ready to handle it had produced a monster that was trying to strangle the weak, struggling infant concern of Miller & Whitney. Despite his thoughts his words were free from recrimination as he traced how "several persons, prompted as we firmly believe by no worse motive than that of committing the same pleasure as they had received in seeing so ingenious an invention, disregarding the instructions we had imposed of them as well as their own engagements, did actually explain the principles of the machine to their acquaintances who were so interested in its success in the upper country and from whom this information became so general that even the boys of Augusta knew that the invention had teeth which worked thro' slats, and a brush. This was easily understood and easily put into practise when known, for as the excellence of machinery consists in its simplicity, the inventor derived his principle credit in reducing his principles to this simple, plain & easy application."

There are several ways to kill a patent. From gossip and reports Miller learned that some planters were deliberately infringing, while others, less brazen, claimed to operate legally under patents issued for improvements to the gin. (Had he not written the Secretary of State a year before not to allow the application for "intended" improvements"?) What Miller did not foresee was the course taken by the planters around Augusta, the heart of the first cotton-growing district; later he confessed that he had "had no idea that the more respectable part of the community would in the least contest the propriety of our having recourse to the law . . . we never contemplated an opposition of this kind from indifferent persons in the community who would be thought to be actuated by the principles of justice, and who are acquainted with the origin & relation of property which is held under the law."

The planters resented having to pay so high a price for ginning—whether in cash or cotton—when a workable gin could be made by any self-respecting mechanic to whom its simple principles and parts had been described. Miller failed to grasp the cotton growers' rapidly solidifying determination not to pay what seemed to them an unwarranted, exorbitant tax. Each spring, as planting time came and hundreds of new acres were seeded with cotton, their indignation mounted, and sustained and nourished their intransigence. As they rode over their fertile fields estimating the crop they would harvest, as they read the prices offered for raw baled cotton, their indignation passed into self-righteousness, and the men who had fought Great Britain to be free of irksome restrictions responded in the way they had been so brilliantly taught: their resentment hardened into resistance. The men of the South had won their Revolutionary victory by guerrilla strategy; seeking freedom in economic enterprise, they remembered the effectiveness of partisan warfare—to wear out the enemy, not defeat him, and even to suffer defeat secure in the knowledge that the enemy's victory would be pyrrhic.

Whatever slogans were used, the issue was who was to get how much from the burgeoning cotton crop. Never before had America seen such a rate of growth. When the sides were drawn in 1795, the total crop was 8,000,000 pounds; by 1800, when the governor voiced Georgia's militancy, the total had jumped to 35,000,000 pounds; and in 1807, when the patent expired, 80,000,000 pounds had been reached. The fight did not smolder and slowly achieve size; the initial intensity of the antagonism to the patent was maintained by the crops' increase in value and volume. From 1795 to 1801, the price of cotton rose from 36 cents a pound to 44.

In Georgia every smart blacksmith and carpenter itched to put his tools to work; they scrambled to replace the gins that had been destroyed in the factory fire. Three men near Wrightboro, one of whom was Edward Lyon, offered an "improved" gin for sale: instead of wire prongs, they used saw-toothed iron discs. Joseph Eve hurried from the Bahamas to Augusta to take out patent rights for his own roller gin, and a local mechanic, Thomas Spaulding, offered to make the Eve gin for fifty guineas. Other workmen associated with Eve made other roller gins, all incorporating an "improvement" to cope with the green-seed cotton. William Longstreet, who had distinguished himself by building a steamboat before Fulton, had moved from New Jersey to Augusta and already had taken out a Georgia patent on a roller-type gin for the long-staple sea-island cotton. Longstreet's main interest was in applying steam power to the ginning machines; in time he actually installed a few engines in ginneries. Whitney's invention let loose a swarm of would-be inventors; the confusion was complete when Robert Watkins assailed Longstreet for infringing on his roller-gin patent and offered gins at less than half Longstreet's price. Belatedly, in May, 1796, Hodgen Holmes obtained a Georgia patent for a saw gin. In the rush of invention and improvement, of state patents and federal patents, a distinction was made between Whitney's gin and the saw gin. It obscured the fact that functionally the two were identical; the difference was one of material and design.

The struggle came into the open in the spring of 1795, when Miller publicly called upon the planters to stop their illegal ginning; and in the long, bitter fight that followed two names became associated with the two kinds of attempted infringements—Edward Lyon and Hodgen Holmes. The first notice, "A Caution," directed to those using machines made by Lyon, advised them that if they were trespassing innocently they had but to desist and "deliver up the machines" and they would not be prosecuted. The second was intended for those using Holmes's saw gin, since to the same warning, reassurance was added that Miller & Whitney "will ever be willing to afford the most ample encouragement to any person who will make appear that they have any real improvement *on their machine.*"

Lyon and Holmes were real men, but they have become names, names that are the archetypes of the two kinds of attack made on the patent. Folklore has busily embroidered details, giving a cunning purpose to Lyon, a certain talent to Holmes. Lyon—it has often been repeated—eager to see Whitney's invention, disguised himself in women's clothes and so gained access to the guarded ginning room. As Miller told Lyon's story, the disguise is pure fiction added at a later time; and there is every reason to believe Miller's facts.

"In the Fall of 1793," Miller explained to the lawyer who was handling the partners' suit against Lyon, "this Lyon obtained from Major Forsyth a letter of introduction to our P. Miller (which will be brought forward as an exhibit to the Court) and came down from Golphinton for the express purpose of seeing our Gin, that he might erect one on the same construction. His rubel [*sic*] pretensions having disagreed with the communication of Major Forsyth's letter—his request of seeing the Gin was not complied with. When he found himself disappointed in this respect he made enquiry of several people in Savannah respecting the principle and mode of construction. But not obtaining information sufficiently satisfactory on the subject, he afterwards went to Augusta, where he found an ingenious mechanic by the name of Tyler—who could give him the most correct description of every part of the Machine, as Mr. Tyler had taken great pains to acquire this knowledge of several persons who had seen the Machine and particularly from Mr. Longstreet who had spent three or four days at Mulberry Grove in making his examination of its principles, construction and operation. After having been thus informed Lyon proceeded to construct gins and put them to work in different parts of the Country and had the vanity to say that he had made improvements on our Machines." Here the name was Lyon, the instance specific; but the trespass, as the Minutes of the Circuit Court for Georgia give strict evidence, applied to many others.

The story of Holmes and his threat to the patentees is soon told; it is worth examining because apologists have claimed for Holmes the honor of inventing the cotton gin itself, while many have credited him with having designed the saw gin, the variant of Whitney's machine that gained general acceptance. Again, by Miller (who was not seeking to argue this point) the true Holmes is presented and his role clearly described. "It was soon found on experience that the teeth cut in circular plates could be made by an ordinary Smith, and the machine be put together by a Common Carpenter. . . . If any credit be due to anyone for introducing into common use this particular variation in the Saw Gin & thereby contributing to deprive the Patentees of the immediate profit of their invention, it is to the ingenuity of Mr. William Longstreet of Augusta, who conversed with me fully on the subject of the invention soon after it was brought into use, & whose candour as well as Mechanical Talents is too great to allow him to claim any merit or reward for opposing the prevailing opinion of the inventor in this particular."

Obviously, Longstreet, for whom both partners had respect, when shown Whitney's invention had suggested that by using saws instead of wire hooks the machine could be produced more cheaply and easily and its efficiency made greater; but Whitney favored wire hooks because the saws, by "their unyielding firmness would also force through the breast work any bunches or lumps of the Cotton which by damp weather, or foul particles, should have a tendency to clog the Machines [Holmes himself blunted the saws so as not to tear the lint.]. . . . On these & other accounts he preferred a less degree of dispatch accompanied with other superior advantages in the use of Wire teeth set in wood, to work through a Breast work of composition metal." Miller's pride in his partner's superior workmanship glows in the gratuitous statement that "among all those Mechanics who have claimed merit for their ingenuity in executing clumsy models of his invention no one, as I can learn, has attempted such a Breast work."

Whitney's insistence on wire hooks was not due to false pride—his original sketch, he himself said, pictured "a whole row of teeth upon a piece of metal—to make them out of sheet iron. . . . [But] not being able to procure sheet Iron or sheets of tinned plates I had recourse to *wire* to make the teeth from necessity . . . one of the

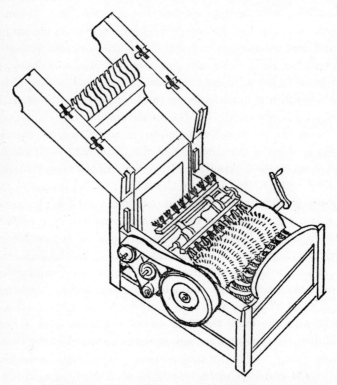

A MODEL OF THE COTTON GIN OPEN

Miss Greenes had brong [*sic*] out a coile of iron wire to make a bird cage & being embarrassed for want of sheet iron & seeing this wire hung in the parlor, it struck me that I could make teeth with that." Wire teeth, used in the first instance out of necessity, remained Whitney's choice—they separated the fiber from the seed with greater precision.

By themselves, the Lyon and Holmes trespasses would not have made the partners prey to "Debts, and claims, and dread of ruin," but like a debilitating disease they prepared the way for secondary attacks. It is a moot point which of the several factors was most pernicious—the competition from infringing machines, the credit situation, or the British spinners' hesitancy in accepting the upland cotton. Combined, their onslaught must have been fatal had the partners been less able to adapt themselves to each new situation, less resilient when almost crushed. From the beginning the danger in all three situations was surveyed and, as far as possible, eliminated. While their enterprise was still in the planning stage, Whitney and Miller knew that because no spinners had used the short-staple cotton, the new crop might present difficulties, since the fiber differed from the long-staple varieties for which the jennies and water frames were geared. It would require the British spinners to make slight adjustments for the shorter fiber to the spindles and rollers.

The partners' original schedule recognized that the need to prepare the way for the new cotton was basic and urgent: Whitney planned to visit the leading British mills immediately after he had delivered the first set of gins. Edmund Randolph, Secretary of State, issued a passport to him a few days after he had received his patent (March 17, 1794). Was this trip postponed because he suffered an attack of "Georgia fever" while supervising the installation of the Mulberry Grove ginnery? And, at the moment when the planters "were running mad" for gins, did the question of their cotton's reception in England seem academic? Did they decide that Whitney must hurry back to New Haven to speed production? A few months after returning to his factory, he told his father that it "does not appear likely to me at present that I shall go [to England] before spring, if at all. My business in this Country must be my first object and I must take particular care that it is carried on in a proper manner."

Had Whitney gone to England, anguish and financial distress might have been spared him. When the bales of upland cotton arrived at Liverpool, the spinners—as had been anticipated—were reluctant to purchase them because of the difference in length of fiber. This difference, slight yet real, made the cotton strange, perplexing; it presented technical problems in the accustomed procedure. There the matter might have rested, awaiting the interest of the spinners in this new source to prod them to experiment;

slowly, steadily, the inertia would have been overcome and upland cotton would have found its market.

But this natural tempo was violently jarred. The planters, fretting under the intolerable restrictions of the patent, grabbing at anything with which to wound Miller & Whitney, deliberately twisted the reluctance and inertia into a vicious weapon. Not content with using surreptitious gins, they extended their war of attrition to deprive Miller & Whitney of its market for ginned cotton. The planters whispered—and their words carried across the Atlantic and the echo came back to Georgia—that the *patent gin* ruined the cotton fiber. Thus the reluctance of the British spinners was transformed into suspicion, and abroad as at home the partners found themselves seriously jeopardized. Miller frantically wrote to Whitney when he first felt the effects: "This stroke of misfortune is much heavier than that of the fire, unless the impression is immediately removed. For with that which now governs the public mind on the subject, our patent would be worth extremely little. Everyone is afraid of the cotton. Not a purchaser in Savannah [brokers] will pay full price for it. Even the merchants with whom I have made a contract for purchasing, begin to part with their money reluctantly."

News of the calculated lie reached Whitney during the hard months when he was rebuilding and replacing what he had lost when his workshop burned. The evil rumor struck particularly at his pride as inventor, since the planters had been careful not to disparage machine-ginned cotton—certainly not their own cotton cleaned by their own crudely made gins. Only the Miller & Whitney gin, they declared, hurt the fiber. Immediately, he set out to counteract their slander. "I have procured Certificates from the Cotton Manufacturers [of New Haven], that cotton cleaned with my Machine is worth at least two pence pr pound more than Cotton cleaned any other way," he wrote to his father at the beginning of November, 1795, and the certificates were published in full in the *Georgia Gazette* that month. Given by Abel Buel, "Superintendent and Proprietor of a cotton manufactory in New Haven" and two of his superintendents, men who stressed their English training, they bore witness that Whitney's patent machine "doth not in any way or manner injure the staple of the cotton . . . that said cotton spins well, makes a strong thread, and requires one operation less in manufacturing than cotton which is ginned in the usual way," and that therefore they were prepared to pay two cents a pound more for cotton ginned by Whitney's machine.

Whitney then tried to account for the British reaction. Their self-interest did not require them to cling to the lie; then why, he wondered, did they continue to grumble? He was forced to conclude that "the cotton which the English manufacturers complain of must have been *naturally* bad. The little knotts . . . are knotts which *nature* has made and not the Gin . . . [and] our last machines take the most of them out. You will always find the cotton which contains these knotts, short and of an imperfect growth. Out of the five hundred Wt of Cotton, of our cleaning, which has been manufactured by our manufacturers here, one hundred Wt was very full of these knotts, and they complained of it very much; but were never so stupid as to suppose that these knotts were made by the machine in cleaning. . . . I think you [Miller] will be able to convince the *candid* that this is quite a mistaken notion—and them that *will not believe*, may be damn'd." And then, to fortify his partner, he added, "I have had several pressing applications from Proprietors of the Connecticut Cotton manufactory for one of our Machines, to pass all their cotton through, in lieu of beating, and have promised to make them one as soon as leasure permits." The textile mills in New England bought Miller & Whitney cotton—unfortunately, their support was negligible in the world market.

Miller's letters spell out the mounting injury inflicted on them by the British prejudice. And always he has but one solution—Whitney must go to England. Like a refrain, in his correspondence with managers, creditors, and lawyers, are the words, "Our Mr. Whitney is expected shortly to sail for England." Whitney was kept in a flurry of imminent embarkation. The year 1795 ended with Miller advising him to "prepare everything for your departure for England very early in the spring. . . . Our justification in the opinion of the English is indispensible to our safety. The utmost stretch of my capital will not be equal to meet the expenses of another year unless this Difficulty is removed—and we have even now trespassed very largely on the funds of the estate of Genl. Greene."

All during 1796 Whitney was on the verge of leaving: he almost engaged passage on the *Ganges*, "a prodigiously fine strong ship with excellent accomodation," sailing the end of July; in December he was so certain of going that he offered Stebbins "one hundred and fifty dollars for the first year if you will come and assist my Brother in the management of our business"; but two weeks later he withdrew the offer and confessed that "disappointment, my constant attendant, has thrown that business back into the same uncertain situation it was when I saw you last."

During 1796 Miller kept writing frantically; perplexity, fear, and even doubts assailed him. If their cotton "should bear the final test of the English factories, we shall struggle through all other difficulties. But if it should be condemned by them we must be ruined. . . . Let us know the truth & the whole truth. . . . I am tired out & my patience quite exhausted in the refutation of the various species of false opinion to which these reports of our breaking the staple of the cotton have given rise. Let us only have a market where our cotton will sell at an equal price with any other & then they may talk until their lungs are exhausted." Vainly Miller offered to pay 30 per cent interest if he could but borrow $1,000 for Whitney's expenses—the gesture of a desperate man.

Whitney never did go to England. Now he was not detained by illness or business pressures; the unpleasant fact was that Miller & Whitney could not raise enough cash to pay his expenses. "The process of Patent Ginning is now quite at a stand and I hear very little of it excepting the condolence of a few real friends who express their regret that so promising an invention has entirely failed." Miller's sad words sound with the finality of an obituary; the poisoned rumors of the planters had found their mark.

Or so it must have seemed as 1796 came to a close. How brief had been their bright hopes! The only alternative now left was to sue. Just before the year was out, to save the stricken business from death, he decided to start the lengthy and uncertain remedy of legal redress. Energetically he instructed his managers to collect the "names of such persons as are setting up Gins on the construction of ours . . . in order to enable us to commence suits against them previous to the next court."

The suits (brought against the Lyon group) were expected to do more than halt their trespass. The partners felt that they could stay in business only if they fought for their rights; that soon British spinners, alert to their own interests, would cease to be guided by slander and accept their patent-ginned cotton on equal terms.

Faith that they would eventually be able to sell in the world market armed Miller as he haled the trespassers into court, trying meanwhile by letters to urge a few British mills to test samples of his cotton. In particular Miller calculated that the damages collected from the trespassers would help repair their credit. So convinced was he of a victory in the courtroom, and of collecting treble the damage sustained, that he counted on this success to make good his heavy mortgaging of Greene property. To safeguard Catherine's position as executrix, he had deeded her two ginnery sites, but even that had not prevented the loss of some property. "I have been reduced to the cruel & mortifying necessity of appropriating the property of the Estate to prevent this Bankruptcy from becoming public. In consequence of which a Plantation belonging to the Estate of General Greene in Carolina will this spring be sold for half its value. Some extra compensation must be drawn from our profits should they ever arrive to meet this loss." (In 1802 Miller had the satisfaction of knowing that as the Greene estate had saved Miller & Whitney, so the latter, in its turn, played a helpful part in the estate finances.) Miller wanted to remind Whitney how deep was their dependence on Catherine and how much he had staked on the outcome of the trial.

But the trial proved even more disastrous to Miller & Whitney than the fire had been. Lyon was "vindicated," and the adverse decision sanctioned the trespass in the eyes of the whole countryside.

Relating the particulars, Miller wrote to Whitney: "The event of the first Patent suit after all our exertions made in such a variety of ways has gone against us . . . the imperfections of the Patent Law frustrated all our views and disappointed expectations which had become very sanguine." His letter dated May 11, 1797, was written ten days after their stunning defeat. Poor Miller, he badly needed a little time to catch his breath.

"We had the Judge with a Party to dine with us twice before the trial came on and got him fully prepared to enter into the merits of the case. We had also got the tide of popular opinion running in our favor and many decided friends who adhered firmly to our cause and interest. Added to this we got the trial brought on, against every measure they could devise for postponement and found them perfectly unprepared as to a knowledge of the strong grounds of their cause and without a single evidence in their favor. We were on the contrary pretty well prepared and neglected no means to become as much so as possible." As an instance of their exertion, he relates how while the court was in session they missed an important paper that had been left at home, how Catherine's son-in-law, "Mr. Nightingale immediately mounted my best horse, in the middle of a very hot day, came to this place [Mulberry Grove], examined my chest &c and after a search of nearly half an hour, laid his hand on the paper, remounted his horse, on the way back met a fresh horse I had sent out for his relief; and returned to the Court House in just two hours and forty minutes from the time he had left it—the paper came in time to procure admittance to the evidence we had brought. . . . The Judge gave a charge most pointedly in our favor, after which the Defendent himself told an acquaintance he would give two thousand dollars to be free from the verdict—and yet the jury gave it against us after a consultation of about an hour. . . . We applied for a new trial, but the judge refused it to us inasmuch as that the Jury might have made up their opinion on the fact of the law which states an aggression to consist of *making devising* and using, or selling, and we could only charge the defendents with using. In a private conversation had with the Judge afterwards, he told me we could have no hope of protecting our Patent rights without an alteration of the law, which he had no doubt but Congress would make for us, on application. Thus after four years of assiduous labour fatigue and difficulty, we are again set afloat by a new and most unexpected obstacle."

Simeon Baldwin, Whitney's lawyer and close friend, recalling the legal aspects of the trial, said: "The first act relative to Patents . . . provided among other things that if any person shall devise, make construct, *use*, employ *or* vend any patented machine &c they shall incur the penalty provided &c. This act was repealed by the more extended act of Febr. 1793 in which the clause prohibiting the infringement of patented rights is thus worded—'if any person shall make, devise, *and* use or sell the thing so invented &c.' This act remained in force until it was revised and extended by the Act of April 1800—by which the penalty was attached to any person who shall make, *devise, use,* or sell the thing patented; the section of the former act by which the penalty was attached to making *and* using was repealed. Mr. Whitney spent much of the winter of 1800 at the seat of Govt & was instrumental in obtaining the alteration. Mr. Whitney has often told me when conversing on this subject that this unfortunate but unintentional wording of the statute of 1793 by using the word *and* instead of *or,* make & use instead of make or use, was attended with incalculable mischief to him." *

"Obstacle," in Miller's lexicon, gradually reveals itself to be a mixture of deceit, conspiracy, and wholesale defiance concocted by the Georgia planters. His emotions were keyed to grave tones. Thus he was amazed—not shocked, not outraged—at the effrontery of a man who installed a gin in "a covert and secret manner in the very Town and in the very same street of the town" where Miller & Whitney operated a ginnery; he was indignant—not wrathful, not infuriated— when confronted with a situation in which "the people of this state openly declare that they will defy the power of the Federal Laws . . . and make no secret of their means of safety in such defiance." Whatever the tenor of his reactions, his resolution did not admit that because the people of Georgia aligned themselves against him he was outnumbered and should surrender. If he did not cry out against his tribulations, neither did he judge them insurmountable. "As to the threat of the people of Carolina that no lawyer dare commence a suit in their country, I consider it in the same point of view as the threat which you mentioned to have been given out in the Upper country of this state, that I should be stoned thro' the streets if I persisted to enforce suits against the trespassers. I must say I never ex-

---

* "A fate of a public policy hangs on the validity of an act; an act awaits the judgement in a case; a case turns upon the boundaries of a word. This is the way of the law." (Hamilton and Adair)

perienced from them the smallest rudeness whatever—and if there are threats thrown out for the purpose of intimidating, it is never contemplated to carry them into effect."

There is bravery in Miller's presence in court, session after session, intent on submitting proper legal evidence that rival gins were being worked, while the very din they made invaded the courtroom and mocked the proceedings. Writing influential senators to enlist their aid in correcting the Patent Act, Miller reveals the simple foolproof method by which the Georgia planters safeguarded their defiance: "They procure a machine and immediately put it into the second story of a building, to which they give admittance to no person but their own Slaves, whose testimony cannot be produced in Court." Slaves, he reminded them, according to the "laws of the Southern states make incompetent witnesses in a Court of Justice: hence it comes to pass that a Man shall with Impunity work a Machine in defiance of Patent rights and all the ordinary provisions of the Law. From all the different works & operations white men are to be carefully excluded which in many cases is not at all difficult; it then becomes impossible formally to prove in a Court of Justice facts which may be indubitably known to a whole neighborhood."

Each new obstacle raised by the Lyon group brought forth the same response from Miller. Steadfastly he pressed forward in his determination "to vindicate our exclusive privilege to the use of teeth and brushes in ginning cotton under the Patent Law." When his lawyer suggested the futility of trying a case before a jury at Augusta, "where the general interest is against me," Miller established this hostility as a fact that was to win him friends in other southern states and in Congress.

He was fighting, as he and Whitney saw it, for a principle—to preserve the sacred rights of private property. He was not asking a jot more than his due. "I am well aware that much obloquy has been attempted to be thrown on the principle, as well as the practice of exercising exclusive rights under the authority of Patents—And to give plausibility to such attempts, the justly obnoxious epithet of *monopoly* (as applied to the forced limitation of a general right) has been constantly misapplied. It is not the use of any general privilege which we would confine to ourselves, but the right of managing as we please our own property, a property which can be rendered useful to us in no other way than by sharing its benefits in some stipulated proportion with other members of the community." Realistically he evaluated the way in which the ginning rights had been distorted and smeared in men's minds. "Politicians of the day, who have thought to enhance their favour with the people . . . have encouraged their trespass by crying out against monopolies, as leading directly to Aristocracy. The effect of this popular clamour was much extended by the direct dependence we were known to have on the Federal Government for the protection of a property which had been created by their legislative Acts."

At the beginning he protested; later he was content merely to sue; season after season the list of defendants was enlarged, though the main offender was still Lyon. "It is my particular wish that suits should continue against several of the most bold & presuming intruders and . . . among the most proper & promising candidates for such Prosecution we believe are the following: Henry Chambers of Greene County, for making, devising & using; Capt. John Hunton, Wilkes County, for devising & using only; James Hutchinson, Richmond County, for selling to others to use." One by one they were discovered, their trespasses analyzed, and suit started. There were many others. Folklore has remembered them all simply as Lyon, since in practice and purpose they were alike.

To procure cash while the legal battle was being readied, Miller engaged in outside ventures. He salted beef and pork for shipment "to the Northward markets"; he offered to sell Miller & Whitney's interest in the Rocky Creek ginnery to their manager for a small amount of cash; he sought to utilize their water-power installation to run a sawmill "besides the Cotton Ginning"; he negotiated for $10,-000 by offering a third interest in the firm itself; he even tried to defray the current expenses of a ginnery by stud fees. "The Jack mule is to stand at the Mills under your care for the Season. His price, I think had better be six dollars, but if you think he will bring eight, you may ask that." Sensible or bizarre, most of the subsidiary enterprises came to naught. He was reconciled to the mule's health "being so low as to induce us to suspend our intentions of advertising him this season." He was chagrined that the prospective partner not only lacked the purchase price but that notes Miller drew on him remained unpaid "to the total ruin of my private credit & accumulating embarrassment of all our Affairs."

Immediately the Lyon victory made it brutally clear that Miller & Whitney faced a long struggle. Miller hired Russell Goodrich, a former classmate from Yale—a man *"sensible, honest & prudent"*—to go "to Knoxville where we were informed that Cotton was saleable & make such inquiries as appeared . . . most judicious on the subject. From whence he was to proceed to Nashville & the Cumberland Settlements . . . from there he was to proceed to Kentucky on the same business & then return by the back parts of Virginia for the purpose of looking for an inland market for the consumption of cotton of our ginning. [The British still were reluctant to buy.] If he should meet with any encouragement in these pursuits we shall come into some agreement for his future exertions in our business but if not he is to lose his time & even his travelling expences."

Goodrich's reconnaissance showed that Miller read his defeat in strictly local terms: "I have just received information that there are now at work 300 of Lyon's Gins in the Upper Country." He did not despair of their patent, merely of trying to enforce it in Georgia. Though neither man made money from the trip—"instead of the large profits, we must now content ourselves to divide the loss"— Goodrich's enterprise and heart-warming allegiance to Miller & Whitney's interests earned him Miller's trust. Had he not joined them at their darkest moment and invested his time and traveling expenses? Miller expressed his gratitude when he introduced Goodrich to his partner: "Every day's experience confirms my belief that the number of persons who deserve our entire esteem & confidence is very small and I am gratified that your knowledge of each other will add an unit to so limited and interesting a selection."

Already, as 1798 came to an end, an idea was forming in Miller's resourceful mind. He was writing finis to a whole series of plans when he notified a Liverpool concern that "we shall clean but little cotton, untill we find better security from the Government. We have gins sufficient to clean a million of pounds of cotton *pr* Annum, but shall scarcely work them this year." He had begun to think along bold new lines when he informed Whitney that "I fear we shall be compelled to sell the privilege without selling our machines. The people of the back country almost uniformly prefer making their own gins to using ours. . . . At the most I do not think it probable we can sell more than twenty or thirty of our machines in the southern States. . . . The prospect of making anything by ginning on toll in this state is at an end. Surreptitious Gins are erected in every part of the country. . . . I am just now making out of a kind of Certificate which I shall have handsomely printed to confirm our exclusive right to individual machines which we dispose of the right of using."

Already—the decision had been reached reluctantly—he had reworked the policy of Miller & Whitney and was willing "to sell or hire out our Gins or the right of ginning with such gins as any person may chuse to construct for themselves on our principles." He was ready to recognize the existence of the surreptitious gins and to legitimize them. His price schedule for the licenses was realistic and modest, for he had become convinced, in talking with Goodrich, that "the reservation of so large a portion to ourselves has greatly increased the difficulty of enforcing the patent." Miller saw how he might get out of the old untenable position: "I have no doubt but that measure . . . were well calculated to promote our interest; if the sales for the whole term [of the patent] could be made in any considerable number the result would prove very beneficial both to you & us. Even renting for a year, as you very justly observe, will be a beginning to turn the stream—which is certainly more easy to divert than to stop when once fairly in motion."

x *Arms for the Government*

THE almost total devastation inflicted early on Miller & Whitney evoked different responses in the partners. Miller knew acute despair and anxiety, but his efforts proved his dedication; from the end of 1795 until his death he stayed in the arena fighting. If Whitney lacked Miller's staying power, the causes are not hard to find. Because his commitment to Miller & Whitney was complete, the frustration and hostility it encountered created for him an unbearably oppressive situation.

To Miller, the ginning concern was but one of many enterprises. He reminded Whitney, restating the gist of their agreement, that in the articles of copartnership he had only pledged his credit "for such sums of money as we should require to borrow," and further limited his participation to "such advances as my other concerns would allow of"; finally, he had obligated himself merely to "devote such a portion of my time as the Business of putting up and working the machines should require." Miller, through the management of the Greene estate, was involved in a continuous round of small quick deals; he also had the opportunities to take on, with some partners, a few sizable, extended ventures. Of these his most ambitious was the ginning business with Whitney. Another, with Catherine's son-in-law Nightingale, was his Yazoo speculation; a third, undertaken with Josiah, Whitney's brother, was a slaughtering business; and a fourth, also with Josiah, of later date, was a Navy contract for furnishing live oak to northern shipyards.* With so many irons in the fire he could be philosophical about Miller & Whitney's reverses. His

---

* "A piece of the live oak sent to Boston . . . has been made use of in repairing of the frigate Constitution."

militancy was inspired by the wish to safeguard his business and social position and to be worthy of Catherine Greene and the Greene children. He stood happily in the center of the pleasant sociable stir that made Mulberry Grove famous for its hospitality and filled the thirty rooms of Dungeness.

And Whitney? His brain child had dominated every facet of his life from the time when "we undertook to render valuable an interest arising from the efforts of your genius & my patronage." How well that word, used thus by Miller, defined the inequality of their positions! And there was little need for Miller to recall that Whitney had agreed that his "whole time and talents should be devoted to improving, perfecting, & constructing the machines." Engrossed by his work, Whitney had no other interests nor activities, and no home but his workshop. Fame could not fill his heart with its capacity for affection, nor could manufacturing gins long satisfy his active mind. His faith in his ability to achieve had been assured him by the importance of his invention; it had been reassured by his quick ability to repair the loss sustained by the fire. Whitney must have been gratified when the New Haven community honored him. On September 9th, 1795, in the Yale commencement procession led by Timothy Dwight, the newly installed president, Whitney walked with those on whom the degree of Master of Arts was to be conferred. This degree had not been earned by additional study; rather, it expressed his Alma Mater's approval of his exemplary conduct for three successive, post-graduate years. In this manner, respectable behavior received recognition.

Thus, when later that fall Miller, on a trip to New Haven, frankly admitted that "no immediate employment can be obtained for the machines," Whitney was suddenly confronted with the threatened loss of work and purpose, hope and prestige.

The despair into which he was plunged could have been occasioned by nothing less than a powerfully thwarted emotion. By itself the stricken condition of Miller & Whitney would not account for the anxious gloom that possessed him during the next two years. Such a prolonged reaction implies causes that are deep and have become fastened over time. It is possible, sometimes, to piece odds and ends together to make a garment—possible, though never as satisfactory as cutting the parts out of whole cloth; and yet, to appreciate certain aspects of Whitney's nature, surmise becomes necessary. And so, out of a few facts, known reactions, and the personalities involved, an explanation can be tailored.

Three years before, when Whitney wrote to Stebbins a few days after his arrival at Mulberry Grove, imbedded in his factual report was a hooded sentence, precise in tone, its wording vague. "I find myself in a new natural world and as for the moral world I believe it does not extend so far south." Something was troubling Whitney, something he dared not put into words. What, or whom, was he censuring? In the few weeks since he had joined Mrs. Greene and her party, had he become aware of a strange ease that lay between Catherine and Miller? He would have been reluctant to find fault: he was grateful to have been welcomed into the family circle; he was charmed by Catherine and pleased to find Miller congenial; he was impressed by the splendor of Mulberry Grove. But at the same time he felt the need to pass judgment; he was shocked, puzzled. What, he must have asked himself, was Miller's real position in the family? In a hundred small gestures, in tones of voice, in the attitude of the children, it must have been apparent that between Catherine Greene and Phineas Miller there was a strong, well established tie. Such conduct would have shaken the deep respect Whitney gave General Greene's widow. And it would be hard to believe that Catherine, responsive to people's sensibilities as to their capacities, did not perceive her new friend's attitude and tell him, soon, quite simply what there was to tell.

Almost a year before, in August, 1791, a marriage settlement had taken place between Catherine Greene and Phineas Miller—he was eleven years her junior—by which he renounced all claims to her property so as not to disturb the Greene estate. The paper—recorded in the county courthouse—also stated that a marriage was soon to take place. In the following years veiled references are scattered in letters written by Miller, Catherine, and Whitney. But the facts are so few they do not serve as guides; they are pegs whereon to hang questions. Was this paper, legally phrased but awaiting implementation by marriage, legal benediction to a long-standing, unsanctioned relationship? Then why did they delay? It is hard to believe that their disparity in ages made it more seemly to maintain secrecy or that Miller would have felt the necessity of achieving financial independence before publicly assuming control of Greene's estate. Was the marriage postponed because Catherine was loath to relinquish being Mrs. Nathanael Greene? (Had not Washington himself made a special point of calling on her to ask her "how she did"?) Or was it delayed because she needed the help of Greene's friends and as his widow commanded more of their efforts than she would have as Miller's wife? The motivating reasons can be only surmised; the reticence they themselves showed still conceals the full answers.

According to Puritan standards Whitney should have called a spade a spade and fled. Yet he accepted the unconventional relationship and returned to Mulberry Grove, relinquishing the position at Major Dupont's. Could he have stayed on with Catherine and Miller for six months simply to construct a machine that might make his fame and success? Or was his invention a reason he could accept and his return to Mulberry Grove permitted because his emotions had been so deeply stirred as to recast his responses? From the first, Whitney had been deeply attracted to Catherine; if it was love, he never admitted it. The picture he must have had was of two young men, of almost the same age, embarked on a brilliant and promising enterprise, united in friendship with a delightful, intelligent woman, older and warmhearted, to whom both were devoted.

One is forced to hazard the further guess that when Miller, in the fall of 1795, explained the serious condition of Miller & Whitney, he also told his partner the plans for his marriage to Catherine. (They were married the following spring, on May 31, 1796, in Philadelphia; the marriage settlement was sworn to and entered in Georgia on April 5, 1799.) It may well have been discussed as part of the business arrangements, as a way to give legality to Miller's using the Greene estate funds to finance Miller & Whitney. If for three years Whitney had been bracketing himself with Miller, could he suddenly step aside and accept the differences his relationship to them would now have? He knew what would be the rich texture of Miller's life as Catherine's husband; he knew too well how for all his superior gifts his own would continue bare, bleak. What is more likely than that, possessed by self-pity, he fastened his unhappiness on the one engagement Miller had undertaken of which he could express disapproval—Yazoo?

Neither reason nor sense drove Whitney to complain of Miller's Yazoo speculation. Had sense or reason prompted his behavior, he might, with equal propriety, have protested the time and money Miller was spending on his other transactions—such as the one with Whitney's brother Josiah. It was the gesture of a man deeply disturbed that made him suggest (in the very next breath), that his partnership with Miller in the ginning business automatically gave him the right to a half-interest in Miller's Yazoo gamble. Whitney's letter presenting this "most unexpected & extraordinary demand" is missing; his attitude and arguments can only be conjectured from Miller's answer. That long reply shows the acute state of Whitney's discontent. "Permit me, my good friend," Miller said pointedly, "to ask you one simple question on the subject. Suppose my speculations should happen to fail—on what person would you direct me to call on for half my loan? This is an indispensible condition of all speculations." The subject was never again mentioned, but that it continued painful is implicit in Whitney's insistence, almost twenty-five years later, on collecting damages for the harm he was persuaded Miller had done the partnership.

In the succeeding months Whitney's despair increased; the letters written then confirm a dark constancy of mood. "This day has been spent thro' Connecticut in giving *Thanks*, talking and preaching Politicks, sleighing, dancing, laughing, eating *Pumkin*-Pie, Grinding Salt, Kissing the Girls, &c. &c." But he was alone, alone in his rented room, after having dined at the home of Elizur Goodrich, his old tutor, when he wrote to Stebbins a few days before Christmas, 1796. The gay sociability of the season sounded all around him, but merriment could not cross the threshold of his loneliness. "As for myself, (this day) has been spent mostly in that kind of anxious solicitude with which I have for some time been encumbered."

The months dragged on. To Miller he itemized his fears and worries, but Miller was powerless to do anything but console. Miller was "much distressed at the embarrassments which you are compelled to sustain to keep alive the little credit we may still have re-

maining at New Haven." Or he was "quite uncertain what we ought
to do relative to continuing the workmen you have now in employment. It may be attended with many inconveniences to discharge
them, but if you could find them some temporary employment which
would be bringing in a profit for a few months, I do not know but
it would be well." In September, 1797, when Miller learned how
desperate Whitney was for cash, he still regretted "that I can furnish
you with no other aid than that of sympathy." There was no use
asking Miller for help.

The crisis, so long dreaded, had come. He had to meet it alone.
His sense of abandonment and failure was magnified by the crowds
of jubilant students who took over New Haven for commencement
week. "I am mortified, sorry and ashamed beyond description"—so
he excused himself to Stebbins. "All the apology I can make is my
extreme embarrassment. On Tuesday last I was obliged to pay 980
Dollars, a part of which was to be raised. I knew not how, nor where,
untill the Day on which it fell Due. This embarrassment mixed with
and succeeded by the bustle of commencement together with the
load of anxiety which has lain so long and so heavily upon my mind"
made him oblivious of everything. He confessed his perturbation,
his confusion: "I can write you nothing concerning my own affairs
because I know nothing about them, myself. 'To be or not to be' is a
question which I cannot decide. All is doubt and uncertainty."

As an aching fester slowly becomes an angry circle when the
particles of decay and dissatisfaction separate themselves from
what had been a bodily malaise, contract, and then burst, so Whitney's anguish at last broke through the barriers of his habitual
reticence. His letter to Miller on October 7, 1797, is a terrifying,
heartbreaking act of emotional catharsis. "The extreme embarrassments which have been for a long time accumulating upon me are
now become so great that it will be impossible for me to struggle
against them many days longer. It has required my utmost exersions
to *exist* without making the least progress in our business. I have
labored hard against the strong current of Disappointment which
has been threatening to carry us down the Cataract of distruction—
but I have labored with a shattered oar and struggled in vain unless

some speedy relief is obtained." Briefly he framed the cause of his unhappiness; and if his phrases do not wear modern dress, his anguish does.

He was thirty-two, intelligent, fiercely ambitious, and proud. In his heart the fear of failure, the doom of loneliness became inextricably mixed. "I am now quite far enough advanced to think seriously of settling in life. I have ever looked forward with pleasure to a connection with an amiable & virtuous companion of the other sex. It is a source from whence I have expected one Day or other to Derive much satisfaction & rational enjoyment. I would not be understood that I have, or have ever had any *particular* person in view—pointed attachment of this kind I have studiously avoided, because I have never been in circumstances that would allow me to enter into such a connection. The situation of our affairs for three or four years has been such as made it necessary that I should hold myself in readiness free from any embarrassment, to go into foreign Countries for the promotion of our mutual interest. You have yourself several times expressed to me your apprehensions that I should get married and by that means be prevented from prosecuting our business in the way which appeared most advantageous. The accomplishment of my tour to Europe and the realization of something which I can call my own appear to be absolutely necessary before it will be admissable to *even think* of Matrimony. Three years have already elapsed since the former of these was to have begun & in that case it would have been finished before this time. There is a greater prospect now that it will be delayed three years longer. . . . Life is too short at best and six or seven years out of the midst of it is to him who makes it, an immense sacrafice. My most unremitted attention has been directed to our business. I have sacraficed to it other objects from which, before this time, I certainly might have realized 20, or 30, Thousand Dollars. My whole & sole prospects have entered in it, with an expectation that I should er'e this time have realized something from it."

He reminded Miller that he had married, had "estates, separate from this to which you can look for support, and, tho' you are under some temporary embarrassments, you are enjoying life. You have devoted no inconsiderable part of your attention to other businesses since ours was undertaken. After all these considerations can you think it strange that I should be desirous of realizing something? . . . Can you be surprized if I am unwilling to put our business on such a footing as shall oblige me to pay my whole attention to it for seven years to come without a prospect of realizing anything from it till the expiration of that time? Of what value is property to me without any prospect of enjoying it? It is better not to live than to live as I have for three years past. Toil, anxiety and Disappointment have broken me down. My situation makes me perfectly miserable." For the briefest instant, there sounds the sickening, uncushioned crash of a man's hopes.

And then, without pause, Whitney reaffirms his conviction in the importance of what he has created. "Yet my ideas of the utility of the invention and the emoluments of our business (if rightly persued) are not in the least abated.

"You may perhaps conclude from what I have said above that I am in a foolish teaze to get married. But you can readily conceive that a person who has no idea of marrying immediately, might be very unwilling to enter into obligations or put it out of his power ever to marry. If this letter should appear incoherent and foolish my circumstances will be some apology for me. I address it to you as a friend and a man of candor. I am willing to do everything in my power to promote your happiness at the same time I cannot be indifferent to my own. I am too much confused and perplexed to write any particulars of our concerns. . . . I had rather be out of Debt and out of business without a shilling than be in a situation half so much embarrassing as my present one."

Whitney had stated his position. He continued promoting the affairs of Miller & Whitney; he wrote long explanations to congressmen appealing to them to support a revision of the patent-law wording; he forwarded to Miller additional testimonials of the excellence of their ginned cotton being spun at nearby factories; he tried to sell some of their machines to the West Indies. He was noticeably changed. Except for this activity, he remained apart, writing little, visiting less.

His withdrawal from all contacts but those made necessary by business caused one of his Yale classmates to write him, after months had passed without a word, "I conclude you are in the land of the living & on the soil of N. Haven, but your silence and obscurity are so great that if you was buried they could not be more profound to me." Artless, garrulous, filled with flowery sentences and arch allusions, the classmate sympathizes with a stricken, gifted friend; the letter is evidence that Whitney's failure was open talk in New Haven. "Don't think you are always to be shut up in N. H. & renounce all connexion with your Friends till you can . . . grow richer than all of us before you can be sociable again. Come break out & run away, get relaxation & courage & you will be better prepared to go back & accomplish your present, & strike out some new invention which will astonish the World & command all their Purse Strings."

Whitney had anticipated this advice. His isolation ceased serving his wounded spirit and became, rather, a concentrated experimenting with ideas. His acute depression yielded to the energy of his active mind, to his deep impulse to create something new, something that would be his own.

As 1798 began, Whitney had already found the way to obviate his single greatest handicap, the lack of funds to finance a business. He knew what perils could befall the inventor who tied himself to the "patronage" of a man of wealth, even a man as honorable and generous as Miller; and having once grasped the fact that Miller & Whitney's troubles had not been due to some untoward act on Miller's part, Whitney saw that his major problem could be solved by engaging in business with the government.

The advantages to be gained were plain. Instead of taking a partner, he would enter into an agreement with the Federal Government; instead of the limited cash and credit at the command of any individual, the Treasury would finance his project. He realized also that, instead of being overwhelmed by more customers than he could supply, he would be producing for a single buyer. That he made this basic decision first and then looked about for a likely vehicle is clear. Appraising him as he stood poised to go forward, one sees his stature assume new dimensions. He was no longer a young man who had made a happy strike; his was an incisive mind that was not afraid to think in wholly new terms. As in his boyhood he had stopped making nails and turned to hatpins and canes, so now he turned from an unremunerative manufacturing of gins to the production of something profitable.

Chance had sent Whitney south, and to the invention of the gin; but it was a cleanly thought-out plan that directed his efforts toward his next enterprise. His first step secured him nothing, but it is the point necessary to plot the straight line of his attention and activity; it also brought him, for the second time, directly to the notice of Oliver Wolcott, now Secretary of the Treasury.

Acting on his new decision to do business with the United States Government, Whitney worked out a screw press with "presses and dies for the execution of the Stamp Act," and forwarded a "drawing of the machine, & a written description & instructions for working & keeping it in repair," to the Supervisor's Office. John Chester, by whom it was received, allowed that he had "neither the time nor ingenuity sufficient to . . . understand the nature of its operation. From a slight examination it appears to be very complex, though I cannot doubt of its possessing sufficient force to answer all requisite purposes. . . . I have only to lament that the thought of your contracting for the making of these machines had not occured to my mind some months sooner than it did." The last sentence makes Whitney's motive very clear; he was trying to secure a contract. Unfortunate he must have felt, on learning that his ideas had been anticipated and that the business had been given to someone else; yet he drew encouragement from the fact that Chester had forwarded his drawings to the Secretary of the Treasury, and that Wolcott had noted upon the Supervisor's reply, "I am not able to employ the ingenuity & talents of Mr. Whitney, of which, however, I entertain a high opinion." The machine Whitney submitted was lost long ago, and save for Chester's letter even the knowledge of it would have disappeared.

A more momentous step followed. On May 1, 1798, Whitney, thus encouraged, wrote directly to Secretary Wolcott; the boldness and magnitude of his new proposal announced—it can now be seen—the advent of America's industrial future. "By the Debates of Congress I observe that they are about making Some appropriations for procuring Arms etc for the U.S. Should an actual War take place or the communication between the U.S. and the West India Islands *continue* to be as hazardous and precarious as it is now, my present Business of making The Patent Machines for Cleansing Cotton must, in the meantime be postponed. I have a number of workmen & apprentices whom I have instructed in working Wood & Metals and whom I wish to keep employ'd. These circumstances induced me to address you and ask the privilege of having an opportunity of contracting for the supply of some of the Articles which the U.S. may want. I should like to undertake to Manufacture ten or Fifteen Thousand Stand of Arms.*

"I am persuaded that Machinery moved by water adapted to this Business would greatly diminish the labor and facilitate the Manufacture of this Article. Machines for forging, rolling, floating, boreing, Grinding, Polishing etc may all be made use of to advantage.

"Cartridge or Cartouch Boxes is an article which I can manufacture. I have a machine for boreing wood of my own Invention which is admirably adapted to this purpose. The making of Swords, hangers, Pistols etc I could perform. There is a good fall of Water in the Vicinity of this Town which I can procure and could have works erected in a short time. It would not answer however to go to the expence of erecting works for this purpose unless I could contract to make a considerable number. The contracting for the above articles will not I suppose belong to the Department of the Treasury; but if you will take the trouble to mention me to the Secretary of War, I shall consider it a particular favor. I shall be able to procure sufficient Bonds for the fulfillment of a contract of the kind above mentioned and will come forward to Philadelphia immediately in case there is an opportunity for me to make proposals."

Ten or fifteen thousand stand of arms! A notion as fantastic and improbable as aviation was before Kitty Hawk. Only three years before, Whitney had bemoaned the loss of twenty gins, and now he was calmly offering to manufacture muskets in astronomical numbers, though he had never made a firearm before. To his way of thinking, familiarity with a particular article—be it a gin, a screw press, a cartridge box, or a gun—was a secondary consideration, since

* A stand of arms in this instance refers to the complete arms needed to equip a soldier—the musket, bayonet, ramrod, wiper, and screw-driver.

the operations of forging, boring, grinding, or polishing could be
directed to form any object.

Whitney, it is obvious, was not conscious of the future implications
of such a method. His only aim was to establish a business, and he
thought in terms of what steps might secure him his goal. He was
not a prophet but an instrument of the industrial order. The time
had come for a new technique to give form and force to industry
that it might change the face of a nation that had a continent to conquer and exploit and but a thin scattering of hands to accomplish
the task. The great countries of Europe had thousands of men, long,
unbroken lines of fathers and sons trained to the fine skill of arms
making; there was no need to create new techniques in the ordered
armories of England and France, Spain, Holland, and Sweden. Whitney sought to compensate for the dearth of artisans in America, and
the system he had been evolving since he had been faced with the
need to make gins in number and in haste for the cotton growers
by-passed the time required to train workmen such as Europe had.
Whitney was but taking the next step to expedite production—that
it was the decisive step that carried an economy from the watershed
of handicraft organization over into the unexplored watershed of industrial manufacture has been revealed by time.

Whitney's proposal might have been postponed or mutilated by
heartbreaking hurdles had it been put forward at any other time.
Normally, new ideas have to fight for their lives—the slightest jolt
to an accepted way of looking at things automatically, as it were,
mobilizes the words that defend habitual techniques: "impractical,"
"visionary," "dubious," "rash." Familiar words to safeguard familiar
ways. A grim need can override this hostility to an original way of
looking at an old pattern; extreme danger permits people to grasp
at straws. Certainly President Adams, Wolcott, and Timothy Picker-
ing, Secretary of War, were eager to make the United States as self-
sufficient as possible; but stated policy could not have pierced
through their normal prudent attitudes. (Wolcott's thoroughgoing
conservatism was overshadowed only by his bitter hatred of Gallican
and radical ideas.) It was the face of war that made possible a speedy
acceptance of Whitney's radical proposal.

On March 19th (the very day Chester was writing to Whitney)

President Adams announced to Congress the failure of the Pinckney mission to France. "Millions for defense but not one cent for tribute" —words later put into Pinckney's mouth—were the measure of the militant excitement that swept the American people at the revelation of the crisis. The allies of but a few years before had become the enemies of the moment—the rebuff accorded the American envoys aroused the nation, while the news that France would regard American seamen found on British ships as pirates erased the last traces of former amity. Congress nullified the treaties with France, the size of the army was increased, new naval ships were ordered built, the country prepared itself to resist an invasion, and Washington was called out of his retirement to head the armed forces.

War with France! The unthinkable might happen at any moment. The more cautious remembered that it was the 80,000 muskets bought from France that armed the soldiers of the Revolution and that most of the materials used in making arms came from Europe; the most foolhardy was sobered by the knowledge that since that war the country had remained dependent on imported arms.

War with France would mean facing, not a small army of professional soldiers, but great numbers of an embattled citizenry. The wars of defense of the young French Republic had, for the first time in history, mobilized an entire nation. "All Frenchmen are permanently requisitioned for service in the armies"—so the Convention in the summer of 1793 had decreed the *levée en masse*. "Young men will go forth to battle; married men will forge weapons and transport munitions; women will make tents and clothing, and serve in hospitals; children will make lint from old linen; and old men will be brought to the public squares to arouse the courage of the soldiers, while preaching the unity of the Republic and hatred against kings." This innovation of total mobilization remains the heritage willed the modern world by those encircled people. Before that time the size of armies ran to thousands and hundreds of thousands; henceforth armies would be counted in the millions. All citizens became soldiers, and the professional soldier became a type apart in the national body. The need for weapons multiplied as did the size of the armies; expanding demands must outstrip the old production methods.

Another innovation of the French Republic had a bearing on Whitney's next enterprise. There is relationship between France's standardization of weights and measures and Whitney's standardization of the component parts of a musket. Both derived from the same concept—establishing uniformity to make like units interchangeable.* Among the inequalities wiped out by the French Republic were those that had characterized the units of weight and length. Replacing outmoded confusion wherein a pound represented 391 different local units of weight, and 282 different units of length were called a foot, they decreed that such units be given precise, national definition. It would make goods flow more easily over wider areas. France commissioned her greatest mathematician, Laplace, to effect the change. The significance of this uniformity impressed Stiles, who succinctly recorded the result and its implications. "The French Republic are introducing a new Test on *Measures* & weights, founded on the arc of the 45th degree Latitude, assumed a medium between the equator & polar degree of the oblate spheroid of the Earth. They divide this degree into 10 million parts. . . . The *standard weight*, a cube of distilled Water, one side of the Tenth part of the standard measure. This is the basis."

Metric uniformity widened and quickened trade in France: uniformity in the parts of a musket would increase the rate at which they could be produced. France had wiped out local variations on the pound and the foot; Whitney would replace the individually made, unique musket with thousands of mass-produced, standardized muskets that resembled one another as exactly as possible. The concept was as elementary as his making a model quill pen for his students to copy, thus ruling out individual taste and skill. "This is the basis" —apocalyptic words, but Stiles did not live to see Whitney's genius express the concept in an article as complex as a musket.

Tense weeks followed President Adams's announcement. The President and his Cabinet discussed how best to prepare: Should they rely on a large navy to repel the invaders or on an army to de-

* Shortly after 1763, Jean-Baptiste de Gribeauval, of the French army, had standardized the calibers of cannons and their carriages. But, as Major James E. Hicks points out, this standardization "was not important from the point of view of technical improvement, it showed the part which artillery was to play in military affairs."

fend the land? The same question, with the size of appropriations required, was debated in Congress. Inevitably, as the problem was argued, it must have started Whitney thinking in terms of his own experience, of manufacturing a single item as quickly as possible to satisfy a hungry market.

Wolcott received Whitney's letter even as Congress voted $800,-000 for the purchase of cannon and small arms (May 4, 1798). It is probable that he discussed Whitney's offer at Cabinet meetings. Quite possibly his mention of Whitney's ten thousand muskets made the fifty thousand the administration called for seem more likely of attainment and it went far to help President Adams "form an opinion with respect to the probability of obtaining within the United States by contract the number conceived to be necessary and the period within which it will be practicable to procure them."

The need for small arms was already acute in 1794, when relations with France began to grow uneasy. Congress at that time had established two national armories—one at Springfield and another at Harpers Ferry—and, until they should produce arms sufficient for national defense, voted sums to purchase arms abroad. The sum of $100,000 was sent to the American minister in London during 1794–1795 to secure cannon and muskets. Soon ships from London, ships from Hamburg, sailed into Philadelphia loaded with cargoes of armaments. In all, about 7,000 muskets were bought at a price of $9 apiece. This was the last sizable shipment of arms from abroad (French privateers later made the ocean crossing hazardous), and it was but a fraction of the desired total.

The output of the Springfield armory was discouragingly small. Two years after it had been created, it had made 245 muskets; and in another two years its total, though it had increased sharply, was just over 1,000. The need for private contractors was obvious. Until the receipt of Whitney's letter with its promise of impressive production, the government, in its moment of national emergency, had wondered how it might arm for defense. Both Whitney and the government had reasons that made them rush to enter into contractual relations; each party was well aware of the substantial rewards that would accrue from fulfillment—the negotiations moved into final form smoothly and with incredible speed.

Wolcott's answer reveals the government's eagerness. "Knowing your skill in mechanick, I had before spoken of you to the Secretary of War as a person whose services might possibly be rendered highly useful. I do not hesitate to advise you to come to Philadelphia as soon as possible." By the 24th of the same month, May, Whitney had arrived at the seat of government and three days later could write to Baldwin, "I have not yet closed my contract; it is however probable I shall before I return."

To Baldwin, whom he had consulted as to the form the contract should take, Whitney gave the tense atmosphere which gripped the Capitol. "The probability of a War is daily increasing. It is said there is a French Privateer in the Chesapeake who brings to and examines all vessels that pass. An Act was passed yesterday authorizing the President to instruct the Commanders of vessels belonging to the U.S. to capture and bring in all privateers belonging to the F. Republic who may be found hovering round our coast with apparent intention of committing Depredations on the commerce of the U.S. This the Federal Party in Congress call a *Peace* measure—the Jacobins call it War."

With rapacious privateers raiding within coastal waters, time was a precious commodity. The importance of each passing moment of peace drove the officials to accelerate what otherwise would have been a leisurely, protracted transaction. A month after he had made his first inquiry, Whitney submitted a draft contract to supply the government "with Ten Thousand Stand of Arms, on the following terms & conditions."

On June 14, 1798, just twelve days later, the contract was executed, the terms Whitney had suggested remaining substantially unchanged. Two further facts should be added to give this document its full, proper setting. The contract was unique in form as well as content. Of the twenty-seven contracts given out that year for small arms, only Whitney's was completely written out; the contracts for the other twenty-six men who agreed to manufacture a total of 30,200 muskets were made on regular printed forms with terms and conditions as orthodox as the methods they proposed using. The urgency of the government's rush to build up adequate supplies of arms made it brush aside the considered opinion of the Purveyor of

Supplies, to whom Wolcott submitted Whitney's draft for speedy comment: "I have no hesitation in declaring that the Secretary would be right in closing with Mr. Whitney provided he was satisfied he can accomplish so great an undertaking in so short a Time. I have my doubts about this matter and suspect that Mr. Whitney cannot perform as to time." The caution had been sounded; it would be remembered.

According to the agreement signed by Wolcott "for and on behalf of the United States of America of the One Part, and Eli Whitney of New Haven in the State of Connecticut of the Other Part," Whitney contracted to manufacture and deliver "Ten Thousand stand of Arms, or Muskets, with Bayonets and Ramrods complete fit for service, Four thousand stands of which arms shall be delivered on or before the last day of September, One thousand seven hundred and ninety nine, and six thousand additional stands, on or before the last day of September, One thousand eight hundred.

"2nd. The said Arms shall be delivered at New Haven . . . and shall be made after the Charleville model. The Barrels shall be proved and the muskets inspected, agreeable to the Rules now practiced and required by the United States. The stocks shall be duly hardened. The Ramrods and Bayonets shall be tempered, and the mountings, stocks and every other particular shall be finished in Workmanlike manner, in all parts precisely or as near as possible, conformable to Three patterns which have been marked and sealed by the contracting parties to this Instrument. . . .

"3rd. The Barrels shall be proved and the muskets inspected at New Haven aforesaid by a person or persons to be appointed by the Secretary of the Treasury or the Secretary of War. When due notice shall have been received by the party of the first part of this Contract that Five hundred Barrels are ready for the Test, the proof shall commence; on like notice, that a Second number of five hundred barrels are ready, the same shall also be proved, after which the United States shall not be required to prove less than one thousand barrels at one time. The wages of the Inspector, the expence of powder and ball and all other expences of proving and inspecting shall be borne by the United States.

"4th. The United States shall cause to be delivered at Philadelphia to the party of the second part, One thousand well seasoned black walnut stocks in the rough as they have been received into the Public Stores, within sixty days after the time of executing this Contract, at the rate of twenty five Cents each, and a further number of Nine Thousand of the aforedescribed stocks shall be delivered to the second party aforesaid at said Philadelphia, from time to time as they may be wanted and at the said rate of Twenty five Cents each.

"5th. The party of the first part contracts for and on behalf of the United States to pay or allow in settlement Thirteen Dollars and forty cents for each and every of the stands of arms which shall be manufactured according to the pattern, and delivered after proof and inspection as aforesaid.

"6th. Five thousand dollars shall be advanced to the party of the second part on closing this contract, and on producing satisfactory evidence to the party of the first, that the said advance has been expended in making preparatory arrangements for the manufacture of arms, Five Thousand dollars more shall be advanced. No further advances shall be demanded until One thousand stands of Arms are ready for delivery, at which time the further sum of Five thousand dollars, shall be advanced. After the delivery of One thousand stands of arms, and the payment of the third advance as aforesaid, further advances shall be made at the discretion of the Secretary of the Treasury in proportion to the progress made in executing this contract. It is however understood and agreed by and between the parties to this instrument, that from time to time, whenever the party of the second part shall have the second thousand ready for delivery he shall be intitled to full payment for the same, so with respect to each and every Thousand until he shall have delivered the said Ten thousand stands."

With the contract for $134,000 safe in his pocket, Whitney took the stagecoach back to New Haven. Despite the magnitude of the task to which he was committed, despite the fatigue of conferences and negotiations with harassed officials, he felt, for the first time in long months, free and light. The relief was shared with Stebbins. "Bankruptcy & ruin were constantly staring me in the face & disappointment trip'd me up every step I attempted to take. I was miser-

Justice from South Carolina

From 1798 to 1801 there was, in the affairs of Miller & Whitney, a calm, a lull; it was caesura dividing the initial clash from the second major conflict.

"I have been so long and so continuously placed in the very vortex of error & of prejudice, of complaint & abuse respecting our unfortunate cotton gins, that some new evidence against a suspicion of insanity would seem requisite, to enable me to stand thus alone in opposition to public opinion." Miller was not asking for help—he was stating a fact; his worries were of a different order. By then he had learned that credit is but another name for debt. He advertised Mulberry Grove for sale in October, 1798. He found no buyers. Finally in 1800, it was put up at auction to satisfy a debt of $38,124.99; it was knocked down for $15,000.

Yet the firm's activity did not pause. The letter books repeat their detail of lawsuits and licensing fees, of Yazoo reverberations, and frantic finances of ginnery troubles and Greene estate embarrassments.

With the coming of 1799, Miller could report events to satisfy his sanguine nature: "I have just returned from the upper Country much mended in my health . . . . The Rocky Creek works which now belong entirely to us . . . is a property of great value should we ever make *oil*. The stream is durable & sufficient. The building large & substantial, & the Dam extremely well made. . . . In the future I begin to hope our concerns will look up, since I have been able at last to draw from Liverpool favorable accounts of the staple of the cotton, and thro' the interest of some Gentlemen am just beginning to sell our Gins under the most favorable auspices."

The "Gentlemen" were customers from South Carolina. Unlike the Georgia planters who "join in pilfering (I believe the epithet appropriate) the hardly earned and expensive profits of the invention from the Patentees rather than see the law for the Protection of the arts supported at the expence of a few Dollars from their private purses," a few South Carolinians sought out Miller & Whitney to buy gins. Here was the first sign that the attitude of the Georgia planters towards patents might be unique and that people did exist who would pay for using Whitney's invention. In some measure these planters would ease Whitney's bitterness at his ill treatment. "At some future period," he commented to Stebbins, the gin "will be deemed a usefull machine and be of immense value to the Southern States—but all this will do me no good. I shall then feel no pleasing satisfaction from the consideration of having been the inventor."

Subsequently, the partners gained an improvement in their legal position which encouraged them and alarmed and angered the Georgia cotton growers. In April, 1800, largely through the exertions of Whitney and Miller, the patent law was amended, and by the new wording the ambiguous sanctuary to the trespassers was wiped out. At once Miller started after the most arrant offenders. He instituted a series of suits to be tried in the fall session of the Circuit Court—principally, as he told his chief counsel, Seaborn Jones, "to decide the dependence which can be placed upon a Jury of Augusta." He got his answer from Augusta. He also got a prompt answer from the governor.

In a speech to the Georgia House Governor James Jackson lashed out against the federal law that protected "the patent gin monopoly"; he called it "a manifest injury to the community and in many respects, a cruel extortion on the gin holders," and declared that Georgia and South Carolina, where cotton "appears to be becoming the principle staple, are made tributary to two persons." Expressing the mood of the Georgia planters, he invoked the phrases and names that would dignify their cause: "Monopolies are odious in all countries but more particularly so in a government like ours. The great mentor, Coke, declared them contrary to the common and fundamental law of England. . . . The celebrated Dr. Adam Smith, observes, that monopolies are supported by cruel and oppressive laws, such is the operation at present of the law on this subject; its weight lay on the poor industrious mechanic and planter." He did not stop with his denunciation of monopolies; his words were a rebuke to Congress for having changed the Act, and an invitation to "our sister state of South Carolina . . . cheerfully [to] join Georgia in any proper application to Congress on the subject. I am likewise of the opinion that the states of North Carolina and Tennessee must be so far interested to support such application." And midway in his speech he mentioned—he was but echoing the planters—that the patentees, "it is supposed on the lowest calculation, will make by [their patent] in the two states one hundred thousand dollars."

Georgia was aroused. How would their cry of "odious monopoly" sound were it to be found neither odious nor a monopoly outside her borders? The cotton growers' dignity was at stake as well as their profits; if they were to be damned as rascals, they must all be damned together—there must be none to escape the epithet. The appeal to hysteria had been sounded.

Alas for Georgia! South Carolina, different in origin, composition, and tradition, was not to be pushed into a course of action foreign to her. Georgia, from the time of her settlement on, had been a frontier, Britain's southernmost outpost in North America, an outpost designed at once as a bastion against the Spanish in Florida and the French in Louisiana, and as a base from which to harass these enemies. Compared with Charleston, Savannah was a shabby country town, and it and its surrounding area was largely populated by colonists who had chosen the dangerous southern frontier in preference to their depressed condition in England and Europe. Georgia never had the social position of South Carolina; it had no fur trade nor plantations of rice and indigo to bring it wealth; it had no Pinckneys or Rutledges who had studied law in England; and neither as colony nor state had it ever enacted a patent law.

South Carolina, on the other hand, was the first colony to frame a general patent law in America (1691), reaffirming the English principles, and one of its earliest acts as a state was to revive its statutes to protect inventors (1784). Two years later the exclusive privilege the state conferred on any inventor of a useful machine for fourteen years was made contingent upon several conditions, one of which was that he deposit a model with the Secretary of State. In South Carolina many factors made the climate more salubrious for patentees.

"Our friend Mr. Goodrich has just returned from the upper Country," triumphantly Miller wrote on September 4, 1801, to Whitney, "and brings us the pleasing intelligence that a prospect is at last opening of an advantageous disposal of our Patent right to the Legislature of *So.* Carolina. The foundation is already laid for such a proposal to come from the Legislature to the Patentee's and it is deemed perfectly essential that either you or myself be present. As you are the original inventor and generally known as such, the pretentions of the present administration in favour of genius & the arts might with great propriety be wrought upon in your favour." Miller then named political elements which would have influence and make Whitney the better negotiator. "The personal acquaintance you have with the President and the heads of the Departments . . . would enable you to present yourself to a Democratic Legislature with letters of recommendation from the Demigog of their party. You have also the advantage of me in having been able to sit down quietly under the protecting branches of the great tree of life, of honour and happiness to our Country. While I have been exposed to the hollow murmurs of sedition, and often have had to combat a whole company of the Satellites of such men as Abram Bishop and Genl. Jackson. . . . Hence it is probable that I have become somewhat obnoxious to the undertrappers of administration and should meet them in a negotiation under some disadvantage."

"Probable" is an exquisite understatement. Bishop, the most articulate of the anti-Yazoo men in Connecticut—where Miller was suing to collect from northern buyers—used his tongue and his pen to excoriate the men behind the land-grab. Among the most conspicuous offenders he named Nightingale, Miller's associate and Catherine's son-in-law, and of the leaders he said: "Unto such was given power, as scorpions have power and their power was to hurt men."

Immediately Whitney prepared to go. His traveling writing case was jammed with letters of introduction, for, in addition to one from President Jefferson, the "Demigog," Whitney had asked Timothy Dwight, president of Yale, and Oliver Wolcott, former Secretary of the Treasury, both staunch Federalists, to commend him to the Honorable Charles Cotesworth Pinckney and other influential friends. He was thus putting into practice the lesson he had recently learned in Washington: Business knows no party politics. He acted on the theory that it was unimportant if a man be a Democrat or Federalist; the point was whether he would advance Miller & Whitney's patent rights.

Whitney made the long trip south by "horse & sulkey," without company. Conditions, after he crossed the Potomac, must have seemed as foreign to him as to the Englishman, Thomas Cooper, Priestley's friend, who but recently had sought refuge in America. Cooper remarked: "Hospitality is relative. From Massachusetts to Maryland, inns are plentiful, and strangers frequent them when they travel; from the south boundary of Pennsylvania to South Carolina, taverns are scarce and dear, and hospitality is on the most liberal scale."

Whitney dated a letter, "Virginia Nineteen Miles North of the Northern line of North Carolina—at no place at all (Sunday Evening) 22d Nov. 1801." He must have been lonely that Sunday evening, grateful for the crossroads shelter where he recorded for his boyhood friend Stebbins, who was now living in Maine, his plans, his experiences, his impressions. "There is a prospect of selling my Patent Right to the Cotton Machine to the Legislature of So. Carolina & it is that prospect that has induced me to take a jaunt to this state to meet their Assembly which is now sitting & I am thus far on my way by land & expect to be at Columbia in about Eight Days. So you see I am still pursuing *prospects*. . . .

"At the great City of Washington I was detained by business a week. I had letters of Introduction to Mr. Jefferson & Mr. Maddison with both of whom I had several interviews. I am much pleased with Maddison, he is a sensible and at any rate appears to be a candid man. The Great City has increased a little since I saw it last winter but I fear it will require an eternity to fill up the great casms which still remain. I obtained letters from Mr. Jefferson & Mr. Maddison to Governor Monroe of Virginia, with whom I had an interview at Richmond where I tarried half a day & which is the handsomest place I have seen in passing thro the State.

"My journey thro this State has been solitary and dreary. The roads are very indifferent & the land—except a little just on the banks of the Rappahonock is 'poor Miserable blind & naked.' It is either old Barren fields lying waste or half wooded with wood of half size but which will never grow any larger. Except a few small towns thro' which I have passed, I have only seen a Miserable hut once in about 4 or 5 miles. Their main crop is Indian Corn of which their land produces from four to Six Bushels *pr* acre. [He was the son of a farmer and saw with a farmer's eyes]. Some Wheat & Some Tobacco are made for exportation. I have met from 30 to 50 Hogshead yesterday & today going to Petersburg. The mode in which they transfer it is to put a pin in each end of the Hogshead to each of which is hooked a Shaft, like that of a Yanke Pung *—in these shafts is tackeled a little horse & a second horse put before with a Negro to ride one of the horses & another with a withe hooked to said pins to assist in holding it back. In this manner the hogshead is rolled thro' thick & thin from one to two hundred miles as the case may be. There are, however, about as many white people as Negroes employed in this business of transportation . . . & the people while engaged in this business stop in the woods by the side of the road when night comes on, build a fire by which they & their horses or cattle stay thro' the night & they never go into a house to lodge during the whole journey."

Whitney reaching Columbia on December 3rd, had to stay there a "little more than two weeks attending the Legislature." Of this he also wrote an account to Stebbins: "They closed their sessions at 10 o'Clock last evening. A few hours previous to their breaking up they voted fifty thousand Dollars to purchase my patent right to the Machine for Cleaning Cotton, 20 thousand of which is to be paid in hand & the remainder in three annual payments of 10 thousand Dollars each. This is selling the rights at a great sacrifice. If a regular course of Law had been pursued, from two to three hundred thousand Dollars would undoubtedly have been recovered. The use of the machine here is amazingly extensive & the value of it beyond all calculation. It may without exaggeration be said to have raised

* The New England pung was a low horse-drawn box sled slung between two long poles that served both as runners and as shafts.

the value of seven eighths of all the three Southern States from 50 to 100 *pr* Cent. We get but a song for it in comparison with the worth of the thing, but it is *securing* something. It will enable M & W to pay all their debts & divide something between them. It established a precedent which will be valuable as it respects our collections in other states & I think there is now a fair prospect that I shall in the event realize property enough from the invention to render me comfortable & in some measure independent. Tho' my stay here has been short I have become acquainted with a considerable part of the Legislature & most distinguished characters in the State."

For the first time Whitney was face to face with the deep-seated hostility, hiding behind half-truths and twisted logic, with which for so long Miller had had to deal. To handle this, he had been "very busily employed in removing the prejudice & ignorance which greatly prevailed respecting our Patent Rights." "His modest and even diffident manner had procured him some friends—the value of his invention had procured him many more." So wrote an eyewitness, Henry William de Saussure, former Director of the Mint, adding: "But he still had many prejudices & difficulties to overcome. Some doubted the originality of the invention, tho his proofs were strong and they could not point out any other inventor, others doubted the utility of the invention: or at least were fearful that the use of it in cleaning the black seed cotton, where it was not absolutely necessary, was more prejudicial to the character of that staple in foreign markets, than the use of it was beneficial in cleaning out the green seed cotton, where it is indispensible. Truth & public spirit prevailed—The legislature purchased Mr. Whitney's patent right to the Saw gin, & its improvements, for the use of the inhabitants of the State, for 50,000 dollars, of which 20,000 are payable immediately—10,000 in the autumn of 1802—and the remainder soon after.

"Our Treasury, thanks to the assumption and funding the State debts, was full; and we were enabled to make these payments without any additional general tax, altho we have agreed to lay a small tax on the persons who use the Saw to re-imburse the State gradually." A tax of fifty cents was imposed on every saw or annular row of teeth in every gin, to be paid by owners who had used the gin since the 1st of October or who should use it before the 1st of the following

April. "It is with pleasure that I make this communication, because it furnishes proof that the States will do Justice to the talents of our Countrymen: and it will take away the Reproach cast upon republics, that they are never the patrons of the arts, nor the rewarders of ingenuity. Mr. Whitney, relieved from the embarassments which oppressed his genius, will, I hope, go on to exercise his faculties for the benefit of his Country."

Miller & Whitney had asked $100,000, a figure that, the partners argued, indicated their willingness to dispose of the invention to South Carolina "for a sum far below its value." However reasonable, the sum was an asking price; in Miller's opinion the settlement whereby they received even half the amount was due to Whitney's quiet authority and polite insistence, "for without his presence I should have feared that twenty or five and twenty thousand alone would have been obtainable, and the advantage of increasing the price will operate by precedent as well as present benefits."

The sale was consummated six weeks later, when, on February 16, 1802, Whitney received the first payment from Paul Hamilton, Comptroller of Revenues and Finances of South Carolina. In return he conveyed their patent rights and signed an agreement to fulfill two additional provisions: "to refund to the Comptroller . . . all and every Sum of money and to deliver to him also such obligations of Notes as we and our agents have received for Licenses. . . . And to deliver to him two of the said Saw Gins of the most approved Size and construction for the use of the State within a reasonable time." Brief, explicit, Whitney must have thought the agreement; yet it was to cost him years of effort and endless argument to have its spirit honored.

Whitney spent the intervening weeks traveling. He had never seen any of their installations—all these years he had been busy in New Haven—and so from Columbia he went by way of Augusta to the ginnery nearby Rocky Creek which Miller had described so glowingly three years before. The stagnant years had left their mark; it was "in a miserable condition & fast going to decay. I think it had better be sold for what it will bring." He visited happily with the Millers at Dungeness, the plantation to which they had moved when Mulberry Grove was sold. Though bare of all elegancies, it was a handsome property, for when Greene had bought it he had erected a four-story thirty-room mansion solidly constructed of tabby, the local concrete made of lime and shells mixed with water.

Whitney's itinerary, with sidetrips and stopovers, was arduous. Covering about 2,800 miles, it was made "in a Sulkey & the same horse performed the whole journey," and brought him back to New Haven the beginning of May. He laconically summed up the whole jaunt by saying that he had "met with some difficulties and delays but finally closed up the business of the Sale to S.C., recd part of the money & obligations for the residue."

Whitney, no less than Miller, failed to gauge the true temper of the Georgia trespassers, who knew that as long as moneys were due and obligations remained the sale was not finally closed; there was still ground left to contest, still space to maneuver. To them, any agreement spelled defeat. They feared that were the sale to be concluded, the idea would take hold and infect other states. It was not to give Miller & Whitney recognition now that Georgia planters had killed the patent, starved out the firm's ginneries, and reduced the partners to insolvency. Suddenly the South Carolina sale made it apparent that what had gone before was not finished; it was but a first act, formless, impromptu, dispersed, disguised. Everyone could plainly see that now the great struggle to apportion the raw cotton profits was approaching its real climax. The protagonists spoke of honor and justice and genius, knavery and fraud, monopoly and freedom—but these were grace notes embellishing, almost obscuring, the drab theme of profits.

Half of the life of the patent was passed when Miller & Whitney sold their rights to the State of South Carolina in February, 1802, and the objectives and policy of the partners had changed as events had forced their change. Where they had tried to shut down every illegal machine, they now fought for their right to sell licenses. It may be that this new approach divided the opposition: some planters, notably those in Georgia, remained unreconciled and adamant; a few South Carolinians, respectful of the law, were unwilling to base their new economy on anything as insecure as the use of surreptitious machines. (Even in Georgia there were those who thought it advisable to settle with the partners on a licensing basis. "The grand jury of Hancock County, at the last February terms, among other present-ments, recommend to the legislature of this state, at their next ses-sion, to purchase for the use of the state, the right to use Whitney and Miller's patent cotton gin; and that the state do indemnify itself, by levying a tax on the use of said gin.") Between the two extremes were to be found the fast-growing audience of southern cotton grow-ers. They watched the incidents unfold, the tension mount; they were swayed by local pressures and prevailing moods; they seesawed between expediency and honor, ill at ease in subservience to the former, reluctant to pay too high a price for the latter.

As the conflict moved out of the undeviating atmosphere of the Georgia upcountry, and cotton cultivation began to be important in regions where other points of view were allowed expression, a settlement became possible. The one thing the Georgia planters could not do was to stop the spread of cotton growing, and it was this factor that cleared the way for Miller & Whitney's sale of their patent rights to South Carolina, North Carolina, and Tennessee. Yet at that time the intransigent planters who had successfully used Lyon to ruin Miller & Whitney's ginning concern within Georgia thought that Holmes might be effective in stopping neighboring states from reaching an agreement with the patentees. Holmes, who had lost his case in court, and paid the partners a license fee, was resurrected and, dressed in his pristine pretensions, presented in a frantic effort to nullify the sale made to South Carolina.

This phase of Miller & Whitney's struggle for survival Whitney attended to personally. He had started the negotiations with South Carolina at Miller's request; he continued his active role not merely because of the enormous sums at stake, but because his opponents still denied him his invention and disparaged his good name. He was aware that to the negotiations he would have to bring heroic patience and unflagging energy. Great numbers of Carolinians were acting, as he put it, "much like children & much more like rogues"; their behavior caused him, he confessed, "much vexation of Spirit in this Business." In the light of all he had suffered, he would have been foolish not to reckon that many Carolinians would be selfish enough to begrudge him the $50,000 the legislature had agreed to pay.

Whitney knew that he and Miller were in real danger of losing what little they had just gained from the gin.

It would seem that until Hamilton, the comptroller of the state, on November 3, 1802, notified Miller & Whitney that the sale had been revoked by the state legislature, neither Miller nor Whitney had any idea that things had gone amiss. (Hamilton's notification and Miller's letter to Whitney are missing; their contents can only be inferred.) To Whitney, who was just then in Raleigh negotiating to "sell my Patent Right to the Legislature" of North Carolina, the news sounded absurd; it left him "more vexed than alarmed," but he warned Miller "to be very cautious and circumspect in our measures and even in our remarks with regard to it. Be cautious what you say or publish till we meet our enemies in a court of justice when, if they have any sensibility left, we will make them very much ashamed of their childish conduct."

Both partners learned that the contract had been broken because their Georgia opponents had persuaded many South Carolina planters that they had much to gain by not paying Miller & Whitney; and that the excuses were decoys set out to give the opposition time to commence the legal harassing that had worked so advantageously in Georgia. For in Miller's sixteen-page reply to the comptroller he stated that "it has been privately reported and in a manner to gain belief, that the representations of a man by the name of Hodgen Holmes acquired so much credit with the legislature as to form part of the secret ground of their proceeding"; he also noticed "that the pretentions of a Mr. Lyon have been revived." Lyon he dismissed quickly: "We had supposed that his vanity and weakness on the subject had ceased to engage the attention of any man of sense." But Holmes he discussed minutely, giving the full schedule of his unworthiness.

Miller also replied to the state's contention that the firm had failed to honor its obligations under the agreement Whitney had made with the comptroller. "The one which bound the Patentees to the return of Notes of money received from individuals for the Sale of Licences, . . . it is admitted to have been uncomplied with . . . it was expected that Mr. Russell Goodrich, the special agent of the Patentees,

would have attended to the fulfillment of this stipulation, but unfortunately he went on a Journey into the State of Tennessee and to
the Natches, where he was detained by indisposition and other unexpected events until the time had elapsed for the payment. This
failure then, being admitted, it only follows to ascertain the amount
to which the legal or equitable forfeiture of the Patentees could
fairly extend. In respect to the notes, no possible injury could arise
. . . by their detention. . . . In respect to the money they detained,
the amount is exactly $580. . . . [Mr. Goodrich] will probably have
the honor to wait on you with this money about the first of next
month which will extend the detention to five months, the interest
of which for this period of time amounts to a little short of Twenty
Dollars, and this sum very small and trifling as it is, is all that a court
of law or equity would allow for the failure of a similar engagement
between individuals, and it can hardly be supposed that the State
of So. Carolina would avail itself of the power of State Sovereignty
to make a greater exaction."

He offered to pay $50 if the state should want to charge the pat-
entees as high as 20 per cent. He suggested to the comptroller the im-
propriety of any penalty, since "It will appear I presume on examination that the Citizens of So. Carolina have made a net profit out of
the use of the invention the last season of at least fifty Thousand
dollars." Then Miller exposed the mean spirit that had directed the
rescinding: "Much more is it the subject of astonishment that the
Legislature of a State could not only proceed to sanction such a
measure, but to pass a resolution, as I am informed, they have done,
directing a detention of the whole Balance of money due the Patentees, and ordering a suit to be commenced for what has been already paid . . . for a cause so very unimportant."

The second specific charge lodged against the firm concerned
Whitney directly, and, since it was his responsibility to provide model
gins, he was mortified "that I am by anyone accused with any omis-
sion or neglect." He recalled, to Major General Charles C. Pinckney,
the discussion that preceded the agreement. "As to the Models I
believe it had been the understanding of the Gentlemen at the
time, that . . . I should engage to deliver them previous to the
[next] session of your legislature. I declined stipulating to furnish

them at so early a period observing it was doubtful whether it would be in my power to perform it, that I was desirous those models should be constructed in the best manner, and contain some improvements which have never yet come into general use; that in this case I should have no other alternative but to make the models myself, there being now no machine in existence after which I could employ workmen to copy; that by a previous understanding I was pledged to the government of the United States and could not consent to engage to do a thing which I might not have it in my power to perform. Mr. Hamilton, the Comptroller will I presume recollect this to be the import of the conversation which passed between him and myself at the time . . . and it will be observed that the engagement which I have entered into with the Comptroller does not require the Models to be delivered at the same time the monies are to be refunded. . . . I have certainly been actuated by the best of motives and if I have done wrong I must say I am not sensible wherein. Permit me to ask the favor that you would speak to the Comptroller on the subject and name the circumstances to any Gentlemen who may feel dissatisfaction. I would come to Columbia before the rising of your Legislature if it were possible, but it is not in my power. . . . I shall immediately after my return [to Connecticut] proceed on in making the models for So. Carolina the materials for which I began to collect six months ago."

To the voluminous statements sent Hamilton there has remained but one reply: "In answer to yours . . . I am to say that I can only act under the directions of the Legislature; and that I have the honor to be respectfully yours—"

What doubts possessed Whitney when he learned, as he was closing the sale of his patent rights to North Carolina, that the fine fabric of his previous year's efforts had been unraveled? 1802 was ending. South Carolina had rescinded the sale. Once again he was selling, but this time he wondered how good the new contract might be. He had a copy—he underlined the last words—of the resolution passed by the General Assembly of North Carolina that pronounced the "contract is beneficial, advantageous and generally satisfactory to the Citizens of North Carolina and ought to be strictly fulfilled on the part of the State with *punctuality and good faith*." He must almost have had to remind himself that the payment schedule was different and that the names were, too. To John Haywood, treasurer of North Carolina, he gave "an amplified copy of a Patent granted under the authority of the United States," and was assured that a "tax of two shillings and sixpence for each and every saw or annular row of teeth, which shall be used in said gins, in each and every year for the term of five years thereafter shall . . . be paid to Miller & Whitney . . . first deducting the Sheriff's usual commissions of six percent for collection." On their part, the patentees bound themselves to the same obligations they previously had. Would the contract born with 1803 die as that year died?

Bewilderment was Whitney's companion as he drove north in his sulky, through the dismal winter weeks, north to Washington where he might rest and plan what to do. His perplexity expressed itself: "I cannot now tell what, whence or when I wrote you last. I have been here three weeks & am now laying by to regain the health of which the severity of the winter has deprived me." He wrote to Stebbins in March from Washington. "The weather this season has been constantly & suddenly changing from one extreme to the other, which has rendered this journey very tedious & fatiguing." His remark on the fickleness of the weather seems to have been his way of commenting on human inconstancy. "I find my personal attention [to the Patent concerns] to be of the first importance. Nothing has been effected in that business but what I have done myself & I am well persuaded that no person or persons could have effected any thing had I been absent. The Cotton Machine is a thing of immence value & by pushing hard I hope to realize something for it . . . but so large a proportion of Mankind are such infernal Rascals that I shall never be able to realize but a trifling proportion of its value. You know I always believed in the *'Depravity of Human nature.'* I thought I was long ago sufficiently *'grounded & established'* in this Doctrine. But God Almighty is continually pouring down *cataracts* of testimony upon me to convince me of this fact." His anger seems to have needed a thunderstorm to clear the heavy atmosphere which had so long oppressed him.

The very next day he again wrote Stebbins. He wanted to gather together the loose strands of fact from which to make a sturdy rope that would tie the slippery southern planters to his contract. "When I returned from Georgia in the year 1793 [Whitney was once more himself], we were in the habit of communicating freely with each other upon every subject which occupied any part of our attention, especially what related in any wise to my Invention of the Cotton Gin. . . . Several Patents have been issued for Machines of my principle."

And then Whitney told how Holmes had been used to discredit him. "One of the Patentees claims as his invention making the rows of teeth of sheet iron instead of wire. The fact is he was told that was my original Idea, & my machine was particularly described to him, even by drawings of every part. . . . We commenced a suit against this man to have his patent vacated,—after a tedious course of litigation & Delay we obtained a judgement on the ground that the principle was the same & that his patent was surreptitious—his patent was vacated & Declared void. He came forward & paid up the costs & purchased a License of us to use the Machine for which he had pretended to get a patent & we now hold his note [for $200] given for that License.* By some neglect of the Judge or mistake of the Clerk in entering the Judgement, upon a new Democratic District Judge being appointed he found means to revive the cause. After a series of delays etc. his own judge was obliged to give judgement against him. Still these designing rascals pretend to hold up his claim & make a handle of it to our disadvantage. & although I have no idea that any court can be so abandoned as to take any serious notice of it, I should like to obtain such testimony as will shew it to be my invention & thereby put a complete stopper on that business. We already have one positive witness of the fact [Judge Nathaniel Pendleton]. The first person to whom the machine was shown (besides Miller's family) which was in the spring of '93."

* Holmes's patent was issued on May 12, 1796. From then until 1804, Whitney counted ten other such patents granted. Miller & Whitney's attitude toward Holmes is unexpected. While their suit against him was pending, Miller instructed Goodrich that "if a dispute at law becomes necessary, I prefer to have it with principle planters rather than with the Mechanics. I would have no objection to a compromise on easy terms with Hodgen Holmes . . . as he is a Mechanic he might be usefull to us and I would rather make him serviceable to us & himself than do him an injury. But keep *this to yourself* unless you actually settle with him."

Whitney would return to South Carolina prepared to destroy the hydra-headed lie which claimed for Holmes the honor of inventing the gin. To arm himself with proof of his being in fact the inventor, he asked Stebbins for a deposition—reminding him of events of the summer of 1793, when, as Stebbins could truthfully testify, they had "many frequent conversations on the subject of mechanics & Natural Philosophy in general and particularly relative to said invention. That I [Stebbins] transcribed his specifications or descriptions of said machine several times & that he conferred with me relative to the various parts of said Description." Whitney's lawyer, Simeon Baldwin, took another deposition from "old Mr. Chittenden, a brother of Gov. Chittenden of Vermont, one of the most distinguished Mechanics & Machinists of his day. (He was the inventor during the Revolutionary war of a machine for cutting & forming card teeth by a single stroke & with great rapidity, of vast importance at the time & said to have been afterwards patented in England & to be the basis of Wittimore's improved machine for making cards.)" Whitney requested of James Madison, Secretary of State, "an exemplified Copy of my Patent . . . with the principal Specifications, References & Drawings included in the copy." Nathaniel Pendleton, General Greene's aide-de-camp, the first person outside the immediate family to have seen the gin, wrote to General Pinckney—giving Whitney a copy of his letter—asserting that when he was shown the gin in the spring of 1793 he had "no doubt then, nor have I any now that Mr. Whitney was the inventor of that machine during the previous winter. Soon afterwards a machine house was put up at Mulberry Grove by Mr. Phineas Miller and several of those machines worked in it by Cattle, which I frequently saw."

Such documents could silence the whispering campaign in South Carolina; but Whitney knew that he must also win a clear court victory in Georgia—there lay the taproot. He had learned that his opponents would not scruple to waste his time and deny his talent. How exasperating to be repeatedly summoned from his manufactory in New Haven, how repugnant was the necessity of having to prove his honesty by evidence. "I have a set of the most Depraved villains to combat & I might as well go to *Hell* in search of *Happiness* as apply to a Georgia Court for Justice."

| XII | *Judge Johnson's Decision* |

THE bitterness toward the Georgia planters was further justified in Whitney's heart when, arriving at his destination, he received "the Mellancholly tidings of the Death of my friend & partner Phineas Miller Esq.," on December 7, 1803.

Not even Stebbins could replace Miller. Miller & Whitney, he knew now, was a symbol of a shared adventure—the golden hopes, the long gray fruitless years of struggle against opposition and misrepresentation. It must have been hard to remember a time when their partnership was not an expression of their friendship, a joining of names and efforts. Miller had assumed the financing of a business whose kind and scope had not existed before in the United States. Singlehanded, Miller had stood off a hungry countryside and had preserved part of their property; as much as possible he had shielded Whitney from any duty, burden, or harm that might interfere with his freedom to explore and conquer his own special world of mechanics and production. From the very beginning Miller had valued Whitney's gifts and sought to advance them. Whitney appreciated Miller's unique devotion to their firm and to him. When he had moved on to his next great project he had not entered into another partnership, partly because he preferred independence, partly because no man could have replaced Miller.

The thought of Catherine, and the memory of how generously she and Miller had welcomed him into their home and lives, made Whitney leave immediately for Dungeness. Traveling there, his mind and heart must have been crowded with the events of the past decade —their plans for quick sure riches and the sequel of anxious toil, uncertainty, disappointment.

Miller's death—"the very unexpected event," as he characterized the death of a man not yet forty—was tragically timed; it came as good tidings were beginning to attach themselves to their firm, with the decision of Tennessee to purchase the patent rights and North Carolina's reaffirmed intention to abide by her contract. Had this been bought at the cost of Miller's life? Whitney must have asked the question, for again and again he openly expressed the hatred he felt toward those who had tried to kill Miller & Whitney.

Reinstatement of the sale to the South Carolina legislature had to be postponed to the next year; he would have to return for the legislative meeting of December, 1804. During his short visit at Dungeness, he attended to the more pressing matters: with Catherine, executrix of Miller's estate, he gave Goodrich authority to assign the patent rights to Tennessee. He instructed his lawyer in Columbia, South Carolina: "Should any of those persons from whom we have recd money for Patent Licenses commence a suit . . . to oblige us to refund the money which they have paid, you are hereby authorized to accept service in my behalf and answer to the Cause in Court. I shall have no defence to make—they are fully entitled to recover the money & it would have been paid to them long ago had it not been for the improper interference of the Comptroller." To whom the moneys were to be refunded seems to have been a point of discussion. Whitney thought they should be paid directly to the individual, whereas the comptroller claimed "that the said monies and obligations were to be delivered over to him for the use of the state." Whitney may have suspected that the comptroller had deliberately created new obstacles. By the time the legislature met again, Whitney wanted a performance by the firm of their part of the agreement, since he was convinced that now he could answer by proof the insinuation that he was not the true inventor. He was nailing shut every exit through which they might try to run out on their contract.

"My time, since my return to [New Haven] last spring," he wrote to Catherine at the end of September, "has been almost wholly occupied in constructing Models of the Cotton Machine for the Southern States & for the last three months my labour & anxiety have been incessant." He was as tense as a general on the eve of battle. "These Models are of full size for general use in which I have endeavored to bring together all the useful improvements & alterations which have occured to my mind in contemplating the Subject for Several years past. Delicacy in their opperation, Durability & a more compleat Development of principle have been primary considerations in their construction & I flatter myself they will be found superior to any which have before existed. They are not quite finished, I hope however to compleat them & start from here for So Carolina in ten Days. I anticipate a very fatiguing & perplexing tour." "Fatigue" and "perplexity" were the words he habitually used for a southern trip, but this time they bore no relation to what befell him. The acute panic that seized his enemies was proof of how well he had sealed all loopholes. When, at the end of November, 1804, he appeared in Columbia, their use of force was their confession of weakness.

Once, Miller had been warned that if he persisted in bringing the trespassers to trial, he would be "stoned thro' the streets"; his exemption from violence was the measure of the planters' certainty that he would be unable to collect from them. This kind of threat had prepared Whitney for a contumacious foe—but no more.

But Whitney's "opponents in Georgia had the address to influence the Legislature of S.C. to rescind their grant, & on his going there to meet the Legislature in 1804 he was by their order arrested in a suit to recover the money previously advanced."

Had they thought thus to intimidate him, they were wrong. Angry, indignant, Whitney accused the legislature directly. He stated that he conceived himself "to have been treated with unreasonable severity in the measures recently taken against him by and under their immediate direction. He holds that, to be seized and dragged to prison without being allowed to be heard in answer to the charge alledged against him, and indeed without the exhibition of any specific charge, is a direct violation of the common right of every citizen of a free government; that the power, in this case, is all on one side; that whatever may be the issue of the process now instituted against him, he must, in any case, be subjected to great expense and extreme hardships; and that he considers the tribunal before which he is holden to appear, to be wholly incompetent to decide, definitely, existing disputes between the State and Miller & Whitney."

Pride illuminated his avowal that he had "manifested no other than a disposition to fulfill all the stipulations entered into with the State of South Carolina, with punctuality and good grace; and he begs leave to observe further, that to have industriously, laboriously, and exclusively devoted many years of the prime of his life to the invention and the improvement of a machine, from which the citizens of South Carolina have already realized immense profits,—which is worth to them millions, and from which their prosperity, to the latest generations, must continue to derive the most important benefits, and in return to be treated as a felon, a swindler, and a villain, has stung him to the very soul. And when he considers that this cruel persecution is inflicted by the very persons who are enjoying these great benefits, and expressly for the purpose of preventing his ever deriving the least advantage from his own labors, the acuteness of his feelings is altogether inexpressible."

Miller & Whitney's opponents had played their last desperate trick. Whitney had left them no hiding room for whispers and lies, insinuations and trickery; ten years of antagonism had created a climax that demanded a settlement. And the planters, confronted by Whitney, who not only had invented the machine but was able to prove that he had invented it, knew their cry of "monopoly" was but a querulous counterpoint to his passionate plea. "On a full hearing before a committee embracing at his request his strongest opponents, the committee reported so full and favorably in his favor that the Legislature restored the grants & made extra provisions for the payment."

From the report of this committee, it appears that its principal task had been less one of deciding for or against the patentees than of arranging a retreat in which the trespassers could retire with a minimum of discomfiture. Why else should they have inserted the last clause: "And although from the Documents . . . they are of opinion that said Whitney is the true original inventor of the Saw Gin, yet, in order to guard the Citizens from any injury hereafter, the Committee recommend that before the remaining Balance is paid, the said Whitney be required to give Bond & Security to the Comptroller General to indemnify each and every Citizen . . . against the legal claims of all persons . . . to any patent or exclusive Right to the invention or improvement of the machine for separating cotton from its seeds." The wording of this communiqué conceals the fact that the final clash in the committee room was short and savage— as Whitney indicated in a quick note to Baldwin. "The boisterous session of the Legislature is just closed [December 26, 1804]—it commenced on the day of my arrival. My constant & utmost exertions have, without interruption been engaged in getting thro' my business & have been so fortunate as to have succeeded equal to my expectations. It was carried by a large majority in the Lower House but it was won by a hard fought Battle in the Senate."

Miller & Whitney had at last achieved their first real victory: their patent rights had been sustained, their credit reestablished. And yet it was but a beginning. Even as Whitney was fighting in South Carolina, he heard that the "contract which has been made with the State of Tennessee now hangs *suspended*"; but he was reassured by the news that though "two attempts have been made to induce the State of *No* Carolina to *rescind* their *contract,* neither . . . have succeeded."

The report of Whitney's thundering success was dressed up to suit people's fancies. "Common *Fame* is a common *liar*—and though she sometimes fabricates her globes of falsehood round a little nucleus of truth, . . . still a large proportion of mankind will for awhile believe every word of her gab." He wrote Stebbins the latest distortion of facts. "She has undertaken to report that in consequence of great success in the Southern Country the winter past, I have become very *rich*. My friends are rejoiced—& I should not be disposed to undeceive them were it not from the consideration that the longer they continue in the delusion the greater will be their mortification when they find it is not true. . . . A report was circulated some miles about the Country that I brought home with me the enormous sum of 80,000 Dollars! What a pack of *fools*—to think any man would be such a *foolish fool* as to travel with half that sum about him. The truth is I brought home the remnant of what I carried away with me for my travelling expences, which, (as I always calculate to have the means of purchasing another horse in case mine should die on the journey) amounted to the sum of 225 Dollars 37½ cents. I have borrowed 500 Dollars since I returned to pay some of my most pressing Debts & now want 500 more & can't obtain it."

The sale to South Carolina and other states had not halted the law suits of Miller & Whitney against the Georgia trespassers. The minutes of the Circuit Court speak eloquently of the firm's determined spirit. Its name appears in more than sixty suits against several dozen separate defendants, as the partners continued over a full decade seeking legal redress despite adverse verdicts and hostile juries and calculated delays. (Was it prearranged that "as the last counsel was arguing this case, George Henly, one of the Jury was taken with a fit" and the case put over to the next session?) Somehow, despite years when they struggled to stave off bankruptcy, the campaign was kept alive. Miller's death did not interrupt the firm's appearance on the court calendar; if anything it committed Whitney more firmly to continue Miller's program. He understood how vital it was that they win a verdict in Georgia. On it rested their strategy. Emotionally, too, it was necessary, for Whitney had long been outraged by the insinuation that his invention was ill begotten and his patent a kind of blackmail to secure him a wealth he had not earned; he noted as "a solemn truth that many of the Citizens of Georgia are amassing fortunes, living voluptuously and rolling in splendor by the surreptitious use of [the gin], while I am, and for more than six years past have been, chained down to this spot, struggling under a heavy load of debt contracted for my very subsistence and expenses while I was solely employed in inventing and perfecting this machine. This, my Friend, is the simple fact."

He was better prepared to fight for his rights, for now Miller & Whitney had sufficient funds to press the law suits. Adam Gilchrist, a Charleston merchant, had been instructed to accept the money to be paid by South Carolina; in July of 1805 he wrote that he had "received the whole amount, altho' a part was not due,—say $22,418." From this sum Whitney directed Gilchrist to send $5,000 to Miller's executor, Dr. Lemuel Kollock, "to be paid over on a Judgement against the Estate of Genl. Greene."

But something less tangible than a substantial bank account operated in Whitney's favor. The attitude of the other cotton-growing states—South Carolina, North Carolina, and even Tennessee—made it almost impossible for Georgia to stand alone in denying Whitney's rights. Her lofty moral reasons suddenly had the sound of cheap and shabby excuses; her pride in defending economic freedom appeared to be a cloak covering the swagger of a highwayman; the long list of verdicts against Whitney could be interpreted as a sharp scheme to legalize a robbery. The planters found the climate they had created unpleasant. Everything had been changed by the action of their sister states; to neighboring planters the Georgians found themselves obliged to defend their behavior. Such a situation quickly became intolerable. And those men who had been rejoicing that shortly the patent would expire—its fourteen-year period started on November 6, 1793—began to worry at how little time remained in which to extricate themselves from their predicament. Their best way out, they must have reasoned, was through the courts; since they had used the courts to sustain their trespass, by the same method they could make redress and remove the stigma.

A scant three years was left between the time Whitney defeated the opposition in South Carolina and November, 1807, the expiration date of his patent; but to the Georgia planters who now had to buy their self-esteem from him, this length of time was whittled down to five court sessions, held semiannually. Their change of attitude is the most likely explanation for the change to be noticed in the court proceedings, whose minutes are as cryptic and indicative as the readings on a thermometer. Spring and winter, session after session, the entries dully repeat "non suit" (a way of terminating a case apart from its merits without precluding a retrial at a later date); then, while the struggle took place in the South Carolina legislature, the Georgia juries were content to mark time with "case continued" or "continued on Defendants Affidavit" or "continued by Consent."

Abruptly, after an arresting entry for May, 1806, these stop. "On Argument a perpetual injunction against Jno. Powell ordered." He was one of the two defendants whose case happened to come at that session. The other was Arthur Fort, who had been sued since December, 1802. Fort was the lone defendant at the following session in December. A new theme had been introduced; it was developed skilfully and majestically at the next session, "before the Honble William Johnson & the Honble William Stephens on Bill, answer, replication, testimony, & exhibits in behalf of the complainants [Eli Whitney et al.]. It is ordered, adjudged, & decreed that the injunction prayed for by the complainants in their bill be granted them & that the same be made perpetual and that the Defendant pay the costs of this Bill. Dated Louisville [then the capital of Georgia] this 19 December 1806 & in the 31 year of American Independence."

This occasion was made lustrous by Judge Johnson's celebrated decision. One by one he considered the arguments advanced by the defendant's lawyer: that Whitney's invention was not original, that it was not useful, that the machine his client had used was different in that it was an improvement and had been invented by another person. Here, raised again, was the thrice-slain specter of Holmes; but this time Whitney was present and fully prepared. He had offered in evidence two models he had made—one with wire teeth, the other with teeth cut out of an iron plate—and he demonstrated that in practice, in principle, even in appearance, the two were identical. His exhibit earned the comment from Judge Johnson that "Mr. Holmes has cut teeth in plates of iron, and passed them over the cylinder. This is certainly a meritorious improvement . . . but at last, what does it amount to, except a more convenient mode of making the same thing. Every characteristic of Mr. Whitney's machine is preserved . . . and all the merit that this discovery can assume is that of a more expeditious mode of attaching the tooth to the cylinder."

Of the first two arguments raised by the defense, the judge spoke out eloquently. "To support the originality of the invention, the complainants have produced a variety of depositions of witnesses . . . whose examinations expressly prove the origin, progress and completion of the machine by Mr. Whitney. . . . Persons who were made privy to his first discovery, testify to the several experiments which he made in their presence, before he ventured to expose his invention to the scrutiny of the public eye. But it is not necessary to resort to such testimony. . . . There are circumstances in the knowledge of all mankind, which prove the originality of this invention more satisfactorily to the mind, than the direct testimony of a host of witnesses." And then Judge Johnson drew out of the stream of history the salient facts which when considered together constituted an irrefutable argument. "The cotton plant has furnished clothing to mankind before the age of Herodotus. The green seed is a species much more productive than the black, and by nature adapted to a much greater variety of climates; but by reason of strong adherence of the fibre to the seed, without the aid of some more powerful machine for separating it than any formerly known among us, the cultivation of it could never have been made an object. The machine of which Mr. Whitney claims the invention, so facilitates the preparation of this species for use, that the cultivation of it has suddenly become an object of infinitely greater national importance, than that of the other species ever can be. Is it then to be imagined that if that machine had been before discovered, the use of it could have been lost, or could have been confined to any tract of country left unexplored by commercial enterprize?"

Whitney must have smiled inwardly, since this had been his argument and Miller's; always it had been deemed insufficient proof, and now, when he had produced incontrovertible evidence, it was charmingly dismissed as superfluous! He could relax but not rest, since he was deeply committed to the idea that the prolonged fight touched his honor and affected his purse. Vindication was right and pleasant, but not enough. Soon after the decision he wrote from Savannah that he had "claims against the citizens of this State to a large amount, which still remain unsettled & although these claims have been placed upon elevated ground by a late very pointed decision of the Circuit Court in my favour, one year more, at least, must elapse before a general and final adjustment can take place."

He felt certain of his sense of timing, his ability to perceive the drift before anything visible had occurred. Had he not, upon receipt of the verdict against Powell the previous May, written Catherine: "From the course of events & the present aspect of things I conceive it will be a more favourable time than has heretofore occured or will hereafter present itself"?

Yes, one year more—and he must have wished that Miller, his fellow warrior, his close friend, had been beside him when he was accorded the award they had always merited.

Judge Johnson's further remarks probably sounded banal to those who heard them. But across the intervening years of incredible growth, they speak with an immediacy that makes the events in the courtroom high drama in the life of a nation. "With regard to the utility of this discovery, the court would deem it a waste of time to dwell long upon this topic. Is there a man who hears us, who has not experienced its utility? The whole interior of the southern states was languishing and its inhabitants emigrating for want of some object to engage their attention and employ their industry, when the invention of this machine at once opened views to them which set the whole country in active motion. From child-hood to age, it has presented to us a lucrative employment. Individuals who were depressed with poverty, and sunk with idleness have suddenly risen to wealth and respectability. Our debts have been paid off, our capitals increased; and our lands are treble in value. We cannot express the weight of obligation which the country owes this invention—the extent of it cannot now be seen—some faint presentment may be formed from the reflection that cotton is rapidly supplanting wool, flax, silk and furs in manufactures, and may one day profitably supply the use of specie in our East-India trade. Our sister states also, participate in the benefits of this invention; for besides affording the raw materials for their manufactories, the bulkyness and quality of the article, afford a valuable employment of their shipping."

The resounding truth of those Ciceronian phrases must not have carried beyond the courtroom walls. Judge Johnson's verdict did not appear in any newspaper until a year and a half later, when Whitney at last won the next step and collected "Two thousand Dollars & costs of suit," which the jury considered "treble the damage sustained by the plaintiff."

This last engagement in Miller & Whitney's battle had elements of comedy broad enough for the plaintiff's side to enjoy. Because Whitney did not go south for this trial, the ludicrous details were described to him. Dr. Kollock, Miller's executor, attended "the examination of their new witness & model at the Court House. I found a little bit of a Scotchman they had picked up who lugged forward the model of a machine which he swore he had seen operate in some of the manufacturing Towns in England anterior to the date of your patent—& which he said was called a Devil. You have had, I recollect, this thing brought forward in a former trial & layed aside again. But they seem to me to have remodeled the thing—adding appendages which resembled your machine just enough to impress a jury with a verisimilitude & to have been made for the purpose which the little Scotchman had not hesitancy in swearing (though no mechanic) that to the *best of his Knowledge & Belief* the principle is the same & any man"—Kollock adds the qualifying—"(of Genius) who had seen a draught or description of this could have made yours." (Picking, a step preparatory to carding the yarn, was so well known that ten years before, when Miller was trying to have fair tests made by British spinners, he had advised them that one great advantage of the patent-ginned cotton was that "it would require but little whipping or beating before it is put on the Cards, and will derive no advantage from the use of the Picking devil.")

The final years of the struggle lack the compact intricacy and tension of the earlier period. The savage clash deteriorated into a routine of small, scattered courtroom incidents, and by comparison Whitney's final victory in Georgia was an anticlimax.

It is impossible to state the exact sum realized from the invention. Some money was made by ginning and by selling gins; some damages were collected from trespassers; some royalties based on the gins used in North Carolina and Tennessee were collected by those states and paid to Miller & Whitney. The only definite item was the $50,000 paid by South Carolina. The amount taken in by Miller & Whitney was for those days impressive, but it did not approach the golden harvest of which the partners had dreamed. Their reward was piecemeal and purchased at a great cost; the return on their ingenuity and enterprise was, despite the moneys they did secure, largely moral. It was this imbalance between honor and cash that made Whitney twice attempt to have Congress pass an Act extending the period of his patent. (His petitions are dated April, 1808, and July, 1812.)

On their side, the cotton growers felt that they had paid him once and that once was enough. The accusations their representatives leveled at him resurrected charges a dozen times disproved. They implied that he did not deserve consideration because he had not taken part in the Revolutionary War (he was born in 1765!); or that he was not the original inventor but had merely adapted from this or that machine, and, at the same time, that though he was the original inventor, the gin now in use had been so improved as to leave his invention without much merit. Finally, it was argued that were Whitney's request granted he would thereby become too rich. All the reasons aired in the congressional committee room were fancy ways of saying No.

In the year 1811 Whitney, answering a letter Robert Fulton had written, summarized for his fellow inventor the steeplechase into which the patent had led him. "The difficulties with which I have had to contend have originated principally in the want of a disposition in Mankind to do justice. My Invention was *new* & distinct— it stood alone & was not interwoven with anything before known. And it can but seldom happen that the Principle of an invention or improvement is so strongly marked & can be so clearly and specifically identified—& I have always believed that I should have had no difficulty in causing my rights to be respected if it had been less valuable & used only by a small portion of the community. But the use of this Machine being immensely profitable to almost every individual in the Country all were interested in trespassing & each justified & kept the other in countenance. Demagogues made themselves popular by misrepresentations & unfounded clamors, both against the Right & the Law made for its protection. Hence arose associations & combinations to oppose both. There was a time when there were but few men in Georgia who dared come into court and testify to the most simple facts in their knowledge relative to the use of the machine. In one instance I had great difficulty to prove that the machine had been used in Georgia & at the same moment there were three separate sets of this machinery in motion[within] 50 yards of the building in which the court sat & all so near that the rattling was distinctly heard on the steps of the courthouse." *

More than a hundred years have passed, and the passions all are spent. As Whitney drew generalized conclusions when writing to Fulton, so must an appraisal be made from the vantage point which the intervening decades and complete freedom from participation in the heated clash afford. It must be said that financially and morally Whitney had been wronged; but it should also be added that

* See Appendix B, Oliver Evans to Whitney, Oct. 29, 1811.

he was not, as it appeared to him, the victim of rogues, rascals, villains, and ingrates who deliberately deprived him of the rightful fruits of his invention. Rather it would seem that both Whitney and the planters were unhappy actors in a situation in which right and wrong were categories not of their making.

Whitney and Miller always denied that they sought to establish a monopoly, yet that was precisely the effect of the ill conceived initial policy of the firm. The planters did not want to trespass, yet they were forced into such action by the excessive tariff they were asked to pay. Reviewing events as they happened makes it easy to say that if the partners had had the foresight, had they had a model to guide them in setting up their business so as to exploit their patent without threatening to control a whole industry, if immediately after the fire in New Haven they had licensed the infringing gins as later they were forced to do, they might have maintained their patent rights from the beginning and never aroused a just public opposition. But too much was at stake to expect the impoverished Georgia planters either to share so much of their profits or to wait while Whitney manufactured enough machines to install in enough ginneries; they would have been lacking in initiative had they not processed their harvest when the British mills stood ready to buy all the cotton they could raise.

Could Whitney, even with his genius for creating manufacturing techniques—but without the necessary previous experience—have been able to make enough gins to satisfy such a demand? By 1797 there were already three hundred surreptitious gins in operation, and the amazing growth in cotton production was made possible by the large number of such gins. When Whitney cited the total cotton exports and on that basis bitterly figured the vast sums of which he was being defrauded, he forgot that those figures had been reached because the illegal gins existed and were able to process the increasing volume of cotton being planted. The pressures created by local conditions and the world market generated an explosive power that could not and would not tolerate any restrictions or controls such as were imposed by the patent provisions. The answer, a black market in gins and ginning, was acquiesced in by all because all were affected by the same pressure. Thus was created a climate that channeled the planters' moral indignation away from their own trespass and into defiant indignation toward Whitney, and justified in their minds their stratagems to deprive Whitney of his property rights in his invention.

Whitney shared the lot of most inventors, and compared to what he had every right to expect he could truthfully assert that his invention brought wealth to everyone but himself. That, however, would not be a just statement: if his hopes for the invention were blasted he himself did not end pitifully. His intellectual vigor enabled him to scrutinize the labyrinth into which he had wandered by chance, analyze its structure, and estimate where and when and how it might be breached. The story of the cotton-gin fiasco is not just another example of an inventor's loss; its details are the final part of the curriculum of Whitney's mature education. As Stiles had introduced him to the intellectual and scientific world and Catherine had made him at home in genteel society, so his experiences in Miller & Whitney taught him certain fundamentals of the new business order. He used them to good advantage.

XIII

The Birth of
the Machine-Tool Industry

As his invention of the cotton gin altered forever the history of the American South, so Whitney's sustained work in the manufacture of muskets changed the social and economic growth of the North and gave it its industrial might.

Whitney's success in the manufacture of guns can be stated in its most tangible terms by a comparison of the items in the little Expence Book that detailed the beginning of his adult business efforts, with the inventory of the impressive estate he left. But the full measure of the man is not so neatly bracketed. Such a comparison does not reveal that Whitney fathered the American system of interchangeable manufacture which shortly was producing quantities of cheap, serviceable clocks and watches, hardware, and sewing machines—the first fruits of the new industrial era to enter into the everyday life of peoples all over the world. Nor does it disclose that men who were trained by him continued the method he had pioneered and translated its concept into other fields. Whitney invented many tools and machines, but the one that assumed a major role in the genealogy of machine tools was the milling machine. Lastly, he established a business that remained, in the hands of his son and grandson, one of the country's leading private armories for ninety years, until it was sold to the Winchester Arms Company—a clear indication that from the onset Whitney understood the economics of the new business structure and that he was able to analyze problems very different from the mechanical ones which gained him his fame.

To assess Whitney's achievement, it is necessary to measure it against the contemporary level of technology. In England, where

Hargreaves and Arkwright and Crompton had set the pace in textile machinery, where Boulton and Watt merged their complementary talents to produce steam engines for the world, where the Darbys and Cort and the Wilkinsons had brought coal and iron together to start the metal industry, where Bramah and Wilkinson and Maudslay in small shops were designing and making the tools for industry's new needs, where Samuel Bentham and Brunel projected a series of machines to produce the huge number of wooden pulley blocks the British Navy required annually—in England, Whitney would have found a score of extraordinary men whose language he talked, whose world was his world, whose thoughts his way of thinking, who were making the future.

These men were not statesmen nor political leaders; they were not outstanding in religion, the arts, science, nor finance; neither were they great landowners nor powerful merchants. Mostly they were mechanics; all had energetic minds and came from the sober, thrifty, disciplined-to-work, free-to-think dissenters. Reading their life stories, one finds a common thread: their tradition was to teach themselves and think for themselves. Their approach to a specific goal might be summed up in a maxim of Maudslay's: "First get a clear notion of what you desire to accomplish and then in all probability you will succeed in doing it." Whatever their personal fate—kind or tragic—their work and their names are forever tied to Britain's economic supremacy. The magnitude of their triumphs makes it easy to transpose them into familiar modern settings; it is necessary to take the long road back to the close of the eighteenth century to know what exactly it was they desired to accomplish and how they succeeded.

Sir William Fairbairn (1789–1874), one of England's first great civil engineers, recalled when his profession did not even exist. "The millwright of former days was to a great extent the sole representative of the mechanical art, and was looked upon as the authority on all the applications of wind and water, under whatever conditions they were to be used, as a motive power for the purposes of manufactures. . . . He was the engineer of the district in which he lived and . . . could with equal facility work at the lathe, the anvil, the carpenter's bench. . . . He could handle the axe, the hammer and the plane with equal skill and precision; he could turn, bore, or forge with the dispatch of one brought up to these trades. . . . Generally, he was a fair arithmetician, knew something of geometry, levelling, and mensuration, and in some cases possessed a very competent knowledge of mathematics."

The millwright's staple material was wood, occasionally reenforced by pieces of iron. Machinery was built out of timber, sawed by hand and axe-dressed. M'Connel & Kennedy, "the largest spinners in the kingdom," had a forest in their Manchester mills of "large square shafts and wooden drums, some four feet in diameter. The main shafts seldom exceeded 40 revolutions per minute." Smeaton's first cast-iron axle for a water wheel, made in 1769, became a famous tourist attraction. His familiarity with technical problems made Smeaton appreciate that even the famous Carron Iron Works lacked the men and means to make a cylinder sufficiently accurate to carry out Watt's idea. That awaited the special skill of John Wilkinson, who designed a hollow, cylindrical boring bar, mounted on bearings at both ends, and produced (1775) "the first metal-cutting tool capable of doing large work with anything like modern precision."

Smeaton's failure and Wilkinson's success were predicated on the difference in their primary interest and training. Smeaton, like Watt, had been apprenticed to a mathematical instrument maker; Wilkinson, on the other hand, grew up in the new iron industry, his father having been one of the first to copy the Darbys' coke furnace. He spent his life indicating the endless uses to which iron could be put: he made iron chairs, and with Abraham Darby (the third) he built the first iron bridge (1779). Cast with a single arch, it had a hundred-foot span and rose forty-five feet above the Severn. He planned and launched the first boat formed entirely of iron plates bolted together (1787); he filled the order for forty miles of cast-iron pipes for the water system of Paris and supervised the furnaces ordered for the Creusot foundry; he coined his own copper and silver money, which, bearing his profile and the legend, *Wilkinson, Iron Master,* passed for currency in the Midland and Western counties; he was buried, by his own order, in an iron coffin. Throughout his long life he boldly advocated iron's unique properties, its cohesion and strength, and proved its versatility. Iron, which is both fusible and malleable, has the capacity to keep its shape, whether formed by casting or wrought by hammering. John Wilkinson was the great virtuoso of the new industry, but he was that because others before him had worked out means to produce iron with coal. The Darbys had started before him, and during his lifetime Henry Cort added notably to the processing and production of iron.

From the prehistoric age, man had known how to extract iron from its ores, but always charcoal had been used to melt and fine the ore. In Elizabeth's England forests had been leveled to work the furnaces, and as the forests receded the furnaces followed them, ever hungry for the fuel they were devouring. By the eighteenth century most of the iron furnaces were starved and had been abandoned; they stood cold—ghostly reminders of a once thriving industry. Coal, it is true, was everywhere; its plentiful presence was known, and many men sought a way to use it to work the iron ores. Unlike the cotton-textile industry that was built upon mechanical inventions, the metal-working industry depended on chemical inventions, and chemistry was still far too inadequate to be of any help.* Advances in the processing of iron and steel were made by experiment, by combining substances to be melted together, by methods learned directly at the furnace, the foundry, the forge.

With the modern rebirth of this industry, the name of Abraham Darby is usually associated. The Darbys, father, son, and grandson, have been called a dynasty; they were known as the Darbys of Coalbrookdale. The dynasty lasted eighty years, and provided Britain with world leadership in the metal-working industry.

By the close of the eighteenth century, cast iron had become available in sufficient quantity and at a price low enough to force millwrights to consider using it for the wooden gears and shafts and pulleys that made maintenance of the textile mills costly. This would have been eminently desirable, but with what were they to

---

* The chemical properties of iron and steel were not investigated until Torbern Bergmann (1735–1784) of Upsala made a start by showing the role carbon played in determining the different physical properties of the combinations of iron and carbon. He found that the carbon content of steel was low, running from 0.3 to 0.8 per cent, while that in cast iron amounted to 1 to 3.3 per cent. He also noted the important variations in the amount of "phlogiston." (Another century would pass before chemistry would corroborate what had been empirically learned.)

shape the iron machinery? The millwrights were aware that their tools were neither reliable nor powerful enough to work this new medium. Save for Wilkinson's borer, the tools at their disposal were crude, inadequate, and pitifully out of step with the great advances recently made in the metal industry. The tools they had can be quickly enumerated. The lathe was still chiefly made of wood and designed for the working of wood; it was powered by a crank or foot treadle, and the cutter was held by the mechanic. The lathe could shape circular or cylindrical parts, but what if the iron were expected to have a surface flat and true? For that there was no tool; the standard method was "chipping and filing." A steel chisel painstakingly chipped off bit by bit to secure an approximately level line, and then the pitted surface was filed smooth. The method was tedious, very expensive, and only fairly accurate.*

Cutting screws, similarly, was a hand process. Either the threads were cut out of an elementary die or, if the screw was to be of some size, a strip of paper was wound around the metal, the paper's center line marked with a punch, and then the marks slowly traced out with a cutting tool. The thread on screws so made was individual. Basically, the millwright's chief reliance was on his superlative mastery of hand forging, and on the hammer, the chisel, the file. For measuring he had calipers and a foot rule made of wood with a "fine 32nd" to assist his trained eye. To comprehend accuracy as it was conceived of at that time, there is Boulton's enthusiastic comment that "Mr. Wilkinson has bored us several cylinders almost without error; that of 50 inches . . . does not err the thickness of an old shilling in any part."

Wilkinson's borer was not merely the first metal-cutting tool capable of anything approaching modern precision in large work. Its invention made it very clear, as Mantoux points out, that "with the reign of iron and steel came also that of machinery, one being the indispensable condition of the other. Watt would never have been able to build the steam engine which, in 1775, Wilkinson ordered for his Bradley ironworks, had not Wilkinson provided him with metal

* Professor Roe says that "Watt's beautiful parallel motion, invented in 1785, was made necessary by the fact that there were no planers to machine a crosshead and guides. Planers were not developed until thirty years later."

cylinders of perfectly accurate shape, which could not have been made by old-fashioned methods—a most significant occurrence, which illustrates the essential interdependence of these two simultaneous facts, the development of the iron industry and that of machinery." And yet twenty years were to pass before the next important machine tool was perfected. Slowly, during those years, the embryonic state of engineering, with its leisurely methods, its high costs, its small output, its dependence on obsolete tools, became the bottleneck of the Industrial Revolution. How serious this was is implied in Fairbairn's statement that when he "entered Manchester [Cottonopolis], in 1813, the only important tools then in vogue were a few common lathes, a screw-cutter, and a boring machine for a steam cylinder." His own machine shop could boast of a lathe of "considerable dimensions . . . we were, nevertheless, without a steam-engine, or any other power, except Murphy, a muscular Irishman." And yet, by that time, to the problems presented by this situation, a number of men, mechanically creative, had already started the revolution in machine making by tools as before them Watt had provided the way to harness the power of steam, and Hargreaves, Arkwright and Crompton had begun the mechanization of the cotton-textile industry. Joseph Bramah (1748–1814), Henry Maudslay (1771–1831), Sir Samuel Bentham (1757–1831), and Marc Brunel (1769–1849) were Whitney's contemporaries. A review of their particular contributions makes Whitney's achievements clearer; an evaluation of their triumphs gives Whitney's success in manufacturing muskets greater stature. What joins them is the fact that at the same time, on either side of the Atlantic, men were responding to the same set of economic and industrial imperatives; unknown to each other, independently, they had set their feet on the same road.

Bramah, the oldest of the group, had been apprenticed to a cabinetmaker after a severe foot injury had made doubtful his ability to be a farmer. His first invention is almost in the nature of a commentary. A farmer's son pursuing his cabinetmaking trade in the homes of London's well-to-do, he designed and patented the first modern water closet (1778 and 1783), substantially unchanged since his day. In 1784 he patented a virtually pick-proof lock.* In 1802 he constructed his wood-planing machinery, and one of his machines was used for fifty years in the Woolwich Arsenal. Four years later he made a machine which automatically stamped serial numbers on the Bank of England bank notes. It is not Bramah's versatility in inventing that makes him noteworthy (a man with his mind and hands and training was, at that period, like a daring navigator in the sixteenth century—whatever the course he set, important discoveries awaited him); it was his insistence on quality workmanship. A whole generation of younger men, rigorously trained by him, bore witness that his measure as a teacher equaled that as inventor.

One of these younger men, and the greatest, was Henry Maudslay, the son of a soldier employed at the Woolwich Arsenal. His biographer deplores the scant formal schooling he had, for as a child he was taught little outside the arsenal workshops. While still an adolescent, his exceptional qualities were the boast of his fellow workers, and, when only eighteen, he was sought out by Bramah, to whom he had been recommended. Despite the high prestige of his shop, Bramah had no mechanic who could impart to metal the necessary precision, and no tools to manufacture his lock in great numbers. As previously the precision instrument makers had made orreries and chronometers and quadrants for the astronomers, now mechanics were to come to the aid of inventors, translating production processes into machines with which to make machinery. Maudslay was the man to help Bramah. Roe describes his talent: "To dexterity he added an intuitive power of mechanical analysis and a sense of proportion possessed by few men, and from the beginning he showed a genius for choosing the most direct and simple means for accomplishing his purpose."

Maudslay's qualities complemented the imagination, quickness, and originality of Bramah's mind; the eight years they worked to-

* Bramah proudly displayed one of his padlocks in his shop window with this sign: "The artist who can make an instrument that will pick or open this lock shall receive two hundred guineas the moment it is produced." Not until 1851 did an American mechanic, Alfred C. Hobbs, after working fifty-one hours (the Committee of Referees allowed him a month for the task) with a complete toolshop at his disposal, pick the sixty-year-old lock and collect the reward. Subsequently, he made his living by the reputation it brought him.

gether (1789–1797) were decisive—it was then that the slide rest was built. This idea, in part or whole, had occurred to many men; but credit for it goes to Maudslay, who gave it shape and developed its possibilities. "Maudslay's Go-cart," as it was affectionately called, began a new era in mechanical engineering: it allowed for larger and heavier work to be done. Speed, accuracy, and uniformity, the desiderata of the new industry, were controlled by gear wheels and lead screw. Turning and screw cutting, operations that before had demanded ingenuity and produced pieces individual as to pitch and size, now were subject to standardization.

James Nasmyth, Maudslay's pupil and himself a famous engineer, wrote glowingly of the slide rest: "This beautiful and truly original contrivance became, in the hands of its inventor, the parent of a vast progeny of perfect screws, whose descendants, whether legitimate or not, are to be found in every workshop throughout the world where first-class machinery is constructed." The combination of mechanical elements Maudslay incorporated in his slide rest is found in some form in almost every machine tool; it can claim to be one of the major inventions of history.

Maudslay set up his own shop in 1797, when Bramah refused to raise his salary, and shortly thereafter started making the machines conceived and designed by Sir Samuel Bentham and Marc Brunel. Bentham, touched with the same brilliant inventiveness as his famous brother Jeremy, expressed it in different terms. Today he would be called an efficiency expert. Though such a category did not exist in his lifetime, the opportunities did. His special love was naval administration and construction, and his studies carried him to the principal ports and dockyards of northern Europe. He went to Russia when the Empress Catherine invited him to examine the mining and engineering works in her vast empire. There the lack of skilled workers was most acute—to assist him in his survey, he had a Danish brass founder, a British watchmaker, and a few Russian sergeants who could read and draw.

Under such circumstances Bentham began to speculate on the possibility of designing machines that would permit unskilled hands to perform skilled tasks. He thought only in terms of woodworking machinery, for his training and outlook were conditioned by the

Navy, where the use of iron was negligible. Slowly his ideas took form, and after his return to England (1791) he took out two patents. The second (1793), long regarded as one of the most extraordinary ever issued by the British Patent Office, described an entire series of machines to expedite the manufacture of pulley blocks. Since each full-rigged frigate used about fifteen hundred, and the Admiralty alone required over a hundred thousand a year, it was an ideal item to inaugurate the idea of interchangeability. These machines were first installed in the new prison that Jeremy Bentham had designed, where an essential element in the handling of prisoners was a system of labor. Since the prisoners were both unskilled and transient, Samuel Bentham's machinery implemented his brother's reforms.

Bentham was fortunate in meeting Brunel, or perhaps it should be said that their meeting was a happy event for both. They had much in common. Brunel was a French naval officer who, escaping the revolution in France, spent five years in America working on various engineering projects. He had been appointed chief engineer for New York and, as such, had assisted Major Pierre L'Enfant, the man who had drawn the masterplan for the City of Washington, in laying out the fortifications of the Narrows of New York harbor. In America, Brunel saw the crippling handicap imposed by the scarcity of skilled labor, and there he first thought out a machine for shaping wood. In 1799 he went to England, and two years later he had completed working models of his machines. Presenting them to the Admiralty for consideration, he was introduced to Bentham. At about the same time each had been preoccupied with the same problem; they felt no rivalry, but rather an awareness that their efforts had a common goal. But though both were inventive and clever and capable of original designs, neither was a skilled mechanic. This need brought them to Maudslay's small new shop.

The famous Portsmouth block machinery was the product of their joined efforts. Forty-four machines in all, each was a unit designed to perform its part in an ordered series of operations. When the machinery was in full running order—in 1808, after almost eight years of planning and construction—ten unskilled men did the work of 130 craftsmen, producing 130,000 blocks annually, supplying the needs of the Royal Navy as long as wooden pulley blocks were used.

A basic prerequisite was common to the thinking of Whitney and Bentham and Brunel. Mass production was their response to supply cheaply and quickly the demand for a single item bought regularly and in great quantity. That pulley blocks for the Royal Navy and muskets for the American Army were first chosen simply means that at that time governments were the only purchasers able to set such a demand.

The British toolbuilders had grown up in the industry which they brilliantly advanced, or served apprenticeships in organized shops, or received technical instruction in naval academies. None of this marked Whitney's preparation and training. From the farm he went to college, from college to inventing. Certainly, neither his father's farm nor work shed was equivalent to their systematic education, nor was Yale comparable to the British and French naval academies; and yet, because Whitney had mechanical genius, he could create, as he himself phrased it, "a new principle"—whether to clean the green-seed cotton or mass-produce muskets—and invent the machines and tools to endow the principle with life.

Whitney stands apart from those contemporaries in another respect. Always, at a critical phase, they could turn to one another for assistance. So Boulton and Watt asked of Wilkinson; Wilkinson relied on Darby's superior iron casting; Bramah and Bentham and Brunel depended on Maudslay's mechanical artistry as, in turn, they gave him the "clear notion" of what was needed. This luxury of having another head, other hands, to call on in a crisis, was denied Whitney. He was utterly alone as he worked out his principle, translating it into methods and machines.

Looking at the goal Whitney had set himself, one can see that at various times since boyhood he had been concerned with the same problem. When he had made a model pen for his pupils to copy, he had intuitively expressed his awareness of the benefits derived from setting a model for form and size and demanding that each replica reproduce the pattern as exactly as possible. Later, when he made gins, the advantages of standardizing the machines became obvious; in the presses and dies for the screw press he had again dealt with the concept in another form. He knew that this way of manufacturing was engaging the ingenuity of other men, for machinery that automatically made nails and card teeth was being used in Rhode Island; these industries were the pioneers in producing cheap small, uniform metal objects. What most delighted Whitney was that the contract to produce ten thousand muskets provided the only opportunity he could have found to allow him to develop his ideas.

He concentrated on the intricate anatomy of the Charleville musket; he had brought back with him two of the French guns made in 1763 and sold by the French government to the American colonists. These models had been made by a system in which each small part was fitted to its particular gun and each gun, though it might seem like every other, was different and individual. Whitney's familiarity with production problems had convinced him that for the United States the solution lay in reducing a complex which formed a labor skill to simpler procedures which workers could learn in a short time. This had been demonstrated by Hargreaves, Arkwright, and Crompton when they replaced the spinner's skill with cunning machines. But Whitney, exploring still further the laws that govern production, concluded that to increase the production of an article as intricate as a musket, methods and tools and machines would have to be created which would themselves be endowed with some of the armorer's skill and which would give uniformity and accuracy to make the parts interchangeable. The system would also solve the related problem of maintainance by making available parts for repair. A logic derived from his experience and mechanical instinct assured him it was quite reasonable to assume a contract for ten thousand guns when the other twenty-six bidders, manufacturing by existing methods, together dared undertake a total of slightly over thirty thousand.

Whitney's friends knew that he had embarked on a venture worthy of his talent. He had their faith and support. Henceforth his would be a lonely search for the ways and means of attaining precision. Precision was an ideal to be approached, and each step forward defined and clarified this ideal. Whitney's genius seized on the concepts of standardization and precision which were abroad in the minds of men and translated them into tangible tools and processes.

Now it is possible to see what forces—industrial, economic, social, political—were created and set in motion by Whitney's initial effort in mass production. At that time, an economist like Saint-Simon could perceive from the lusty beginnings that had occurred in Britain the nature of the industrial and social problems which would arise from the new organization of production. But to Whitney there were no such overtones. He saw his successful completion of the contract as the chance to reestablish himself.

The 1763 Charleville muskets, to whose specifications Whitney had to conform, deserve to be dusted off and their unique story told. The glitter of great names and events had made the voyage of the muskets from France to America the joyous, triumphant climax of a little comedy of high politics. The Abduction from the Arsenal, might be the title, and, like the contrived stage pieces of that period, everyone but the wicked enemy (who makes his appearance at the end and to no avail) schemed, intrigued, and indulged in mysterious theatrical tricks. The time: early spring, 1776. The principal actors: *Silas Deane*, the Connecticut Yankee sent to the court of Louis XVI by the Continental Congress that was grimly aware of what it meant to start a shooting war without adequate arms to fight; worldly, energetic, determined, experienced both as lawyer and storekeeper in bargaining and promoting; *Pierre Augustin Caron de Beaumarchais*, France's leading dramatist (his *Le Barbier de Séville* had just appeared, his *Le Mariage de Figaro*, wherein his passion barbed with wit demolished a corrupt aristocracy, had not yet been written), the friend of Voltaire, the trusted servant of his king, and a courtier who had the confidence of the king's foreign minister, *Vergennes*. The minister, secretly sympathetic to the rebellious American colonists, was officially unable to commit an act hostile to Great Britain.

Adept and experienced at political manipulation, Vergennes was enchanted with the plan Beaumarchais devised whereby Deane could get arms for his compatriots and he could remain friendly to Britain. The plot, broad and direct as the action of a comedy should be, achieved a happy conclusion: the action called for Vergennes, with the king's consent, to order Penet, the chief armorer at the Royal Arsenal at Charleville, to dispose of thirty thousand muskets of the 1763 pattern—it was explained that they were obsolete, changes and improvements having been made in 1766, 1768, 1770, 1771, 1773, and 1774—to armorers in various French cities. Meanwhile Beaumarchais, with Deane as a silent, very active partner, organized Hortalez & Co. (how partial Beaumarchais was to the Spanish disguise!), a firm favored by large loans from the French government. The performance was thoroughly professional, the timing perfect. By the beginning of 1777, three ships left France. One was intercepted by the British blockade (the wicked enemy), but the other two brought their cargo of 23,000 muskets safely to American ports. They were distributed in time to share in the honor of defeating Burgoyne at Saratoga.

Thus muskets made to serve a feudal France assisted a revolutionary America; formed by the time-honored skilled handicraft system, thirty-five years later they became the models for the first article produced by the new industrial system.

XIV

The Arms Manufactory at Mill Rock

NEVER, in the breathless rush to get started, did Whitney doubt his ability to manufacture the muskets for which he had contracted. Reading his letters, written in the summer and fall of 1798, one is aware of his sure touch. No aspect of the complex structure seemed alien to him, though the whole enterprise was wildly novel. Intuitively, he knew what landmarks were significant in the world he was about to create.

Had Wolcott suggested the advisability of another contractor establishing himself in the vicinity of New Haven—making of that town a small Birmingham or Sheffield? To do so, Whitney argued, "would be like an attempt to plant a forrest with full grown trees." The limited local labor supply would be instantly disturbed. "I have not only the *Arms* but a large proportion of the *Armourers* to make. My intention is to employ steady, sober people and learn them the business. I shall make it a point to employ persons who have family connections and perhaps some little property to fix them to the place, who consequently cannot be easily removed to any considerable distance." Let the unattached, the restless go westward; he would not invest time and money in teaching a man who was not tied to New Haven by family and property.

Workers, he explained, "must necessarily learn the business at my expence. When they are learnt, they may easily be led to think they ought to have higher wages; without considering at whose expence they got an insight into the business. If there is another manufactory in the vicinity where workmen are wanted, and higher wages offered, they will either be discontented or go off and leave me—it matters not which—for I would as soon have a workman taken off as made dissatisfied." And then he points out that "a rise of Wages of only 6*d* per Day will be a serious evil," striking off "all the profits at once." Having stated his argument against inviting ruinous competition for labor, Whitney pointed out that another gun manufactory in the neighborhood would inflate the price of certain materials, "particularly Charcoal; the demand for which will be so suddenly and so greatly increased beyond what it ever has been, that it will not be had without paying an enormous price for it. These are considerations which materially affect the Contractor and are not uninteresting to the Public."

Until his business had taken the form he wanted, Whitney was on guard lest the same aggressive enterprise and competition that had so quickly killed Miller & Whitney's ginneries in the South should gain a foothold and ruin his workshop in the North. Once was enough to be robbed of the returns his genius and efforts could claim; this time he had also to protect his "new principle." As the Lyonses and the Holmeses had slapped gins together, so other mechanics, incapable of artistry or precision, by their crude efforts could justify those who ridiculed the principle of interchangeable manufacture. He had to make certain that his second venture did not carry the seeds of calamity. Out of a wish for self-preservation, he warned Wolcott that "perhaps Mr. Dixon or some of his connections may send propositions to contract to manufacture Arms, proposing to make the Locks, Barrels, and all the principal parts of the Musket at a Distance from New Haven and have them only stocked and finished at this Cotton factory here. Should this be the case, I beg leave to observe that I apprehend it would be only an indirect method of procuring that, which they despair of obtaining by direct means. It would fix their general rendezvous here, and afford them, perhaps a better opportunity of tampering with my workmen than if their whole business were carried on here."

In the same letter of August 2nd he enclosed the bond, "executed 31st ultimo by Mr. John Innes Clark and myself for the faithfull performance of my Contract," and requested Wolcott to forward the $5,000 advance to which he was entitled. He himself, he wrote, was going "to Massachusetts to procure workmen" but had arranged to send a small vessel to bring four thousand gun stocks, since "it will be more troublesome and expensive transporting the stocks from Philadelphia in the winter after the Delaware closes." A clearly thought-out schedule can be discerned behind the arranging, assembling, building, organizing. Calmly, and with confidence, he declared, "I shall use every exertion to put my business into effectual operation as fast as it can be done with a suitable degree of prudence and economy."

His careful program was disrupted almost immediately. Yellow fever had already struck in Philadelphia with such virulence that the government moved to Trenton so that it would not be cut off from the rest of the country. The epidemic forced Whitney to postpone getting his stocks from the public stores; but, even worse, it also deprived him of that market for his iron and steel. This, he told Wolcott in October, "has been a very considerable disappointment to me because the Iron which is manufactured in this part of the Country is generally made in the winter Season, the Streams on which most of the Forges Stand being nearly dry thro' the Summer and untill late in Autumn." He was worried not only for the quantity he needed, but had serious doubts about the quality. "None of the various kinds of Iron which are made in New England, except that of Salisbury, have been tried for musket barrels. . . . After making particular enquiry, I found but *one man* who had it in his power to procure the genuine Salisbury refined Iron. This man, Mr. Wm. Charles Loveland of Canaan, would contract to furnish me with my Barrels welded up ready for *boreing* and *finishing* but would not undertake to supply me with Iron. Under these circumstances I concluded to enter in a contract with him to deliver me Ten Thousand musket Barrels at New Haven—and I think there is a fair prospect that he will fulfill his engagement."

In arranging to have his supplies ready to be called in as required, Whitney knew that either he must give his subcontractor the security and protection of a contract or rely on other sources whose iron might or might not make satisfactory barrels. In this situation he wanted the government either to take any surplus barrels he might have on hand when his contract had been filled or allow him to experiment with the other kinds of iron. Welding iron barrels, he assured Wolcott, was "so simple that good common Blacksmiths will pretty readily turn their hand to it—but the Boreing and fitting up cannot be done to a profit without an expensive apparatus and is a Branch which they do not understand." The loss of the Philadelphia source made him revise his estimation of time and money. "I find it will take a longer time and be attended with more expence to establish the Business than I was aware of at the time I contracted," he admitted to Wolcott, but hastened to add that "the prospect of finally placing it on an advantageous footing appears to me to be more flattering."

No factory, no workmen, no materials—to these he had already added no time and no money. But whereas he was certain that the lack of men and machines and supplies would soon be met, the passing months only increased his feeling that he was racing against time. He had intended "to have done a considerable part of the work in the town of N. Haven, in the Buildings which I own and then occupied there. [The shop where he manufactured gins.] But after viewing the works at Springfield [Armory] where their water works are at some distance from the principal Armoury, I relinquished the idea of doing any work in town and determined to do all my work on one spot. The Superintendent at Springfield told me that it would cost 4000 Dollars a Year more to do the same in 2 places at two miles distant from each other, than if it was all concentrated into one place."

Delay dragged at every step he took. Securing his mill site should have been simple and quick. He knew exactly where he wanted to build his manufactory. "There is a good fall of Water in the Vicinity of this Town which I could procure and could have works erected in a short time," he had written to Wolcott. Mill Rock, the spot he had chosen, was where the founders of New Haven had built the first dam and set up the first corn mill. Mill River, as the stream was called, offered great opportunities. At all seasons an ample flow of water guaranteed him a steady source of power, the fall at the dam was sufficient to turn the necessary machinery, and the river up to that spot was navigable for scows carrying from twenty to thirty tons. (Timothy Dwight averred: "No position for a manufactory could be better. From the bleak winds of winter it is completely sheltered by the surrounding hills; to the delightful breezes of summer it is perfectly opened by the valley through which the river

flows. No place, perhaps is more healthy; few are more romantic.")
But it was September 17th before Whitney was able to purchase "the
Mill and Stream just above Neck Bridge—where Buel's factory
stood—Called Sabin's Mill—and the farm adjoining which belonged
to Capt. Daniel Talmage."

He confided to Stebbins that because he has encountered "some
difficulties and much delay in compleating the purchase I was unable
to commence my opperations in erecting the necessary buildings and
machinery for executing my contract, till about the first of November." Six precious weeks had been lost. To get his dam built and his
buildings up before winter, he hired every workman he could. He
ripped out the old mill; he collected the material needed for the
new buildings. The mill site, "tho' firm and well founded by nature,
was rough & irregular and it required a considerable expence & some
time to lay the foundation of regular works so as to take the best
advantage of the water & situation. Three days more would have
completed the foundation of my principal building when the first
snowstorm (which was terribly severe) happened. This occasioned
so much delay that I did not compleat the raising of my building till
the 4th Dec." By the slim margin of three days he had lost the race,
but even to winter he would not yield, and between snowstorms
(there were twelve—impatiently he had counted them) he and his
small army of workmen toiled. He might complain that he was
"worne out with fatigue & anxiety"; but fatigue was forgotten and
anxiety stilled when on January 13, 1799, he could triumphantly report that "My building which is 72 feet long by 30 & 2 stories high
is nearly finished!"

In this letter to Stebbins he briefly sketched the outlines of his new
world. "There are three things called houses on the farm which I bo't
of Talmage. I moved into the best of these (the one he used to occupy
& which is the nearest house to the Mill) about the first of last month.
Mrs. Ogden is my housekeeper & I have two girls in the kitchen—
and I have at present only twenty in family." Were these the workmen he had secured in Massachusetts? From the start he kept watch
over his employees. For the unmarried he ran a boardinghouse, close
to the factory, where, in fatherly fashion, he supervised their lodging

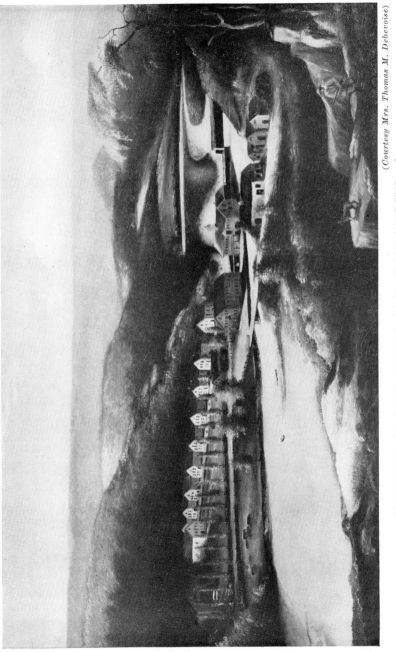

WHITNEY'S GUN MANUFACTORY ABOUT 1825

(Courtesy Mrs. Thomas M. Debevoise)

and feeding and had their clothes washed and mended. Later, for married men, he built homes—the first mill village in America.

"I continue to Date from N. Haven tho' in fact I live in the bounds of Hamden. My situation here may be made a pleasant and a valuable one. The New Turnpike Road from New Haven to Hartford which is laid out, granted & subscribed for, passes directly by my Door— between the house and the mill—indeed it cuts off a part of the House and comes hard on my New buildings which I have erected for my waterworks. This will be one of the most beautiful and most considerable roads in New England; being nearly in a straight line from N. H. to Hartford & the distance between the two places by this new Road but a little over thirty-four Miles." In the turnpike his friend Senator James Hillhouse had promoted, the arrow-straight highway that would connect Boston with New York, carrying travelers past the front door of his manufactory, he took a certain pride. That autumn he had frantically told Stebbins that it would "be a ruinous thing" should winter retard his activities; but when winter had come he accepted the fact that he would "not be able to do much till the Spring opens." Looking out over a world buried under deep snow, he could quietly admit that "I have now taken a serious task upon myself & I fear a greater one than is in the power of any man to perform in the given time—but it is too late to go back." It was at this time, that Whitney again wrote to congressmen and influential friends, urging a change in the wording of the patent law.

But it was in Whitney's nature to relax only when he had practical reasons to permit it. His apprehensions were eased when, on proof of his having spent the first $5,000 advance, the second, equal in amount, was immediately forwarded to him. He received it on January 4, 1799. At the same time Whitney must have felt that fortune was favoring him when he read in the "Circular to the Contractors for fabricating Muskets" that Captain Decius Wadsworth had been "appointed Inspector to prove barrels and inspect muskets." Here was a friend in an important position. Wadsworth, a Yale classmate of Miller's, had exerted himself to have the patent law amended; his respect for Whitney's genius was based on intimate knowledge of his cotton-gin invention. Whitney knew that should a critical moment arrive, he would deal with an official willing, on the basis of past accomplishments, to trust his integrity and ability to succeed in his present venture.

That moment was fast coming. As the first year of the contract drew to an end, Whitney felt as though he were being strangled for lack of time and capital. His letters recounting his troubles and pleading for indulgence give the only firsthand account of the beginning of mass production. Wadsworth perhaps paid Whitney a visit, for in April he had been requested by Wolcott to report "what progress Mr. Whitney has made and when his deliveries may be expected to commence." News from Europe made it very clear that the United States would have to rely on themselves for arms. Wolcott, who had won admiration for his hard practical sense and his capacity for taking pains, began to have grave misgivings that many of the men who had undertaken to manufacture them would fail: "The sooner a contractor discontinues a business to which he is unequal, the better it will be for him & the public."

Twice Whitney phrased the long letter before he finally sent it to Wolcott on June 29, 1799. There are a few differences, but both have the same blending of assurance and need, of prevailing business procedures and excited, haphazard references to the new production system. "I do not make that progress in the execution of my contract for fabricating Muskets which I expected at the time I contracted. I have met with many unexpected and unavoidable delays & disappointments which could not have been foreseen and guarded against. I was also myself mistaken in some of my calculations at the time I entered into the Contract. The greatest and principal cause of delay has been the uncommon length and severity of the past winter. Its early commencement prevented the completion of many things appertaining to my water works, such as Dam, flooms, etc, which, had the winter held off as usual, would have been accomplished in a short time. . . . Its long continuance produced a great scarcity of forage for cattle and untill within these few Days, it has been extremely difficult to procure any teamwork even at double the price." Ox teams were the tractors and bulldozers of that period.

Whitney was not alone in lamenting winter's cold and spring floods; established firms throughout New England suffered heavily.

"In the month of February I contracted with Messrs. Forbes & Adam of Canaan, who are unquestionably among the most able and punctual dealers in and manufacturers of Iron in this Country, to make me a number of tools, Mill-iron and other heavy iron work, for all of which I carried them patterns at the time, and to supply me with roll'd iron Rods, etc. of a particular description. All these they were to send me in a fortnight. At the time I was there their Works were frozen up & had been somewhat injured by a late flood. . . . With all their resources and exertions their works are not yet in motion. I had a letter from them a few Days since saying that 'their works were much more injured than they imagined.' . . . At the same time I contracted with another man in the same neighborhood —a man of property and reputed to be one of the most punctual, to supply me with several tons of iron—all to be delivered in the month of April. The season proved such that neither ore could be dug nor coals burned till all the fodder for cattle was expended, then neither ore nor wood could be transported for the want of teamwork & I have not received a single pound of iron from that quarter. The man with whom I contracted to weld my Barrels failed—this would have been a great disappointment if I had met with no other. As it is however I think I shall do as well as if he had fulfilled his engagements. . . .

"At the time I entered into the Contract to manufacture the arms, my mind was occupied in devising the best & most expeditious mode of doing the work & I contemplated the Dispatch and facility with which I could work after all my aparatus was compleat and in motion and did not sufficiently consider the time that must necessarily be taken up in constructing and making this apparatus. . . . I find that my personal attention is more constantly and essentially necessary to every branch of the work than I apprehended. . . . Indeed there is no Branch of the work that can proceed well, scarcely an hour, unless I am present."

Almost from the start, Whitney discovered that he had not completely solved his financial problems. In estimating the size of the government advances, he had counted on obtaining credit, but the credit structure did not accommodate industrial enterprises like his. He explained to Wolcott that "when I contracted I supposed it would cost me from twenty-five to thirty thousand Dollars in money and credit to make one Thousand stands of Arms and be in proper circumstances to continue the business to advantage & I have no reason to believe that this calculation was erroneous. But I do not find that advantage from Credit which I expected. I can, it is true, purchase anything I want on a Credit of Sixty Days, but that is not a credit which, in the present stage of the business can be of much service to me. . . . In mercantile transactions, where quick turns are made and the property for which the credit was obtained can at all times be turned into cash, commodities may be purchased with safety on this short credit. But manufacturing is very Different. More time is required to work up raw materials. . . . Credits which I obtained last fall have expired & I have been obliged to pay up those obligations with the money which I had appropriated for other purposes."

In the draft, he explained why the initial expenses were the heaviest. "The business in which I am engaged is so *New* a business in this Country, that a daily supply of raw materials cannot be had. Most of them must be procured from a considerable distance and the persons must be notified that they are wanted a Considerable time before they can be delivered. The whole quantity of many of the articles which will be wanted in the course of two years should be purchased at once. Procuring these articles takes up my time & draws me from home—when my whole attention is required it is better to procure the *whole* quantity I shall want at once than to procure the tenth part—provided I can pay for them."

Having presented a candid picture of his situation and indicated the reasons for his anxiety, Whitney described the other side of the coin. "My general plan of arrangement is good [and] my confidence in it increases in proportion as the execution advances. My water works are not yet in motion but are in great forwardness; my arrangements for forging, filing etc. are nearly compleated. I have about sixty good men engaged and a prospect of being able to procure such number as I may want. I am persuaded that I can do the work well . . . provided I can be indulged as to time & avoid pecuniary embarrassments in an early stage of the business." Let not Wolcott think this much had been easily attained. "I have constantly and exclusively, Day and Night, devoted utmost attention and exersions to the accomplishment of my undertaking—and tho' the burden of care and anxiety which I have incurred to myself by undertaking this Business, is much greater than I before conceived of, still nothing shall induce me to shrink from the task or for a moment divert my attention from its final accomplishment."

And then, in what must have seemed like a cryptic aside—for with the threat of war still serious, Wolcott was eager for muskets, not theories, and he could hardly have appreciated what a slight alteration would mean to costs and production in this new system—Whitney added: "I might have made 500 stands of Arms by this time but they would have cost me 15 Dollars apiece and would not have been as good as I wish to make them. My Aparatus would have been such that it could not readily have been enlarged with advantage and it would have taken me six months more to make another 500—and it would have been a losing business with me from beginning to end. It appears to me that many who have undertaken to make Muskets will make but indifferent ones; that their system is such that they will not improve much by practice—and that their arrangements are in no way calculated for permanence or increasing progression.

"Tho' I have not hitherto accomplished as fast as I wished and expected, yet I should be perfectly willing to a strict examination by men of sense & information & stand or fall by their decision." The contract, which both parties had agreed upon with swift impulsiveness, was now to have the first demands made on it for understanding. "Cannot some arrangement be made by which I may obtain such indulgences as will enable me to pursue the business with equal advantage to the Government and relieve me from the extreme anxiety which now in some measure overpowers my ardor and damps my resolution." Somehow, somehow the terms of the contract had to be altered in Whitney's favor.

Time and money. Of both, Whitney had great need. When he asked for more of each, half the contract time and all the money advanced had been spent. Whitney regretted his lack of an "opportunity of laying before [Wolcott] my whole plan & manner of executing the different branches of the work," and Wolcott's not being able to afford the "leisure to examine and compare them with the modes practised in this and other Countries." Whitney was well aware that he was asking Wolcott to grant him grace. Today such a request would be reasonable, for it is a commonplace that an industrial enterprise demands a heavy initial outlay and a protracted preparation before the first new article is tooled, assembled, and delivered. But then! Captain Wadsworth, who recommended the weapons Whitney was making as "superior to any muskets for common use ever fabricated in any country," who had examined his factory and heard Whitney explain the advantages to be gained from his system of interchangeable manufacture, and who resented the ridicule of Whitney's idea "by almost all those who pretended to superior knowledge and experience in the business"—even Captain Wadsworth gave as his opinion that "there is more to please the imagination than of real utility in the plan!"

Two factors served Whitney's cause and sanctioned Wolcott's yielding to what then could only have been an inclination. Whitney was known to have discovered the way to clean green-seed cotton, and his invention commanded respect even though as a money earner it was a spectacular failure. And those who derided his new venture as a "vain and impracticable" effort were silenced by the cogent argument that the country was in desperate need of the domestic manufacture of muskets.

During the next two years Whitney was like a man trying to make harbor through storm-tossed seas. It seems little short of miraculous that twice, when disaster was about to wreck him, a single voice, high in authority, should have been able to still the angry doubts that would have submerged him.

As Whitney read Wolcott's stern initial statement that "my mind is inclined to scepticism with respect to all theories which have not been sanctioned by experience," he must have felt discouraged. But then came a gracious offer: "If you feel entire confidence in your project and will furnish me with additional security for a further advance, money shall be granted to enable you to make a fair trial. I should consider a *real improvement* in machinery for manufacturing arms as a great acquisition to the United States. For present purposes & to give you time to look out for good security, I enclose you a [letter] of credit on the Collector of New Haven for 1500 Dlls."

Such encouragement from a man so strictly observant of orthodox business practices was an act of faith in Whitney, his genius, his integrity; faith, too, in the landfall Whitney had sighted—the misty outlines of the vast new world of industry. It surely must have been this that moved Whitney to put on paper the principles which so far had eluded words. The rough draft of the letter he sent to Wolcott on July 30th gives the measure of how deeply he felt the grandeur of the undertaking. "Actual Experiment is the only true touchstone—" such generalities expressed the convictions of men of sense. But Whitney wanted Wolcott to understand the kind of experiment in which he was involved. He explained:

"I find that I can *forge* the *Guards* faster, more exactly in their true shape & so they will require less work in fitting up than they could be cast in Brass after a perfect Pattern by an experienced founder. This is also the case with respect to several of the smaller limbs of the Lock and mounting. I find by experience that I can forge the lock-plates with a solid pan in such a manner that they will require but little filing. And this I have ever considered the most Difficult part of the lock.

"My general plan does not consist in one great complicated machine, wherever one small part being out of order or not answering to the purpose expected, the whole must stop & be considered useless. If the mode in which I propose to make one part of the musket should prove by experiment not to answer, it will in no way affect my mode of making any other part. *One of my primary objects is to form the tools so the tools themselves shall fashion the work and give to every part its just proportion—which when once accomplished, will give expedition, uniformity, and exactness to the whole.*

"If each individual workman must form and fashion every part according to his own fancy & regulate the size & proportion by his own Eye or even by a measure, I should have as many varieties as I have members of each part—many of them would require an inscription upon them to point out the use for which they were designed, & it would require treble the number of hands to do the same work. By long practice and many trials mere Mechanics who have no correct taste, acquire the art of giving a particular uniformity, I hope, to particular substances. But very few really good experienced workmen in this branch of business are to be had in this country. In order to supply ourselves in the course of the next few years with any considerable number of really good muskets, such means must be devised as will preclude the necessity of every workman's being bred to the business. An accurate Eye, close attention and much time are necessary (where experience is wanting) to form things rightly; but few among the great mass can proportion things accurately.

"In short, the tools which I contemplate are similar to an engraving on copper plate from which may be taken a great number of impressions perceptibly alike."

Whitney had found the analogue that touched at the heart of his principle; he gave Wolcott a phrase that he could understand and quote, a phrase that surely must have engaged the imagination of those who heard it. But when he tried to explain how many muskets he could deliver, he must have dumbfounded Wolcott, a systematic and orderly man. The number? Far less than he had expected, "tho I shall have some of the smaller parts of the whole ten thousand made by that time." When would the deliveries start? He had to admit candidly that it was taking much longer than he had contemplated. What kind of sense did Wolcott make of this behavior? "I must not only tell the workmen but must show them how every part is to be Done. They are as good as any workmen but I cannot make them understand how I would have a thing done until it is Done." And then having given no exact promises, he reaffirmed that "I shall produce good arms and introduce some *real improvements* in manufacturing Muskets whereby they can be made *better* and with more expedition."

Wolcott must have been troubled by this mixture of vagueness and bright hope; he replied briefly but pointedly. "I will take no advantage of the strict terms of the contract in point of time. You must, however, produce a number of compleat arms this season. At the next session of Congress I must make a report of the state of the different factories."

To advance an additional $10,000, however, Wolcott required additional security. Reading the agreement of September 8th, one can share the elation Whitney felt when ten of New Haven's citizens agreed to put their names on a bond. "We to aid Mr Whitney & to encourage the manufacture will join in such Bond, provided Ten or Twelve will so join—he securing us by mortgage on his farm & Works. Agreed to by James Hillhouse, Elias Shipman, Timothy Phelps, Peleg Sanford, Elizur Goodrich, Simeon Baldwin, David Daggett, Pierpont Edwards, Eneas Munson, Jr. and Jeremiah Atwater." Yale graduates, mostly, these men represented the leaders in politics, the law, medicine and trade—almost the bond was an expression of civic pride and trust in the gifted young man who had chosen to make his home and his fortune in New Haven.

Relieved for a while of his money worries and the immediate obligation to deliver muskets, Whitney devoted himself to his manufacturing. For the next year a silence covers his activities, unbroken but for his letters to Stebbins. It was always easy for Whitney to talk to Josiah Stebbins, but he might have foregone that pleasure under the pressure of work had Stebbins not continued to write and gently insisted that somehow Whitney find time to answer. Soon after his marriage in 1797, Stebbins had moved to the wilderness that then was Maine, where his college education and legal training brought him eventual prominence, and where his awkward manner, ungainly appearance, and lack of style in argument were regarded as characteristics, not handicaps. Only a handful of the many letters he wrote to Whitney remain. They reveal a man serious, plodding, fearfully respectable, a man who gave the same love and understanding to Whitney when he was grown as when they were boys together at Leicester Academy.

The great need Stebbins and his wife had to continue their New Haven friendships induced him to seek an appointment as "DeputyPost-Master at this place [New Milford, later Alna, Maine]. We have the mail only one day in a week . . . so an office could not be contrived with less inconvenience of attendance. Postage has been a tax to me. You, in your way of dealing and thinking on a large scale do not realize this as I do. . . . I have taken the office solely for the sake of avoiding for the present paying a post-office tax and corresponding with friends unrestrainedly. . . . To you I am glad to offer the *first-fruit* of the privilege." Separated a whole year from his friend, Stebbins urged Whitney, "when you *can*, consistently with your business, *do* (I ask it once for all) drop me everything of your

pains & pleasures, as far as you deem it safe and prudent. . . .
Where do you board? How do you live? etc. etc. Tell as much as you
can."

Fortunately, Whitney wrote. "I meet with many delays which I
did not expect but cannot avoid. I am many times impatient and unhappy that I progress so slowly—at other times I look around & see
that I have done a great Deal and feel more satisfied with the progress
which I have made. But my principal solace arrises from the consideration that my machinery and modes of doing the work will certainly answer a better purpose than any heretofore devised. I shall
be able, by and by, to work well & to execute with Dispatch. My
works will be much superior to any in America & I have the vanity to
suppose they are equal to any in the world. But I have a great task before me and when I shall get thro' God knows. I live constantly out
at my place & tho I have at least forty People around me every day
—I am yet a solitary *Old Bachelor.* I am incessantly occupied in my
Business and after laboring hard thro' the day I am obliged to leave
ten times so much undone (which ought to have been Done) as I
have in the course of the day accomplished, and lie down under a
load of cares already almost unsupportable & still accumulating. I
flatter myself that I shall not sink under it. I think I shall persevere
to the End. . . . I am so totally engrossed at home that I am almost
entirely ignorant of what is passing in the world. I think of my old
friends sometimes—sigh for their society—hope, wish, and believe
that they are happy—curse the stars that have imposed Ixion's task—
& return again to the Wheel. . . .

"Present my most affectionate remembrance to Laura—tell her
to kiss the darling boy for me & teach him to couple my Name with
that of Friend of his Parents."

A few months later Whitney again described himself to Stebbins
as "a poor forlorn Old Bachelor—making guns yet—always in a
Dam'd hurry without bringing anything to pass." Something romantic was afoot that spring of 1800 to make Whitney apply such
a coquettish phrase to himself. Other letters written during those
months hint that Whitney and the Millers had been discussing something matrimonial. What, exactly? And with whom? Most likely it
was one of Catherine's two unmarried daughters, in whom Whitney

confessed himself interested—Cornelia, aged twenty-one, or Louisa, the youngest, then about seventeen. For what other persons would Catherine feel so "principled against using her influence?" How else should Miller warn that "it is not always that young people think in unison with their elders—& we have had some remarkable instances to the contrary of this," and still offer to ascertain for Whitney "what place you would hold in the mind to which you would address yourself." That it was marriage Whitney sought, and that the person was close to Catherine and intimately known to Miller, is all that is clear. Whitney's words have an uneasy sound as he accepts Miller's offer: "I have the utmost confidence in your candour—and wish you to ascertain & inform me particularly & minutely what prospect I may have of success. I will make great exertion & say I wish to come out next winter, but if there be no prospect of obtaining the object of my wishes, providence would perhaps dissuade me from the attempt." And there the matter rested. Miller did not bid him come posthaste, and when Whitney went south a year later it was solely on urgent business for Miller & Whitney.

XV · *Jefferson and a Practical Demonstration*

O N November 8, 1800, Wolcott resigned as Secretary of the Treasury. The vitriol, the violent charges thrown at him were meaningless to Whitney. Had Wolcott's hatred of John Adams, his rage against Adams's policies, his blind attachment to Hamilton—had these passions so possessed Wolcott as to make him commit acts which approached positive treachery? Whitney knew Wolcott as a firm friend, a faithful, farsighted Cabinet member who had given valuable assistance to his efforts to arm the young nation. The political convulsion meant only one thing to Whitney; it broke the precarious ease he had enjoyed.

With Wolcott gone, written explanations and proposals, letters conveying reassurance fortified by impartial recommendations, bonds and sureties—all the paraphernalia by which he had wrested additional time and moneys from the government—were useless; their efficacy had depended upon one man in authority who was friendly to Whitney's talent. With Wolcott gone, it was imperative that Whitney present himself at the seat of government as soon as possible. He was reassured by the progress he had made; he would not have to plead—this time he could show those in authority what he had been doing and the end to which he had worked. The muskets themselves would convince the most skeptical.

As was his custom, before starting, he armed himself with laudatory letters. Decius Wadsworth wrote at length: "I am acquainted with no person to whose care I should be so willing to entrust the making of an experiment. . . . The arms he is making . . . will not only exceed in point of workmanship the best which have been fabricated for that use in this country, but even be superior to any muskets for common use ever fabricated in any country." Wadsworth thought it expedient to spend as much time commending Whitney, the man, as Whitney, the gun manufacturer. He did not dwell on what was known—his mechanical invention, ingenuity, and ability. Rather he listed the "less obvious traits. . . . Patient, prudent, of mature reflection, diligent, economical, blest with sound judgement, it is rare to find a man uniting so many excellencies, free from striking defects. He is therefore entitled to the highest degree of confidence. . . . I entertain a hope that an institution so highly deserving of national patronage and support, will meet with the encouragement it merits."

En route to the new city of Washington, to which the government had just moved, Whitney stopped off at Philadelphia, where from John Nicholson, Inspector of Small Arms, he obtained a certificate. Briefly, it stated that "specimens of Mr. Whitney's work . . . meet my full & entire approbation & I do not hesitate to declare them to be specimens of the best workmanship in the fabrication of War Muskets which I have seen."

Two and a half years before, Whitney had traveled the same road. Then it was summer, and the miles between Philadelphia and New Haven had been easy and swift; then he had with him the Charleville muskets, and his mind was filled with a subdued excitement as he thought of the great adventure on which he was about to start. Now, in the cold, short days of late December, he was retracing his steps. "It was long & tedious, the roads being very deep & bad & the stages traveling very slowly. . . . I carried on a musket of my manufacture & several samples of Locks &c." He was tired, but more than the physical fatigue was the fear that the men with whom he would now have to do business would not see what he was about to show them. Habit, he knew, could make people as blind as prejudice, and men could gaze on the face of tomorrow and swear it was a wishful dream.

Whitney's apprehensions were ill founded. He found friends in Washington; Wolcott was still there—"Everything which I have done was highly approved of by Mr. Wolcott. This gave me peculiar satisfaction as he has ever been a man high in my esteem." Elizur Goodrich, his old tutor's son, was filling a term as congressman. Without fanfare or extravagant notices, Whitney offered the government officials a simple but impressive demonstration.

"Our friend, Mr. Whitney is here, and has exhibited his Works and Specimens to the President of the United States [John Adams], the Heads of Departments and many others of superior mechanical information." Elizur Goodrich wrote to tell Baldwin, Whitney's lawyer and friend, the events of that crowded first week of January, 1801. "They have met universal approbation & are considered as evidence that this Country need not depend on a disgraceful recourse to foreign Markets for this primary means of defence. All Judges & Inspectors unite in a declaration that they are superior to any which the artists of this Country, or importation have brought into the Arsenals of the United States—and all Men of all parties agree that his talents are of immense importance, and must be exclusively secured by and devoted to the means of defence. The arrangements will be made perfectly satisfactory [to] him—and he is requested as the Artist of his Country to suggest from time to time all alterations, improvements &c which may in his opinion, be useful in the Armories of the United States &c.

"We last evening waited upon Mr. Jefferson, in pursuance of a previous appointment. He had while in France & England, by direction of this Government particularly attended to the Manufacture of Arms. On a very critical survey & examination he did not hesitate to say, that he had in no instance seen any work or specimens equal to Mr. Whitney's, excepting in one factory in France in which the owner had defined the various parts of his Muskets, on the principles of Mr. Whitney, that Mr. Whitney equalled his specimens—that his were gaged and made by Machinery . . . that by Authority of this Country at great price he attempted to remove this Artist to the United States—but he was immediately taken into the service of the Crown, and had since deceased. He observed that the manufacture of Arms, even at double expense, must be secured, that Arms however of equal goodness could not be so cheaply procured from any part of Europe. He observed that the State of Virginia had determined to furnish at the expence of the State—a Musket, to each Militiaman in the State—and to have an equal quantity in their arsenals—that they had directed them to be exclusively of the Manufacture of this Country—that they had good Work, but not so good Work from the State factory in Richmond. He proposed to Mr. Whitney—that he would write to Gov. Monroe, advising him to contract with him at the United States price—for any number of thousands which Mr. Whitney would undertake to furnish. Mr. W informed him that it would not be in his power to contract, untill his contract with the Government was more nearly completed—and having spent the evening on the subject of Manufactures &c we returned."

What undercurrents were present when Whitney showed off his musket and heard himself called "the Artist of his Country" are suggested by the note which accompanied Goodrich's "observations which are confined exclusively to that business of Mr. Whitney. As he has had to contend with much ignorance, and some malice, I have written it, with a view that you may read or show it to any persons you think proper."

The malice seems to have been centered in Samuel Dexter, who was named to replace Wolcott. During President Adams's final months of tenure in office, Dexter went from his post as Secretary of War to the Secretary of the Treasury. Immediately after Whitney's triumphant demonstration of his musket, when, by allowing the officials to assemble the parts of the locks—selecting the constituent parts at random—he dramatized the concept of interchangeability and made its advantages obvious, he wrote a long memorandum to Dexter. He wanted to explain the conditions and aims of the original contract and the reason for the delays he had suffered. The story was always the same, yet the addition of significant details makes his methods and basic approach ever clearer.

"I have been under the necessity either personally to form or to be present during the formation of every Pattern, Model, Mould etc. [his method for obtaining uniformity in the parts]. . . . I had not any experience in the fabrication of Arms and . . . I did not associate to myself workmen who had been accustomed to their fabrication. This has, I imagine, been favorable to Improvement but has been productive of some delay. [He did not want his workmen to have to unlearn habitual practices.] I have endeavored to ascertain the qualities of different species of iron & steel and other materials most suitable for muskets." He had learned from the ginning business the importance of testing and experimenting.

And then, having with candor admitted his lack of experience when he had commenced his task, he proceeded with authority and assurance to discuss those "improvements in the construction which in my opinion may be adopted with advantage. The modern French Locks have a brass Pan, which has the advantage of not being corroded by the nitre of the powder, of being placed with greater facility in a more favorable position to receive the Fire from the hammer, & of more effectually securing the priming from the rain—which advantages I think will more than compensate for the expence of the alteration [to the model musket]. . . . I cannot introduce the Brass Pan at all in the first 1500. But if it should be tho't advisable, I will contract to make Brass Pans to the second parcel of 1500 stands, for six cents each in addition to the contract price, and Brass Pans with an alteration in the hammer etc so as to embrace all the advantages, to the remaining seven thousand stands for an additional to the Contract price of ten cents on each musket." Whitney's methods of estimating costs was as new as his system of manufacturing—and an integral part.

"My system I now consider as established and my theory successfully reduced to practice and in order to enable me to proceed, free from those pecuniary embarrassments which are so destructive to all manufacturing concerns, would respectfully solicit the following modifications and arrangements of my contract." He asked for "an advance of ten thousand Dollars and in three months from this time a further sum of five thousand Dollars"; he asked "that the delivery time of any Arms may be suspended for the period of six months—that within that time I deliver five hundred Muskets and receive five thousand Dollars on the delivery—and the like sum on the delivery of each quantity . . . the whole to be delivered within two and a half years from this date [January 8, 1801]." Whitney had calculated that such a schedule of payments for muskets delivered would finance his business and allow him to repay the $30,000 advanced him.

To this the government agreed; now the original advance of $10,000 had been trebled, the original period had been stretched to five years.

February had almost passed before Dexter felt he had protected the Treasury to the degree that he could safely send Whitney his $10,000. To Whitney, Dexter must have appeared unduly fussy in insisting on certain safeguards, and unconscionably slow in answering letters. It was this that prompted him on April 4th to give Dexter a fortnight's notice that the additional $5,000 due three months from the agreement reached on January 8th last and accepted by Dexter on the 16th would soon be due. To preclude further delay, he also forwarded a bond to cover this final amount. On the 15th Dexter answered. He informed Whitney that the memoranda of the discussion held the previous January had been lost in the fire that destroyed the Treasury building; he was suspicious of Whitney's request and demanded further guarantees for the new sum. He declared that Senator Daggett's recommendation of the sureties' ability was too general; he was afraid to risk good government moneys to further such experiments without really substantial security. Plainly, Dexter stood ready to obstruct the agreement that Whitney had so brilliantly maneuvered to obtain. Faced with such malice—Goodrich had translated Dexter's extreme prudence into an antagonism—Whitney found a powerful ally—his second protective, understanding friend.

The previous month Jefferson had been inaugurated as President. Jefferson had been present when Whitney had "exhibited his Works"; his prestige and enthusiasm, his unique familiarity with Whitney's objective—had he not searched the armories of France and England for just such an artisan?—had counted heavily in Whitney's favor. The political change that came with Jefferson's advent to power favored Whitney. Jefferson ordered "the business of the Contracts for fabricating small arms" out of the hands of the Treasury and its new head, Albert Gallatin, opponent of large army appropriations, and transferred it to the War Department.

Henry Dearborn, the newly appointed Secretary of War, was the official with whom Whitney would henceforth have to deal. Whitney gained by this shift in administering the contracts. The emphasis

of the Treasury Department had been on the contractual obligations; those of the War Department would be on securing good
muskets. Of the 40,000 muskets due to have been finished and delivered by September 30, 1800, only a little over one thousand had
been received by the government; of the advances paid out, Whitney
owed the large sum of $30,000. Dearborn wrote to Whitney, as one
of the contractors of 1798 (June 16, 1801), asking why there were
no credits on Whitney's ledger and what plans he had for refunding
the money advanced.

Again (June 27, 1801), this time for Dearborn's information, he
reviewed his original aim in establishing a new system of manufacturing arms, the delays he had met, and the conditions of the agreement made the previous January, reminding him that Jefferson had
been present at an examination of his muskets and that a musket
of Whitney's manufacture was in the Treasury office and could be
examined again. He was able to add: "I shall have five hundred Musketts ready for delivery next month—all the parts for several thousands are in forwardness and some of the limbs for each of the whole
ten thousand are now made." After three work-filled, worry-filled
years, he could start making deliveries.

The question he then asked of Dearborn is characteristic of the
care and foresight he lavished on every detail: "I beg leave to observe that it appears to me the method of packing [the muskets] and
the materials of which the Boxes are made as well as the mode of
making them, is a subject which has not been sufficiently attended
to. In some instances they have been packed in Boxes made of Oak
boards, either green or but partly seasoned, & so slightly put together that they exclude neither air nor water. . . . It is impossible
but Musketts put up in this manner must begin to be corroded by
rust in less than twenty-four hours . . . and in a short time be totally
ruined. On the contrary I have good reason to believe that arms
properly packed, in Boxes of well seasoned pine, made in such a
manner as to exclude the dampness of the atmosphere, will keep
and remain in perfect order for twenty years. . . . I have spared no
pains to compleat my Musketts in the best manner & I feel unwilling
that they should be spoiled by being improperly packed." How justified was his concern that the muskets be properly packed can be

judged by a letter sent from the Springfield Armory concerning two hundred muskets that, "having been placed in green Chests have taken Rust to the degree that in the opinion of the Supt. & Master Armourer . . . they will cost to have them put in proper State $66.67."

When Whitney delivered the first batch of five hundred muskets, properly boxed, inspected, and proved on September 26, 1801, his account was credited with $6,700; he was remitted the $5,000 agreed to. He had reduced the money advanced him by $1,700.

Just then, just when his production was moving along as he had planned, Whitney received Miller's letter making it imperative to attend the forthcoming meeting of the South Carolina legislature to handle the sale of Miller & Whitney's patent rights. Here was a sudden, indefinite delay. "I am litterally in the predicament of the Old Woman who had so much to do, that she knew not what to do first," he wrote to Stebbins on September 25th. "I am a perfect Ass between two bundles of hay—or rather I am surrounded with five or six hundred bundles all of which attract and *repell* equally. I can't attend to *this* thing because *that* thing requires my attention more. . . . I go on in a circle till I arrive at the point where I started." And then, having given a picture of a man riding off rapidly in all directions, he asked Stebbins for specific information about Dearborn. "He is from your country [District of Maine] & perhaps you may know something about him. I know nothing of him but expect soon to have occasion to negociate some business with him & should like to have some Idea of the cut of his *Gib*. Is he a man of talents? Has he extensive information? Is he a man of integrity? in short has he a *soul?*" *

The answers to these questions—the anatomy of Dearborn's soul

---

* Henry Dearborn had lived a career that was romance itself. A village doctor in New Hampshire, when the Revolution began he marched with Stark to Bunker Hill and fought there until his ammunition gave out; he endured the incredible hardships of the march through the wilderness to Quebec, saw Montgomery killed under the walls of the fortress, and was himself taken prisoner. Later exchanged, he wintered at Valley Forge, served at Monmouth, and witnessed Cornwallis's surrender at Yorktown. He succeeded Greene as quartermaster general and gained firsthand insight into military administration. He was fifty when Jefferson appointed him to his Cabinet; in his handsome person he combined highly desirable qualities—scientific training, service as soldier and executive, a fervid Republicanism.

as described by Stebbins—are missing. But Whitney need not have asked them—he had the support of Jefferson, and Jefferson's admiration for his talents. Whitney spent the first week of November in Washington; he had several interviews with the President, who must not only have reassured Whitney that the government would permit his attending to his ginning business but who carried out his earlier offer to write to Governor James Monroe of Virginia on Whitney's behalf. Jefferson's introduction repeated his detailed understanding of the methods used in interchangeable manufacture.

"Mr. Whitney," he wrote, "is at the head of a considerable gun manufactory in Connecticut, and furnishes the United States with muskets, undoubtedly the best they receive. He has invented moulds and machines for making all the pieces of his locks so exactly equal, that take 100 locks to pieces and mingle their parts and the hundred locks may be put together as well by taking the first pieces which come to hand. This is of importance in repairing, because out of 10 locks, e.g. disabled for the want of different pieces, 9 good locks may be put together without employing a smith. Leblanc, in France, had invented a similar process in 1788 & had extended it to the barrel, mounting, & stock. . . . Mr. Whitney has not yet extended his improvement beyond the lock. I think it possible he might be engaged in our manufactory of Richmond, tho' I have not asked him the question. I know nothing of his moral character. He is now on his way to S. Carolina on the subject of his gin."

There was more than Jefferson's long-held enthusiasm for the new method to plead Whitney's cause at each delay, each interruption. Of the $400,000 Congress had appropriated that year for the purchase of cannon and small arms, Dearborn notified the President that as of November 1st, exclusive of sums paid out by the Treasury Department and those allotted for the national armories, his department had paid out a mere $86,000. (Did this brief, informal memorandum of November 17th contain facts which, when considered, set the policy for the questions raised by Whitney's request?) Clearly, the officials knew the need was for muskets, not moneys; they would be patient, they would be generous with time. In all his dealings with the Administration, there was not an inharmonious note.

With the patent rights successfully sold to South Carolina, Whitney must have felt elated when he reached Washington (April, 1802). "General Dearborn, Secy of War told Mr. Whitney that if he would deliver 4000 Stands of Arms (including 500 already delivered) on his contract before the first of April next (1803) he might expect an allowance & extension of time for the term of two years from said 1st of April for the delivery of the remaining 6000 Stands to compleat the number of 10,000 for which he originally contracted." (He was allowed $2.50 per box, for the proper packing of the guns.) Again he had had to ask for time, again it had been granted him.

That June, after Wadsworth had proved five hundred barrels and inspected five hundred muskets, Whitney wrote to Dearborn: "I have packed them up in suitable chests. . . . I am happy to find that this method promises to answer my expectations; the first parcel having been put up in the Boxes one year, are now in the same perfect order as when they were put up." The following September, when trouble flared up in another quarter—"You are undoubtedly informed of the hostile measures adopted by the Emperor of Morocco in relation to the U. States"—Whitney delivered another five hundred muskets, "with Brass Pans at 13.46 ea per agreement."

For some years Whitney had to shuttle between his factory in New Haven and his patent-right interests in the South, where opposition to the sale made to South Carolina continued the protracted struggle. Until that was settled, Whitney knew that much time would be spent in the affairs of Miller & Whitney and that therefore he must arrange a new time schedule for delivering the muskets. He was exhausted by the severe, unexpected attack Miller & Whitney had suffered. When he reached Washington, he made an agreement with Dearborn (February 28, 1803). This final arrangement accepted the realities of the perplexed situation and set the tempo which Whitney could maintain. "In case Eli Whitney shall deliver on or before the first day of May next, 500 Muskets in addition to those already delivered, . . . then the said Whitney shall be allowed the privilege of delivering two thousand stands annually, the terms of the Contract notwithstanding."

Whitney felt these were very favorable terms. He wrote to Steb-

bins: "I have some business to negociate here which I have been
so fortunate to accomplish entirely to my own satisfaction. My contract to manufacture 10,000 stands of Arms was really a very arduous
undertaking. There is yet much to be done to complete it. I have
hitherto gone no faster than I could go safely. It has been an important object to persuade the Administration to allow me so much time
as to go on easy with it, till it is compleat. This they have done. I have
obtained all the time I wished. This has relieved me from a vast load
of anxiety. . . . Besides this will allow me leisure to attend to my
Patent concerns."

The glorious promises solemnly made in the summer of 1798 had
weathered the series of frustrations, and, after four and a half years,
Whitney and the government settled down to a routine which brought
quiet satisfaction to both parties. Whitney had never doubted his
ability to achieve his goal; he had always been fortunate to find
a staunch supporter—first Wolcott, then Jefferson—to indulge him
his need for time and money. The success of this first exploration of
a new system of production rests both in Whitney's genius and the
government's understanding and support.

The first thousand muskets had faithfully copied the Charleville
models of 1763; the second thousand incorporated the brass pans of
the 1777 model; and, beginning with the third thousand, Whitney's
muskets had "Brass Pans and other alterations complete at 13.50."
By October of 1803, a note of spacious ease can be felt when to Stebbins he writes: "My Armoury here has got to be a regular Establishment & progresses tolerably well & I flatter myself that I shall
make something handsome by the undertaking. My works have considerably excited the Public Curiosity & are visited by most people
who travel thro' this country. This, however, is not so flattering to
my vanity that I do not wish to be less thronged with Spectators."
Quite soon, his factory was mentioned even in travel books. Edward
Kendall, in his *Travels through the Northern Parts of the United
States in the years 1807 and 1808*, included the factory and Whitney's
method of manufacture: "For every part of the musket he has a
mould; and there is said to be so much exactitude in the finishing,
that every part of any musket may be adapted to all the parts of any
other."

From 1803 on, a succession of muskets finished, proved, and inspected, in lots of 500, flowed out of Whitney's manufactory, and a succession of $5,000 payments whittled down the advance he owed the government. And then, in 1808, when he had almost completed the contract, he received the first complaint from Dearborn. "In a conversation with a Gentleman . . . I mentioned your muskets as the only ones I had seen, made by contract that were perfectly executed. He being desirous of seeing one of them, I had one procured, he discovered that the pan did not set close to the barrel; that the breech plate was not of the best kind; and then drew the ramrod, which on trying its temper, was found to bend & remain bent like common iron. I then sent for two others: and on taking one into my hand, made a gentle effort to bend it. It broke within about 8 inches of the lower end, & the other part remained in a curve. . . . I hope the same defects will not be found generally. I have given you this information that you may have the Boxes, now at New Haven, opened and an inspection made under your own eyes. These defects are serious evils, and occasion a new inspection of the muskets received."

These defects were serious, but they were not uncommon. Muskets made at the national armories themselves were found to be defective. Some made at Harpers Ferry revealed that "the steel was so bad it ought to be rejected. The bayonet . . . was easily bent at the shoulder so as to be unfit for the charge. The lock . . . would not true up to the hammer . . . the ramrod, bayonet and lock of the sample inspected were defective either in material or workmanship." While of the "several thousand Stands of the Arms manufactured at the Springfield [Armory] . . . fifteen out of twenty of them are defective." Another private contractor was told of the guns he had supplied that "some parts of the locks, particularly the hammers and cocks, are extremely brittle: a great proportion of them break in practising with wooden flints—there must be some defect either in the steel or in the temper, or both. Many of the screws brake. . . . Nearly one-fifth part of the muskets have been rendered unfit for use."

In those days before chemistry had transformed metallurgy from a skill or art into a science, how could they know if the steel were true, the iron strong? It was hard to imagine that materials properly selected might be defective; it was a reflection on a man's experience and judgment to suggest that the metals might conceal flaws; the only explanation was that the workmanship was at fault.

The answer, which Whitney wrote the same day the complaint was received, shows how completely unreliable were the metal supplies which they all used. "A ramrod will break with a slight application of force after it has been passed by a careful and experienced Inspector. I well remember an instance of a ramrod belong to a Musket . . . sent from Harper's Ferry to the War Office as a specimen of their best workmanship—I sprang it to no considerable degree and it flew into three pieces." He mentioned the method by which his inspector tested the elasticity of the ramrod: "If there is the least defect in a Rod it will not ring & he makes it a point to reject all which do not ring when thrown forcibly down the Barrel." He wrote that the "ramrods have all been made at my own manufactory by persons employed by the day—not one of them has been made, nor any opperation belonging to them, been performed by the job; so that no person has had any inducement . . . to practice any deception about them . . . Those which I have manufactured for a long time past are equal to any which have ever been made in any part of the world."

Whitney might exercise caution in purchasing his materials, further caution in testing and experimenting; the government might set up elaborate methods to prove and inspect—a musket was no better than the iron and steel that went into its making. Because of this, it was not surprising that Whitney himself saw what happened to a "Regiment of Soldiers stationed at this place [New Haven] who were all armed with Muskets manufactured at the Armory at Springfield—& tho' these muskets were in the hands of the soldiers but a short time, there was a great complaint of the Ramrods—a large proportion of them broke."

Ten and a half years had passed from the time Whitney accepted the first contract when, on January 23, 1809, he informed the Secretary of War that "you will receive vouchers for a further delivery of 500 Muskets which compleats my Contract for fabricating 10,000 stands of arms for the Use of the U States. Upon the receipt of which be pleased to Direct the sum of Six Thousand Dollars to be remitted to me at this Place. I suppose the whole Balance due me from the U States is about Eight thousand Dollars: . . . I propose to come to Washington in a few weeks for the purpose of Closing up my accounts." When Whitney deducted the cost of the stocks which had been furnished him from the Public Stores, when he added the price of the four hundred boxes he had made in which to pack his muskets properly and the cost of a "Proof House & Battery" which he had been asked to build at the government's cost, the balance owed him on the 10,000 arms he had manufactured and delivered was the small sum of $2,450.

He had succeeded. He had carried through a new system of manufacturing, a revolutionary system that replaced a skill with the uniformity of a machine; he had been able to give tangible expression to an idea that could be adapted to other manufactures. He had, to his own great satisfaction, established his own business.

When Whitney and Jefferson spent several evenings together in leisurely conversation, discussing the problems and possibilities related to interchangeable manufacture, Jefferson related in detail how in France he had seen that very principle worked out in the same making of muskets. It was years before, in 1785, and he had written about it to John Jay, the Secretary of Foreign Affairs for the Confederation government. The details, as he summarized them then, mentioned that "as yet, the inventor has only completed the lock of the musket, on this plan. He will proceed immediately to have the barrel, stock, and other parts, executed in the same way. Supposing it might be useful in the United States, I went to the workman. He presented me the parts of fifty locks taken to pieces, and arranged in compartments. I put several together myself, taking pieces at hazard as they came to hand, and they fitted in a most perfect manner. . . . He effects it by tools of his own contrivance, which, at the same time abridge the work, so that he thinks he shall be able to furnish the muskets two livres cheaper than the common price. But it will be two or three years before he will be able to furnish any quantity. I mention it now, as it may have an influence on the plan for furnishing our magazines with this arm." Four

		Doll.	
1801. Sept. 26	To 500 Muskets dd Simothy Phelps at 13..40 as for original contract	6700	—
1802. June 15	To 500 Muskets .. Timth. Phelps at 13..40 as for Cont.	6700	—
Sept. 6	To 500 Muskets with Brass Pans at 13..46. as per	6730	—
1803 Mar 31	To 500 Muskets with Brass Pans at 13..46. for agreet	6730	—
July 11.	To 500 Muskets with Brass Pans and other alterations completed @ 13..50	6750	—
Oct. 20.	To 500 Stands arms. with Brass &c complete @ 13.50	6750	—
1804 April 4.	To 500 Stands of arms completed @ 13..50	6750	—
July 23.	To 500 Stands of Arms compt. @ 13..50	6750	—
1805 Jan. 16.	To 500 Stands of Arms . do . do	6750	—
May 23.	To 500 .. Do. Do. Do	6750	—
1806 April 16.	To 500 Do. Do. Do.	6750	—
June 26.	To 500 Do. Do. Do.	6750	—
Oct. 1.	To 500 Do. Do. Do.	6750	—
1807 Jany 3.	To 500 Do. do. do	6750	—
Mar. 23.	To 500 Do. Do. Do	6750	
July 23	To 500 Do. Do. do	6750	
Nov. 14.	To 500 do. do. do	6750	
1808 Feb. 27.	To 500 do. do. do	6750	
June 4.	To 500 do. do. do.	6750	
1809 Jany 23.	To 500 do. do. do.	$134,850	
	To 400 Boxes for muskets @ 2..50	1000	
	To cost of Proof House & Battery	178	75
		136038	75

DEBTOR, UNITED STATES, IN ACCOUNT

with	Eli Whitney	Cr.

Date			Amount	
1798 Aug. 21	By 5000	} John I. Clarke surety ———————	10,000	—
1799 Jan. 1.	By 5000			
Oct. 3.	By 4000	} E. Shipman & others surety ———	10,000	—
Dec. 25	By 1500			
1800	By 4500			
1801.	By 10.000 Phelps & Sanford surety ———		10000	—
			30,000	—
Sept.	By ———————————————		5000	—
1802. June 1.	By ———————————————		5000	—
Sept.	By ———————————————		5000	—
1803 Mar.	By ———————————————		5000	—
July.	By ———————————————		5000	—
Oct.	By ———————————————		5000	—
1804 Apl.	By ———————————————		5000	—
July.	By ———————————————		5000	—
1805 Jany.	By ———————————————		5000	—
May.	By ———————————————		5000	—
1806 Apl.	By ———————————————		5000	—
June	By ———————————————		5000	—
Oct.	By ———————————————		5000	—
1807 Jany.	By ———————————————		5000	—
Mar.	By ———————————————		5000	—
July.	By ———————————————		5000	—
Nov.	By ———————————————		5000	—
1808 Feb.	By ———————————————		5000	—
June	By ———————————————		6000	—
1809 Jany	By ———————————————	13	1000	—
	By 10 335 musket Stocks @ 25 Ct each		2588	75
	By Ballance Due E Whitney ———		2450	—
		13	6038	75

years later he consigned "a box of officers' muskets, containing half a
dozen, made by the person and on the plan which I mentioned to
you." The whole idea seems to have remained with the muskets, shut
up in the box marked "T.J. No. 36."

It would be hard to imagine that the conversation did not drift
into speculation: Why did Lablanc's method—its problems of tooling
solved, its advantages appreciated—die with its inventor? It could
not have been the Revolution that put a stop to the contemplated
establishment of "a large manufactory for the purpose of putting it
into execution." A government that was concerned with standardizing weights and measures would be interested in standardizing the
manufacture of arms provided it served a practical purpose. The
French Republic had need of muskets with which to arm her mobilized citizenry, but she had only to take the great stores of arms,
made and ready for use, in the royal arsenals. In the face of such
lavish stockpiling, there was no urgency to develop the newer method.
France had a large corps of highly skilled workers—she felt no need
to rely on machinery to produce muskets in quantity. It may have
been that these workers themselves opposed a system of manufacturing that violated their habits and traditions and threatened their
very livelihood.

The concept of interchangeable manufacture was being experimented with in Europe before Whitney started his work. It was an
idea that took very limited hold in France, where it was first worked
out, while in England it was solely applied to lowering the costs
on the pulleys made for the navy. In America, however, it was applied to the mass production of more and more objects—clocks and
watches, hardware and sewing machines—because it solved the shortage of workers. The American system was eminently fitted to use
the waves of agrarian immigrants who, innocent of the language or
of industrial skills, could tend the machines that made goods shipped
all over the world.

XVI

The Master Manufacturer

I now Set Down to Let you know that I am in good
helth and i hope you engoy the same. I have not
ben to school Sense I hav ben here and I cannot read nor write one
Half as well as i did when i came heare To lieve and i do not wish to
live heare."

So, shortly after his arrival in New Haven, ten-year-old Philos
Blake wrote to his younger sister. Philos was Whitney's nephew,
oldest son of his sister Elizabeth and Elihu Blake. Soon after Whitney established himself in the house near the mill, he sent to Westborough for Philos—as he was later to send for the younger sons,
Elihu and Eli Whitney Blake.

For Whitney, the first decade of the nineteenth century contains
years filled with concentrated work and clouded with anxieties, years
made taut by the pull of disjoined efforts—the exertion to create
a northern business and the fight to save the energies invested in the
southern venture. It is hard to equal those years, before or after, for
intellectual and physical activity. And yet in the dead center of that
whirlwind there was an oppressive stillness. "You will find me a
solitary Being," he wrote Stebbins, "without a companion & almost without a friend—employed in this smutty occupation of Vilean
& living on plain fare in a humble cottage. . . . If I had a house,
a wife & a home—" The cry of a heart that was empty, that recognized its emptiness by the constant use of "Old Bachelor," sounded in
all Whitney's letters to Stebbins. His capacity for affection could
not be denied and, since he had no wife and no home, he reached
back to the home of his childhood to find there someone on whom
to lavish care and thought and love.

With a child's candid eye Philos mixed the wonders of his uncle's manufactory and those of the port of New Haven: "Thare is a driling machine and a boureing machine to bour berels and a screw machine and too great large buildings, one nother shop and a stocking shop to stocking guns in, a blacksmith shop and a trip hammer shop and five hundred guns done. I seen a great menny ships sinse i have ben here and i have seen the sea and i have seen the cannon." It was September, 1801; his inventory must reflect the items his uncle stressed either by tone or manner. The "five hundred guns" were the first to be finished; the machines enumerated were those his uncle must have taken pride in explaining when the little boy asked his what-fors. It is unique, the only precise record of what Whitney had in his "manufactory."

For though Whitney showed off his buildings and machines to hundreds of persons, and dozens of written records are left, they all conspire to speak in general terms; they marvel, they explain, they summarize the techniques. Timothy Dwight's *Travels in New-England and New-York* is a typical example. "In this manufactory muskets are made in a manner, which I believe to be singular. . . . Machinery moved by water, and remarkably adapted in every instance to the purpose in view, is employed for hammering, cutting, turning, perforating, grinding, polishing, &c." And so, when Philos was two years older and his spelling and syntax were impeccable, he abandoned the sure bold pen of his childhood, and wrote to his sister, "I wish I could give you as particular an account of our manufactory as you have given me of Westborough, but I am such a blunderhead that I cannot describe even those things which I perfectly understand."

Elihu followed Philos and, later, Eli, his namesake, joined his brothers in their uncle's home. Seeing Whitney through his nephews' eyes is to catch unexpected glimpses of him, and, seen thus, Whitney's expression is changed. The focus was not on the inventor, not on the industrialist, but on an uncle, preoccupied, frequently away from his house, who tried to satisfy the thousand different demands upon his time, an uncle generous and caring. In 1811 Philos reported home that "Uncle has a widow and an old maid to keep house for him; has got nine apprentices. . . . You ask me why I cannot mention Elihu's wants to Uncle, I have a great many times—but I have teazing enough of my own to do."

Or there was the catch-as-catch-can sequence of events that lasted many months when young Eli entered Yale in the fall of 1812. "Uncle said he was very glad I did not come before for he had but fifteen minutes before arrived from New York. . . . Went back to Mr. Goodrich's for tea and Uncle came there likewise to tea. . . . Uncle was so much hurried that he could not attend to getting me my bed and told me I might continue to sleep at Mr. Goodrich's & he would call for me in a few days and see about it. . . . Uncle returned from New York some time but did not call at my room untill last Wednesday. He called and stayed a few minutes and told me to come out to his house saturday and he would talk to me about a bed. . . . I accordingly went out yesterday about 3 in the afternoon but did not find Uncle at home because two of his boys [apprentices] ran away in the night before & he was putting handbills in circulation &c. But I stayed . . . till halfpast 8 and then he came home. I stayed about an hour and talked with him. Which time was as good as it was short. He said he did not know where he could get me a bed but he would do the best he could about it."

No one but Whitney himself knew how burdened he was with the time-consuming, anarchic trivia connected with running a house. For an unmarried man to assume responsibility for two nephews (Eli was away at school) and at least nine apprentices was a task in itself. Whitney's household Expence Book lists the details that had to be attended to; it also states explicitly what a housekeeper undertook and why, for the seven-year period covered, almost thirty different names are entered—some for a few days, some for many months. A recurrent item concerns the clothes the housekeeper was expected to make and keep in repair: thus for making four pairs of trousers and four jackets and mending ten coats and one pair of pants the housekeeper was paid $6.28. Always she had a helper, since the sewing was added to cooking and baking, washing, cleaning, making fires and fetching water and nursing any who were sick. A Mrs. Mallery "came to take charge of the house 6th May 1812." In August she "agreed to Continue here until Spring. Her wages to be one Dollar per Week. Betsy to continue here and work with her mother for some time, except she is to go to school for three months when the weather is so she can go, in which time she is to work mornings and evenings & I am to pay for her schooling which together with her board is to be the compensation for her work. Mrs. M is also to have the priviledge of doing her husband's washing here." There is the notation about Patty Johnson, who "came to work this afternoon, Thursday, Sept. 21." The very next day, "It appears that Patty had the Disentary at the time she came here, on which acct. She went to her sister's this day & in consideration of destitute situation, I gave her three dollars to be repaid by work when she is able."

Of the three Blake brothers, only young Eli was sent to college. ("I do not know what Uncle's ideas are with respect to me, whether he means I shall go to colledge or not, however I think he means to try me to see whether it is worth it or not.") First, he was sent to Leicester Academy: "I have been studying there about a year and a half the Lattin and Greek languages only, in which time I have made myself fit for Colege."

After their father's death in 1807, Whitney and his brother Josiah watched over their sister Elizabeth; each, in his own way, acted the role of father to her. Josiah was constantly driving over from Boston; he fussed over her, the children, the problems of the farm; he was endlessly preoccupied with health. Each year he went to fashionable Saratoga Springs or Ballston Springs for the cure—each year for a different ailment; once "to get Clean of the Bile & Dermacrotick Blood contracted in the warm climate of Ga!" Whitney, on the other hand, was always intending to visit his sister, always promising, and always forced to cancel his plans. Instead he would arrange with Josiah, "if sister Blake or Eliza are in want of any money this fall, I wish you to pay it to them & charge it to me. You will state this to them. I am excessively pressed at this time with business." By letters and trips, by visits arranged and moneys sent, the family ties were refreshed and strengthened.

A constant exchange of letters passed between the brothers, lengthy, loving discussions of the needs and achievements, plans, and health of Elizabeth's children. Even when Whitney was harassed by those who sought to destroy his business, he found the time to

satisfy a wish that was important to a nephew. Philos, he wrote
his brother Josiah, now established as a merchant in Boston, had
been made "the youngest Lieutenant in the Artillery Company of
N Haven. . . . It is undoubtedly much the most respectable company in this state. . . . [He] is extremely anxious to be perfect in
his *uniform,* to complete which, he is in want of a sash—an article
which is not to be obtained here and as I presume only at an extravagant price anywhere. He wishes for a *good one* which I suppose will cost from thirty to forty Dollars." Before such a request,
Josiah was not easily satisfied with what was available, though "it
is as good as the Commander of any Company in Boston has [and]
can be had at twenty-seven Dollars, not less." He was delighted,
a few weeks later, to find "a Sach, imported for a particular person . . . and from your Letter Judged it best to purchase it for
Philos. Paid for it the *Big* Price of Forty five Dollars and have charged
the same to you in account with me." Or, there was their niece Eliza,
whose delicate constitution worried Josiah; she "has a wish, if perfectly agreeable to you, to pass the comming winter at New Haven
with Mrs. Goodrich. . . . Eliza conducted herself at the Springs
[Ballston Spa, where her Uncle Josiah had taken her for the cure]
with her Usual Degree of prudence and was decidedly as much
respected as any one of her age."

Persistently mixed with the love and care so generously given is
a didactic tone. Under the uncle's watchful eyes the young Blakes
were coached in dress and manners and speech; they were being
prepared to associate easily with the children of their uncle's friends.
Whitney had taught himself the essentials that allowed him to move
unaffectedly in society. His sister's children were molded in the same
image. Whitney's attitude toward his nephews' deportment, the details he valued and stressed, are explicitly stated in a most remarkable letter. Written to a sixteen-year-old, it is a little essay on the
constituents of elegance and respectability.

"It is my wish that your studies be so directed as to prepare you
to enter Y. College next Sept [1812].

"I am pleased to observe that you improve in your handwriting—
there is, however, much room for further improvement & now is your
time to learn. . . . If you indulge yourself in writing a careless,

slovenly hand untill it becomes a confirmed habit, it will be very difficult for you to improve. If you should live to be settled in business it will then be too late to acquire this desirable accomplishment. Your hand writing will probably then grow worse instead of better. You make many of your Capital Letters too large, and of unequal size. The capital letters in an epistle, or any other piece of Writing, should all be of the same height & their height should only be a little more than twice the height of a small *m*. . . . Your small *d*s are awkward & badly made.

"My avocations are such that I have less leisure to give you directions & instructions than I could wish: you must therefore, let my instructions sink deep into your mind & not let me have occasion to repeat them.

"You will make it a solemn point . . . to avoid the use of profane language. Such a habit is not only criminal but it will forever prevent your becoming interesting and respectable in conversation. If you contract the habit of using bad words you will have no stock of good ones at hand. . . . You will also be careful to avoid all obscene language as equally improper & disgusting, & as more indicative of the clown than the polite Scholar.

"In reading, Speaking & in all your Conversation, let your Voice be audible & your pronunciation *clear* and *distinct*. Strive to render your voice harmonious and *pleasant;* but let it be *natural*. By all means avoid affectation. Nothing can render a person more unpleasant to others than Drawling, Muttering or an indistinct articulation & nothing is more painful than to be obliged to ask a person three or four times over what they have said & perhaps not find out at last.

"I am extremely sorry to learn from your Uncle Josiah that you have contracted a habit of sitting, walking & standing very *crooked*. You must make a fixed, *unalterable resolution* to change this habit— if you do not you will ruin your breast and be in great danger of bringing on a consumption. By a little exersion you can mend of this habit—& the longer you practice . . . the more easy and familiar it will be to you—& tho' it may cost you a little pain at first, you must at all events correct yourself in this particular.

"I wish you to read this letter over attentively, at least once a week, for the next three months—and in addition to that, to hand it to your preceptor for his perusal & ask him to have the goodness to admonish you whenever he observes you deviate from the instructions herein contained. All your exersions to improve will be highly honorable & advantageous to yourself & your proficiency will be viewed with peculiar satisfaction by all your friends & particularly by Your affectionate Uncle."

By such tokens a man was judged. Through eyes conditioned to these standards, Whitney had viewed Paine when they had met in the Washington public house. When writing young Eli, he had sketched in the edifying elements of respectability; his description of Paine, as he wrote it to Stebbins, expressed Whitney's automatic feeling of disgust for a man who lacked those fundamentals. "I should judge from his appearance that he is nearly 70 years of age. . . . He is about five feet 10 inches high—his hair three fourth white— black eyes—a large bulbous nose—a large mouth drawn down at the corners with flabby lips—with more than half decayed, horrid looking teeth—his complection of a brick colour—his face & nose covered with carbunkles & spots of a darker hue than the general colour of his skin—his dress rather mean & his whole appearance very slovenly—his hands so convulsed that while his expansive lips almost encompassed a wine glass, he could hardly get the contents of it into his head without spilling it. . . . In short he is a mere loathsome carcase, which has withstood the ravages & rackings of brutal intemperance for an uncommon length of time & from which (were it exposed on the barren heath of Africa) the Hyena & Jackals would turn away with disgust.

"He observed that he had dined with Mr. Jefferson yesterday & the Day before—& I make no doubt he is a 'bosome friend' of the President. . . . Tho' some of the democrats will swallow common carrion with a good rellish, I think most of them will loath the putrid rattle snake which has died from the venom of his own bite. . . . I have consumed more time on this horrid subject than it deserves & will leave it—"

Faithfully Whitney echoed the conservative and clerical diatribes directed at Paine; fulminations which filled long columns in New England papers and repeatedly asked: Why "insult the sense and virtue of the country by professions of affectionate attachment to a man so offensive to decency, so smitten with the leprosy of scorn, the natural enemy of every virtue?" Decency. Virtue. Respectability. The very words tolled like church bells calling New Englanders to conform. Whitney lacked the sharp, clinical eye of Senator Mitchill, who thought Paine looked "as if he had been much hackneyed in the service of the world—his eyes black and lively." Only in viewing his special world of mechanics and technology was Whitney willing to accept any deviation from the orthodox.

It would be an error to classify this letter as anti-Democratic, to find therein Whitney's true, concealed political orientation. The date at which he wrote those phrases makes such an easy assumption dangerous; it was November, 1802; he was most dependent on Dearborn, Jefferson's Secretary of War, for patience and grace.

From politics, the topic that crowds the diaries and letter books of the important men of that time, Whitney remained aloof. Whether because of indifference or extreme discretion, it is impossible to say. Letters written from the new city of Washington to Stebbins, or to his brother Josiah, contain not a comment to color his clean impartiality. His intimate circle of friends included Pierpont Edwards, the ardent Jefferson adherent, and Oliver Wolcott, Hamilton's protégé. The year 1801 is hard to match for tense political passions; yet Whitney, in a few words penned from his manufactory, showed he was immune to the national fever: "Parties are warm in N Haven but I live out—& take more pains to avoid being a polititioner, than to know anything about it." These words were written shortly after the demonstration he had put on to convince government officials of the practicability of his method of manufacturing guns. That meeting had taught him what his attitude must be. Gathered together were men who belonged to opposing political parties; side by side, discussing his work and his methods, stood bitter political foes; Whitney saw that if he was to achieve his purpose, he was obliged to be friendly with both sides. To become partisan would be fatal.

Whitney was a product of the New England world, a churchgoer and a substantial contributor to the New Brick Church in New Haven; if he was on friendly terms with the militant Timothy Dwight and other ministers, it is clear that he was content to take faith on faith. In 1801, when Dwight, president of Yale, jubilantly shook half his students into formal conversion, Benjamin Silliman was touched by the vibrant atmosphere: "Yale college is a little temple, prayer and praise seem to be the delight of the greater part of the students, while those who are unfeeling are awed into respectful silence." Whereas Whitney, engrossed in his nearby gun manufactory, packed the spiritual upheaval into a single sentence at the end of a letter to Stebbins: "You have doubtless heard of the N Haven Remonstrance if you have not I have no time to tell you." Silliman's letter is part of a life compounded of science and sermons, in equal parts; Whitney's reveals a man wholly absorbed in business.

To his family and friends, Whitney always used the words "business pressures" to explain his inattention to their demands, or as the excuse for his inability to visit. But whereas the pressures were constant, the composition of his business activities changed. Until the close of 1802, three themes dominated his time and energy: the cotton gin, muskets, and his restricted personal life. After 1802 new small, transient phrases, some indistinctly heard, some introduced suddenly and as suddenly lost, add richness and variety to the major themes.

His dealings with the War Department widened. Dearborn asked him to advise with Colonel Christian Senf about the government establishment to be installed at "Rocky Mount, S.C., on the Cataba River." He explained that he particularly wished him to "look for a convenient site for the water-works, at as little expense as possible, safety from freshets, the sites for the principal buildings, military stores, house for Superintendant, barracks for Workmen." Very little of this enterprise is clear; the few details that exist are found in the bill Whitney handed to the War Department: "My travelling expences from Raleigh to Rocky Mt—$26.50 [He was in Raleigh arranging the sale of his patent rights]; Expences while at Rocky Mt—$31.25; Chairmens Bill—$9.75; Expences in returning to Raleigh—$24.25; Hire 2 Horses & Chair, 36 days at $2.00 per day—$72.00; Hire of servant—$15.00; Whitney's compensation from Dec. 20, 1802 to Jan. 25, 1803, Inclusive, 36 Days at $3.00 per Day—$108.00." * Whether he ever went there again is doubtful. Mount Dearborn,

* Whitney seems only to have collected $50 against this bill.

as the establishment was called, was soon abandoned. In 1820, when South Carolina petitioned for permission to cut a canal through the lands belonging to the government, the buildings already had become quite dilapidated and had been "plundered of everything that could be taken away"; six years later the recently formed Ordnance Department had no record whether it had been originally designed for "an armory or an arsenal."

Dearborn's continued confidence is shown by his inquiry if Whitney would assume the position left vacant by "the death of Mr. Perkins, Superintendent of the Armoury at Harpersferry." Dearborn hoped, as his letter makes clear, to transplant Whitney's method to a national armory: "It may be convenient for you to transfer a considerable number of workmen now employed in your works, together with some part of the machinery and tools attached to your manufactory."

Whitney declined the position. In the early years of his contract, he might have accepted such an offer—it would have relieved him of worries while he carried out his grand purpose. When he received the letter, in January, 1807 (it was forwarded to him in Savannah) he had completed two-thirds of his contract, the sale of the patent rights to South Carolina had been reinstated, and Judge Johnson's decision—which he had just heard—had established the way for Miller & Whitney's collecting damages from Georgia trespassers. All this was implied when he told Dearborn that the superintendency "would not be disagreeable to my inclinations; but my present situation is such that I cannot discharge the Duties of that important office without a ruinous neglect of my private concerns." James Stubblefield was appointed Superintendent of the Harpers Ferry Armory, and in the following year he presented himself at Whitney's manufactory. The introduction he carried from Dearborn noted that he "waits on you by my desire, for the purpose of seeing your improved Machinery for Manufacturing Arms."

That October, 1807, Dearborn asked Whitney if he would manufacture four thousand horsemen's swords and four thousand artillery sabers with hilts and scabbards. Whitney in his reply tried to explain that it took time to get a factory tooled to make a specific article: "I should have no objection to enter into the contract proposed, provided sufficient time could be given to make those arrangements (as to materials and machinery). . . . In order to manufacture Swords & Sabers well, a regular & well systematized Manufactory of those articles would be indispensible—and to indemnify the expence of such an establishment, it should be carried on for several years. . . . A substitute for European skill must be sought in such an application of Mechanism as to give all that regularity, accuracy & finish to the Work which is there affected by a skill. . . . As to the price, it must depend on the model & the severity of the Proof to which the Blade is subjected. . . . I have no doubt of the practicability of manufacturing in this Country, Swords which would bear respectable comparison with the celebrated Blades of Toledo & Damascus, to which the Age of Chivalry & the less Advanced State of Science in those times has affixed so high a value." The horsemen's swords were to have a blade "two feet ten inches in length and about one inch and a half in width with suitable thickness . . . so tempered as neither to break nor bend, by a full stroke of a strong arm, and with such an edge as will cut bone without injury to the edge!"

And then, answering Dearborn's query about the method suggested by a Daniel Pettibone for making such swords, Whitney wrote: "Mr. Pettibone has been several times at my Manufactory in my absence. . . . I am informed by some of my principal workmen to whom he has communicated his process, that it contains nothing new or important. I have been in the constant habit of welding & working Cast Steel since 1793 & I cannot but entertain some doubts as to the preference to be given to Cast Steel as the most suitable material. . . . An apparatus sufficient & the number of Workmen requisite for manufacturing from 2000 to 3000 Swords pr. year would be an establishment upon as large a Scale as I should be willing to undertake, unless the exigencies of the Country required a great effort."

Whitney noted in his answer that he had intended going to Washington to see Dearborn—he had his own urgent reasons for wanting to talk to the Secretary of War. When he had visited with Dearborn on his way home from the South, it had been early spring; now it was November, and during the intervening months he had delivered fifteen hundred muskets; he had only an equal number left unfinished on his contract. He feared having his machines stand idle, having his pay roll continue—or, worse still, seeing his unused machinery deteriorate and being forced to let his workmen drift away into other employment. His anxiety prompted him to write to Major Hezekiah Rogers, a friendly official in the War Department. Whitney mentioned his wish to be at his factory when Dearborn visited New England, and inquired when Dearborn could be expected at New Haven. "Having been appointed by the Legislature of this State on a Committee to consider the Expediency of erecting a Bridge across the Connecticut River opposite the City of Hartford . . . I fear I may be absent when the Secy comes on. It would give me much satisfaction to shew him my manufactory & give him a fair Opportunity of seeing the manner in which his work is executed."

To Whitney it was very important to show the Secretary of War his establishment and explain the marvels wrought by his machinery. Now, now he must plan for the future! "I am now so far through with my present Contract that I wish soon to determine whether to continue the business of manufacturing muskets, after that is compleated, or not. I should prefer continuing the business provided I can do it on such terms as to make a reasonable profit. Indeed I would be satisfied with a *Moderate* profit—but I certainly will not continue the business without a prospect of making *something* by it. The interest upon the Capital which must necessarily be vested in the business will amount to at least one Dollar on each Ten & the insurance against fire is a serious *Item* in the calculation & one very proper to be taken into account." Whitney remembered how the loss of his own workshop by fire had added intolerably to the debts of Miller & Whitney; he had heard of the huge sums spent by the government to restore the loss suffered when the Springfield Armory burned in January of 1801.

At a time when expenses were estimated on the basis of labor costs plus the costs of the raw materials—with a dollar or so added on to cover all other items—he insisted on including interest on the invested capital and insurance charges as part of the cost of a musket. He was as much an innovator in his method of estimating costs as in his system of production.

The urgency of his need to do something when the contract was completed revealed itself in every detail he wrote to Major Rogers: "I am now thro' with more than half the various branches in compleating my present Contract—Three hands will compleat all the forging except the Barrels in Sixty Days from this time. I can manufacture other articles at my works to a much greater profit than to make muskets but the payments in return will not be as sure & regular which is an important consideration. . . . I would contract to deliver 2000 or 2500 pr year for seven or ten years."

In the summer of 1807 he was already apprehensive about keeping his manufactory in production; by April of the following year he was, with good cause, angry and distraught. Since January he had been in Washington, trying to interest congressmen to extend his patent rights; about the middle of April he was invited to present his arguments to the committee considering his case. During the same weeks he had been negotiating with Dearborn for a new contract. His efforts were futile. "The Patent Law is laid over till next session & I fear there is not much prospect of success then," he wrote to his brother Josiah, "& I have wholly relinquished the idea that it will be possible for me to make any contract with the present secretary of War."

It is possible that Dearborn tried to explain that the Administration had decided that the two national armories, each with an annual production of close to 10,000 muskets, could now handle the needs of the regular army and that it would be left to the individual states to supervise the arming of the entire militia. It is possible that Whitney, conscious only of his dependence on a government contract, could not accept such a change in policy; or it may be that Whitney would not accept the low price offered by the government. On April 23rd, 1808, the day after Whitney wrote so bitterly to his brother, Congress voted $200,000 for "the purpose of providing arms and military equipment for the whole body of the militia of the United States. . . . That all the arms procured in virtue of this act shall be transmitted to the several states composing this Union." How that sum would be spent, what agencies would be responsible for making contracts, were matters left to the separate states. Whitney left Washington conscious only of the double defeat he had suffered.

Whitney had predicated a business on government contracts and

government financing. Soon—and each delivery of five hundred muskets advanced the date—he would be without that solid foundation. The months that followed brought back the same unhappiness
that had held him tightly during the period before he started the
contract. He felt that Dearborn had betrayed him. "A number of
serious disappointments in matters of business together with my
long absences have so deranged my affairs that my utmost personal
& mental exersions have been inadequate. . . . I have for the last
Eight months been trifled with by certain persons whose elevated
station ought to have placed them above such conduct. I have been
held in a state of suspense & uncertainty which prevented making
general arrangements & I have been obliged to have recourse to
temporary expedients."

Again the hopeless mood was broken. The moneys voted by Congress were soon allocated. In October 1808 Whitney signed a contract to manufacture two thousand muskets for the State of New
York, with Wolcott acting as Whitney's loyal intermediary in dealing with Governor Daniel Tompkins. Whitney's relief at having secured this new customer was profound. Though he still had five
hundred muskets to deliver to the army, his new order provided,
as he reckoned it, a year's work, a slight morsel to feed a factory
accustomed to the steady diet of a large contract. For he remarked
to Major Rogers, who later approached him to make musket barrels for the Department of State, "As I have no extensive engagements on hand, I could undertake to furnish the number required . . .
within twelve months." Whitney made nothing for the State Department; to manufacture only musket barrels, "it would be necessary to
enlarge one branch or curtail the others—either alternative would
be attended with inconvenience."

At the end of May, 1810, he was still busy with the New York
State muskets, and he was still the victim of unforeseen delays. "Several of my workmen on whom I relied at the time I contracted . . .
have been enticed away to Springfield, a circumstance which together with my own ill health & the sickness of the man on whom
I depended to forge the Bayonets, has prevented my completing
the Contract sooner. The 2000 Muskets are nearly finished. . . .
My whole exersions, so far as my health would permit, have been

levoted to this undertaking, since I closed my Contract with the
J States." By November he had finished the entire lot and planned
o visit New York "for the purpose of receiving 5000 Dollars to
vhich I shall be intitled for the Muskets now inspecting & more
particularly for the purpose of closing a further Contract." Two
years later Whitney wrote his staunch friend Wolcott that "Gov. T
nay be assured that . . . although unavoidable disappointments will
prevent my delivering the arms at the precise times specified, I shall
pproximate nearer to strict punctuality than any other person he
ould engage to perform the same work in the U. States. I shall be
n NYork if my health will permit."

In addition to the New York State contracts, Whitney secured orders for smaller amounts from Connecticut. Two sheets from Whitney's ledger tell the amounts and dates of this transaction. The first
ontract must have been agreed to in February, 1810, for he re-
eived a cash advance on the 24th of that month. By May 11, 1811,
he had completed "700 Muskets for the use of the State of Connecticut, at 12.50 each as per Contract," and that very same month
he signed a second contract for an equal amount. He made final
delivery a year later, in May, 1812.

It was out of funds providing for the arming of the state militias
that Whitney kept his manufactory alive after his Federal contract
had expired. It is hard to name the article he might have made had
he failed to secure these orders for the manufactory which he had
reated out of his energy and genius.

In the fall of 1810, Whitney was seriously ill. For years he had
been driving himself mentally and physically; only a prolonged sickness could have forced him to yield. To Lemuel Kollock, a doctor
by training (a founder of the Georgia Medical Society), Whitney
gave the details of his illness: "I was attacked with so much severity
s to confine me to the house & with symptoms so alarming as wholly
o unman all my Resolution—& I intirely gave up the expectation
of being able either to travel or attend to any business this winter.
After a fortnight, however, I was in great measure relieved, flat-
ered myself that I should regain my health & resumed my inten-
ions of going to Georgia. But my intervals of convalescence have
ontinued only for short periods & I am now altogether unable to

travel. My face is at this time so much swolen that you would no
recognize it, but cramps in the stomach & breast are more painfu
& excite more apprehension."

Kollock had been an old friend of Miller's; after his death h
helped Catherine handle her affairs—the estate of General Green
was tightly snarled with that of Phineas Miller; she was an executri:
of both. Gradually, Kollock had relinquished most of his own ac
tivities to care for hers: "I have entered upon the business of as
sisting her all in my power." Whitney, reading the letters they wrote
him, may have considered how Catherine's never ending crises ha
absorbed the bright, kindhearted doctor. By 1810 he had become
her arm and her voice and her legs—writing the letters that de
manded to be written, speaking for her in the litigation which fille
her days, running her errands, and when she lay ill with fever, car
ing for her. Here was proof that Catherine knew how to bully thos
she loved.

Business pressures and his own ill health made for Whitney a
fortress behind which he could remain free and still her friend. Sh
accepted his apologies: "For indeed my beloved Mr. Whitney, you
interest is my interest—your health my health—your happiness m
happiness." He was forced to decline her repeated invitations t
visit, as well as her desperate appeals to help her settle a disput
or fight an enemy bent on ruining her. She might scold him for under
taking new ventures even as she implored him to take charge o
straightening out the tangles left her by old ventures. And thoug
she berated him for not writing, for not coming to see her, he wa
always conscious of her great goodness. Long ago he had warme
his hands at it and, reading a letter she had dispatched in haste, h
knew it was that ageless quality that made men happy to serve he
She had "picked up on the Road [between Charleston and Savannah
two little English Boys 10 and 13 years old they are, sons of a Black
smith who were coaxed away by expectations of picking up hat
full of gold in America. The Embargo induced the Captain to throv
them upon the world. I found them starving and brought them home
They are fine Boys and I think will be useful to you and themselve
if you will consent to take them. One of them can make a good ke
to any lock now, and both have great ambitions to excell in this mode

Point out the best and cheapest manner of Conveying them to you for you *Must take them.*"

Kollock's devotion to Catherine invited Whitney's friendship. He was glad of an opportunity to buy the doctor a "Watch Engine [which] exactly met my wishes," and exerted himself to secure for him "a pair of *Full Blooded Spanish Merino* Sheep . . . bought of Coln. David Humphrys at Humphry's ville in this State who did himself import the Stock direct from Spain. I have paid 150 dolls. for each of the Full Blooded & notwithstanding that this price may appear enormous for these dirty looking animals, I have been offered four hundred for the pair. . . . You may justly consider these Sheep as a very valuable acquisition there being no more to be had here at this time at any price; they will doubtless be higher next year as the demand is much greater than can be supplied." The "Merino enthusiasm," as Kollock called it, was then in full swing. After the Embargo the mills were forced to rely on domestic wool, and the price of wool jumped and kept mounting. Merino wool brought $2 a pound, and speculation in the sheep assumed fantastic proportions; $1,000 was considered a good price and a safe investment. War, and the continued absence of British woolens, kept the prices up; the bottom fell out when England flooded the American market with low-priced woolens. (Whitney had an amused, disdainful description of Miller & Whitney's agent, Russell Goodrich, who had "turned Shepherd—has a flock of Merinos about 50 miles from Augusta—dresses altogether in homespun—and is mighty near if not quite a democrat.")

In that decade of business worries and triumphs, Whitney received recognition as a man of science and a man of affairs. He was a charter member of the Connecticut Academy of Arts and Sciences, started in October, 1799, and was admitted to membership in the United States Military Philosophical Society. He was Justice of the Peace in Hamden, the village where his manufactory was located. As an outstanding "artist" in the mechanical arts, he was asked to help "Chauncey Whittlesey, Esqur. He has for some time been afflicted with a painful tooth-ach—I have taken the liberty to recommend him to you for relief in the last resort." Fame brought him an odd assortment of honors.

Despite the apprehension that is repeated—word, phrase, and mood, like a stencil—in Whitney's letters, their contents reflect his improved circumstances. After 1803, when the delivery schedule for muskets was arranged, his tone is calmer; after 1805, when he received the large sum from South Carolina for the sale of Miller & Whitney's patent rights, his business ventures widened. His new subsidiary interests centered largely around Oliver Wolcott. After Miller's death Wolcott became the man to whom Whitney was drawn both as friend and as businessman. Wolcott was careful, systematic, hard-working; his home had an elegance and brilliance that reminded Whitney of Mulberry Grove, where Catherine attracted distinguished visitors; his knowledge of banking practices and his connections in financial circles gave him a secure place in the world of trade and commerce; and his dry wit, reserved for those to whom he felt close, made his company delightful. "The Jacobinical affection in my bowels," he reassured his wife, "has been cured by small doses of rhubarb & drinking camomile tea." When he had held a high government office he had shown respect for Whitney's capacities and sympathy for his disappointments; shortly after he stepped out of public office he invited Whitney's friendly confidence—and business.

Oliver Wolcott & Company—organized in New York City in March, 1803—acted as fiscal agent, private banker, and investment broker. He had correspondents in the principal cities of the United States and connections with the great banking houses of London, Liverpool, Paris, and Amsterdam; he could handle the transfer of funds to his clients and for his clients. Through Wolcott's firm Whitney could receive the moneys due him from the South and pay the obligations he had out of town. Whitney turned to Wolcott when South Carolina deposited money to his credit in Charleston: "$15,000 is the sum which I wish transferred from thence to N. Y. I leave it to you to prescribe the most eligible mode." And when his money had arrived, Wolcott was instructed that "Ten thousand Dollars of the sum . . . is made subject to your order. I propose to vest it in the India concern, as I mentioned when I saw you last."

The pages in Wolcott's account books that detail Whitney's account (1805–1814) depict the kinds of transactions but not their extent. Wolcott was Whitney's financial agent; he was also his partner. They invested together in the China trade, importing teas and nankeens, and seem to have enjoyed immensely profitable returns. Their correspondence is equally inconclusive: it suggests a variety of business adventures, but as it is punctuated by "as I mentioned when I saw you last," or "I shall have the pleasure of seeing you as I intend to be in NYork within a few weeks," the revealing, critical details were cautiously reserved for personal talks.

"I have just returned from the scramble for the Stock of the Derby Bank," Whitney wrote to Wolcott in January, 1810; he had at his request subscribed for him. "Everyone is greatly disappointed in the amount of the Stock which he meant to have obtained." The rush to open banks was on. Two years later the Eagle Bank—Whitney had been one of those who petitioned the state to establish it—commenced subscriptions for its stock. "The crowd of subscribers was so great that the subscription did not close untill the afternoon of the following day. The amount subscribed is vastly beyond my expectations." In 1813 Whitney purchased forty shares of the New Haven Fire Insurance Co., paying $4,000. He was becoming a man of considerable property.

Mysterious allusions to "the Spanish Ship Anna Maria" drift in and out of letters during the summer of 1813. Whitney wrote Josiah that "the whole of the *Capital* & half the *property* and *profits* of this ship and cargo are mine. These circumstances, however, I will thank you not to mention—it will be well to hold up the Idea that no person in the U States has any interest in the property. I consider her safe arrival as a fortunate circumstance for me as I have a large stake in the concern of Wm. Wallace [the ship's captain] exclusive of this Ship and Cargo." The cargo was landed at Boston and passed through the customhouse. Josiah assured his brother that it would be "disposed of without loss of time." And then Josiah reminded Whitney that "I have never undertaken to transact any Business in Boston at a Less Commission than 2½ pr. Cent. . . . I consider the services of Mr. Sherman Entitled to One pr. Cent, consequently I shall make no charge for my attention, at the same time it should be understood that I cannot at any time hereafter undertake the Management of the Sales of any Goods at a Less Commission than 2½ pr.

Cent." A few days later the ship *Anna Maria* and her cargo disappeared from all letters, Josiah remarking, "I think best to defer the subject until I have a Verbal Conversation with you, which will occur by or before the 15th of Sept, say in 50 days because if you do not come to Westborough by that time I shall probably be at New Haven."

Josiah, five years younger than his brother, must have well considered the advice Whitney had given him when he became a commission merchant: "Let me advise you not to be over anxious to dive very largely into business at first. Take care to establish yourself on secure & solid foundations. A small Edifice founded on a *rock* is far preferable to a large Building placed on sand. The regular bred, experienced Merchant is cautious how he trusts his property in the hands of a young man who branches out largely & dashes away on his first going into trade." And now it was Josiah's turn to caution his brother "that Capt. William Wallace has in several Instances attempted too much. If he would have only one ship and keep with her all the time himself, I am of the Opinion the Nett Gain would be more. . . . At the same time he wants Experience to enable him to transact the Business of a Ship & Cargo in a Foreign Country or in this to the interest of the owners."

In investing money, as in politics and religion, Whitney remained rooted in the practices and attitudes of the community of which he was so much a part. His own hard-earned money went into the regular channels of trade and commerce: the purchase of stocks of banks, insurance companies, turnpike companies; in real estate, both residential and farm; in small local paper mills. There was nothing unusual in his staking young Captain William Wallace, a typical Yankee trader who tried to make a fortune out of nothing. Such men cut ice from New England ponds, packed it in sawdust, sailed around the world, and sold it to Indian princes who wanted to chill their drinks; or they dug up the root of the ginseng that grew wild along the eastern coast and traded it for teas and nankeens and silver pieces to the merchants of Hong Kong. Whitney's money was put out for profits on a particular venture, not for interest in industry.

To ask that Whitney should have expressed his genius in other fields is to expect the impossible; it is enough that within the limits of his talent he created boldly and surely. As soon as he went into manufacturing, he came face to face with the problems characteristic of modern industry—how to raise capital and how to figure costs, how to recruit and train workers, how to experiment and devise in order to operate most efficiently. From the very beginning he approached manufacturing in terms of new problems presented by new necessities; not in habitual practices and contemporary thinking. It is possible to place Whitney in a larger context—in the intellectual history of modern times—and see that his method extended into industry the rational approach that had marked social and scientific thinking.

When he was exploring this unknown territory of industrial methods, he was, as any explorer must be, alone. Miller, and then Wolcott, and his other friends and business associates, knew the many moods that beset him in the course of his task, but only Stebbins— "My dear Unforgotten and never to be forgotten friend"—was shown Whitney's portrait of himself. "You ask *how* I am & *where* I am. Do you remember that you & myself went one afternoon onto the mountain east of N Haven from which we saw a small house in the little valley to the westward—that often losing our way in descending the mountain & having many apprehensions that we should be benighted we crossed the small river at the foot of the Mountain & at last arrived at this *sd* little house in the valley where we in vain tried to obtain some refreshment. It is in the same *sd* little house that I now write to you & do enjoy a tolerable share of health. . . . Now if you would know *what* I am—I must tell you that I am an Old Bachelor, overwhelmed in business, constantly forming resolution to curtail my business concerns & like other fools, as constantly plunging deeper into scheams of business; constantly resolved to marry without allowing myself leasure to take one step towards carrying that resolution into effect."

XVII

The Feud with Irvine

O N June 18, 1812, the United States declared war on Great Britain. Eleven days later Whitney wrote to the Secretary of War, describing himself as one with "twelve years' attention to the subject of Manufacturing Fire Arms"; he spoke with the assurance of one who believed "himself to have possessed greater advantages for obtaining information on this subject than any other individual in the United States." Whitney remembered the political fevers that had prevailed at the time he secured his first contract. Now a state of war existed; the country was brutally unprepared; it was an auspicious moment to suggest that the government give him a second contract. To that end his "Remarks" were directed. For all their seeming discursiveness, they were pointed and convincing.

For the benefit—and education—of the Secretary of War, he examined the situation in Great Britain, where, about 1796, the government "raised the price of arms and engaged all the workmen in the kingdom to deliver to the government *all* they could make in 14 years—and about the same time they imported into England 50,000 muskets from Germany. Since that period the term has been extended . . . and a premium is constantly offered by the Government to any subject who will leave the occupation to which he was bred and work at certain branches of this manufacture. So great is the difficulty in fabricating good muskets Locks, that even in G. Britain where there are the greatest number of workmen whose occupation is most nearly connected with this branch, the Govt. find it impossible to extend the manufacture to meet their demands.

Twelve months ago the British Govt. had on hand 200,000 Musket Barrels which could not be made up for want of Locks, etc."

In the United States his great objective had been "to substitute correct & effective opperations of machinery for that skill of the Artist . . . which is not possessed in this country to any considerable extent." Muskets could not be made "in this country without the aid of a variety of heavy and expensive machinery, moved by water. As waterworks are expensive and soon go to decay, the machinery should be so proportioned and the extent of each establishment such, as to keep *all* the machinery constantly employed. Any attempt to carry on such a Manufactory without a solid, fixed and sufficient Capital must be abortive. The amount of the capital must be at least equal to double the value of the Arms delivered in one year [in modern terms, Whitney turned his capital over once every two years]—and this amount will not be sufficient unless the finished work be turned in & payment for the same recd. every ninety days [in order to supply the current funds to meet pay rolls and purchases]. The establishment of such a Manufactory is . . . a progressive opperation—& can in no case be accomplished in less than two years— and should be continued at least twenty years to warrant such an investment of capital."

Whitney asserted that his was now "the most respectable private establishment in the United States for carrying on this important branch of business . . . and he feels himself warranted by his own experience and success in believing that the *New Methods* which he has invented . . . are practically useful & highly important to his country. He would further state that the principal part of his property is vested in Buildings, Machinery etc . . . which cannot be converted to other use without a great sacrafice & he therefore wishes to continue in the business—and begs leave respectfully to submit . . . whether it be for the interest of the United States to give him employment for such length of time & upon such terms as to afford a fair prospect of a reasonable profit for his labour."

Whitney's second contract was for fifteen thousand muskets. It was signed on July 18, 1812, with the Secretary of War, William Eustis. Deliveries were to start "on or before the first of May 1813," and were to be made thereafter at a yearly rate of not more than three thousand, nor less than fifteen hundred; the whole amount to be delivered before the end of 1820. "The said Muskets shall be . . . in all respects conformable to the models of the musket which the said Whitney hath heretofore manufactured for the State of New York—excepting only as to the length of the Barrels, which shall be Forty inches in length." His advances and payments generally followed that of the previous contract. Whitney and Oliver Wolcott signed the $30,000 bond required by the government and had no difficulty in finding sureties to underwrite the "faithful performance" of the contract.

Whitney considered the contract most favorable. The government had accepted the same model he was then making for New York State. (He further obligated himself that very October to manufacture an additional two thousand for Governor Tompkins.) This meant there would be no long preparation, no retooling of the factory, no unsolved problems to delay the actual manufacturing. Because he was in full production, he stipulated that the first five hundred guns would be finished by the following May. The price of the musket—$13—was the same as he was receiving from New York and Connecticut—not the unreasonable price of $10.75, a figure set in 1809 and 1810, for contracts let out for 85,000 stands of arms. Nothing in the terms of his contract gave him cause for apprehension.

He expressed concern over a very different matter: that young Eli Blake pass his examinations to enter Yale, come properly introduced "relative to your character and qualifications," and be adequately provided with clothing. "Your Uncle Josiah will furnish you, on my acct. with as much money as will be necessary to pay off your Bills and expences & bring you on here." And when his nephew was finally "located to my satisfaction," his greatest worry was to get quick delivery on a quantity of emery. He wrote Josiah to make certain that "it should be forwarded as soon as possible as the winter will soon set in and . . . besides, it may be *captured* on its passage and the *want* of it will be ten times more than the *worth* of it. . . . I am, at this moment, subjected to much inconvenience for the want of the *Emery* & it is of serious importance to me that I should receive it within ten days."

The autumn months passed peacefully by. To Whitney the war

was remote, the conditions it imposed hardly differing from those of the disturbed peace that had preceded it. The tight blockade that Great Britain enforced came to him faintly, indirectly, as an echo. "The British armed forces in the Sound who have made some slight attacks on the coast of this State has excited some alarm here & thrown me into some embarrassment relative to getting on some material for my manufactory from Pennsylvania."

More immediate than the war, infinitely more disquieting than the British frigates, was a warning he received. The master armorer at the Springfield Armory "called at my works & told me that Coln. [at the time only Captain] Irvine was very sorry to hear that I had got a contract, because he and Mr. Wickham * intended to introduce a New Model for the Musket." The war itself was, for Whitney, overshadowed by the campaign directed against him by Callender Irvine.

On August 8, 1812, Captain Callender Irvine, who had served as Superintendent of Military Stores, was named Commissary General of Purchases. His office replaced that of Purveyor of Public Supplies, a position that for nine years had been filled by Tench Coxe. It may well be that Coxe was one of Irvine's victims. There was a plan already set in motion when, the previous January, Coxe, as Purveyor, asked Irvine, then Superintendent of Military Stores, for specific information requested by the Secretary of War. Irvine bypassed Coxe, communicating directly with the Secretary. This deliberately hostile tactic made Coxe protest to Eustis (how prescient he was!), "The tendency of such things, which have been stated in his conduct as Inspector, if allowed, will, in my humble opinion, retard, disorder & injure the service." Eustis's inquiry had concerned some Whitney muskets that a field officer had reported to be defective: "3 ramrods and 2 locks broke in manual drill . . . and a bayonet used to strike a man on the cheek, did not damage the skin but bent the bayonet almost perpendicular!"

Tracing back into the records of these guns, Coxe found they were contracted for in 1798, before his tenure, inspected by an office other

* Marine T. Wickham was employed at the Philadelphia Laboratory of the War Department. He designed a new gun in 1812. According to Major Hicks, its "only important innovation was fixing the bayonet to the barrel by means of a screw."

than his, and that the inspector had since been removed from his position. Examination convinced him that "tho there is much good work, the . . . faults in the necks of the bayonet and ramrods are very bad facts." Somewhat prophetically he remarked that the whole episode "will show that a contracting officer, like the Secy of War, may have his designs frustrated as well as a Purveyor. Patterns & Inspectors are of infinite consequence."

When Irvine took over the contracts Coxe had made with nineteen small-arms manufacturers during 1809 and 1810, he found but little more than a third of the 85,000 muskets had been delivered and that rising costs made it unlikely that more would be finished at the stipulated price. In January, 1813, General John Armstrong replaced William Eustis as Secretary of War; the new Secretary relied heavily on his subordinate officers.

Whitney knew nothing of the Coxe-Irvine struggle, and his relations with the arms inspectors had heretofore been pleasant; but he had reason to fear trouble when, in March, 1813, he received a routine notice from Armstrong advising him that "a copy of the contract and bond will be forwarded to Callender Irvine, Commissary General of Purchases, at Philadelphia, with whom you will in future correspond." The warning Whitney had received had been a friendly act, truthfully reported; but it was too limited, for Irvine's plans extended much further than Whitney.

In the light of subsequent fast-moving events, Irvine's ultimate goal becomes very clear: he wanted control over the allocation of funds, supervision of the musket models and their manufacture, and direction of personnel so that the Wickham model, in which Irvine had a stake, might replace all others. To this end he decided to eliminate the private contractors and extend the public armories in size and number. But first he had to undermine the Ordnance Office or make it subservient to his authority. His first success had been to obliterate the office of Purveyorship—and Coxe with it. The Ordnance Department, of which Colonel Decius Wadsworth had been made chief (July 2, 1812) was his next target. He did not attack Wadsworth directly; but by attacking the quality of the muskets made at the Springfield Armory Irvine intended to make him appear incompetent and frighten Wadsworth into submission, or at least into passive acquiescence. Retracing his machinations step by step, reading the interoffice memoranda of that distant time, one becomes uncomfortably aware of the presence of a boa constrictor— the swift lasso of the powerful coils, the gentle, quiet, fatal squeeze, and the final mighty swallow of the broken, still-warm body. It is not a pretty sight. And reading thus, one feels a rush of relief when an intended victim suddenly becomes alert to the deadly danger.

On March 12th Wadsworth answered a report made by Irvine on the bad results shown when the musket barrels at the Springfield Armory were proved. "It is well known that charges [of powder] may be increased so as to burst any barrel," he wrote to Armstrong, "the deficiencies attempted to be shown tend rather to show the insufficiency of the established proof than to reflect on the character of the superintendent, whose duty it is to cause the barrels to be proved agreeably to the instructions received from his superiors." And then Wadsworth protested the animus that Irvine, through his inspector, seemed to have betrayed for the Superintendent, and indirectly, toward him: "It must be impolitic, I humbly conceive, to empower persons to overhaul, criticise, and censure work executed there [Springfield Armory], who have before been in subordinate stations at that armory, or others who are strongly suspected and accused of entertaining sentiments hostile to that establishment and its superior officers. Such a proceeding must have the effect of producing irritations." In another communication (the same day), he explicitly stated that a "pattern" offered by Irvine was badly designed—the "fixing of the bayonet was particularly objectionable."

But Wadsworth had been very disturbed by Irvine's manner and method. Writing Whitney, the next day, about some special equipment, he added a postscript: "Great complaints are made relative to the Springfield Arms, please let me know your real opinion of the Quality."

In April, Irvine began harassing the small-arms manufacturers who had taken contracts in 1809 and 1810. He was very shrewd in the way he explained the situation to Armstrong. "These contracts were founded on imperfect Muskets as standards and at prices for which it is impossible to have made good muskets. So that if the contracts are complied with strictly . . . the Govt. will be saddled with so many defective arms of which there are enough already in store . . . furnished under contracts made with & under the *eye* of Tench Coxe. . . . What cost the Govt about 60,000$, not one arm of the whole is fit for service, or worth one cent but what they may bring as old iron or brass at auction." When one of the contractors, Joseph Henry, of Bethlehem, Pennsylvania, objected to Irvine's highhanded procedure, Irvine, in forwarding the manufacturer's letter to the Secretary of War, sent it with one of his own—he presented the case in the terms he desired Armstrong to see it.

"I have proposed to all contractors as they complain of having a hard bargain, that they may pay up the advance money or deliver as many arms as will be equal to the advance and the contracts shall be rendered void. Some have acceded. . . . Others have refused. . . . It is to me clear that some of these gentry did not in the beginning expect to comply with their engagements, nor do they now intend it. Their first consideration was to get possession of the public money, and their desire is to retain it as long as practicable. Many of them were unacquainted with the manufacturing of arms— expended the whole advance money in the erection of buildings & machinery. . . .

"We cannot rely upon Contractors for a supply of arms. These private contracts are exceptionable in many ways & every respect. Better to increase the number of our public establishments & the number of hands at those already in operation & bring the whole under the superintendence of one judicious & independent man." There: it was out. This was Irvine's goal, and he himself was the "judicious & independent man." Yet his argument was disarmingly impersonal; it was on a lofty, patriotic, and managerial plane: "It will be safer for the Govt. to expend two or three hundred thousand dollars on building armories than to advance so much money to individuals who will expend it in erecting buildings & machinery for themselves and disappoint the Govt. as to a supply of arms confidently calculated to be received within the period specified in their contracts." It is impossible to say whether Irvine did not know the genesis of the private contractors or whether he deliberately obscured it. In seeking to promote the musket model he and Wickham had made, he showed himself indifferent and callous to Whitney's influence in the public armories. Not once, in all his memoranda to Armstrong about Whitney, did he mention that the superintendents of both armories had been directed to visit Whitney's manufactory in order to copy tools and observe methods, to learn from him, to incorporate his newest improvements in their work.

Instead, by the end of June, Irvine was ready to go after Whitney. His belligerence sounds bugle-sharp when he notifies the Secretary: "Mr. Eli Whitney . . . has not delivered a single musket, tho' he should have delivered on or before the 1st of May last, at least 500 muskets. [At that writing Whitney was seven weeks late on his delivery.] When the engagements of these contractors are not complied with as to time, I recommend that the contracts shall be cancelled. I have written today to Mr. Whitney stating that I have a general authority of that kind & that I will most assuredly exercise it. The Govt. has been trifled with long enough, in all conscience, by these contractors." On receipt of his letter, Whitney knew that Irvine was determined to use his power to ruin him. He went to Philadelphia. He wanted to talk to Irvine, to assess him. At that meeting they agreed—so Whitney thought—that when Whitney sent a musket from the lot being made for New York State to Irvine he would immediately receive "the further advance of five thousand Dollars mentioned in my contract." By November he was writing to Irvine, "You will easily imagine that after a delay of a Month, I am greatly surprised and disappointed at receiving the contents of your letter instead of the promised remittance."

The letter Irvine wrote—October 26th—was concentrated venom. It itemized the shortcomings of Whitney's musket: "The bayonet is 2 inches too short . . . the lower part of the butt is too long . . . the barrel is very crooked, and the britch is not water tight . . . the main spring is very indifferent, and the toe of the hammer too sharp—otherwise the lock is not to be complained of. . . . These defects must be remedied, or the Muskets will not be received or paid for by me."

Whitney separated the insults from the threats and answered both. He reminded Irvine that Eustis, with whom he had contracted, had selected that particular model, though Whitney had offered him the choice of "any he had seen elsewhere. On the Model, workmanship and Dimensions (with one single exception) of those Muskets, my present contract with the U States is predicated. . . . From this standard I consider myself as having no right to deviate without the consent of the Government, & I humbly conceive that the Government have no right to require a deviation without my consent." His premise stated, Whitney discussed the defects Irvine had enumerated. His tone was patient, his analysis painstaking: " 'The Bayonet is 2 inches too short.' The opinions of Mankind are very various as to what is the most proper length for a Bayonet. Agreeable to the Standard length of a French Bayonet, which is about 14 inches, the Bayonet in question is too long. Some have supposed that a Bayonet ought to be *thirty inches* long. And several thousands have been made of that length. . . . There is almost as great a variety of opinions on this subject as there can be variety of lengths between 14 and 30 inches." Point by point, conscientiously and fully—was he also pointing up the fool?—Whitney answered Irvine's criticisms.

He was not to be intimidated by threats. "As I understand it, if I will make such alterations in the Model and consequently in the Contract as you may please to direct, the contract will, in that case, be fulfilled on the part of the United States and not otherwise. . . . I am willing to make alterations in the contract, provided I receive a suitable remuneration therefor: but I think it should be done by *Agreement* and not by Order. . . . If you suppose the U States can, at any price, obtain a supply of Muskets, all of which shall be made with the same punctillious exactness which appertains to the Model which has lately been constructed under the direction of Mr. Wickham, you are certainly deceived. It is on that Model, I presume, that your ideas are formed. And I will venture to assert that there never has been a Musket made on that Model . . . which did not cost more than *forty* dollars." He reminded Irvine that the failure to send the remittance promised him "must occasion a serious embarrassment to a person who has fifty people employed." The boa constrictor and the lion had met; Whitney's reputation, his strong conviction in his own achievements, his unequaled knowledge of mechanics and manufacturing, stripped Irvine of everything save his hostility—and his great power.

It would not be easy to defeat such an enemy, and the struggle became doubly painful because Whitney was sick. "My health has been bad for the last three weeks past," he wrote to Catherine Miller on November 20th, "& I am sorry that it is not in my power to say it is mending." (Previously, Josiah had sternly counseled his brother about his attacks of ill health: "Your complaint I think is Rheumatism and if it is not soon removed will become *nervous*, and a nervous Rheumatism, is the mother of the most dangerous disseases.") Another letter from Irvine—it contributed little toward easing his physical distress—expressed Irvine's version of the agreement they had reached: "I requested that a Musket . . . be forwarded to this office, that I might be satisfied with the sufficiency of those making by you for the US or, if found defective, for the purpose of suggesting any alterations not attended with much expence. . . . I did not point out the exceptions to your musket with a view to consult your opinion, which would have been improper for two very obvious reasons. First you are not a practical Gun Smith, as I have been informed, and again, you are too deeply interested in the matter. Therefore your opinions and Criticism . . . have little weight in my mind.

"I have neither the leisure or time to spare for an Epistolary controversy with you or any other man. Your contract with Govt was transmitted to me. . . . You have said that Govt has no right to ask or expect an deviation on your part from the letter of that contract. This being admitted to the fullest extent I have to reply to it. That Govt had a right to expect and will insist upon a compliance in every respect with the terms of your contract. . . . You have failed to execute your engagements. . . . It is therefore my duty to require of you to refund promptly, the money with interest, which has been advanced you by the United States, which I now do."

Irvine had made a sad blunder in estimating that the carefully dressed, elegantly spoken gentleman who had called on him could not possibly be a "practical Gun Smith." On this point Whitney undeceived him: "I can, with my own hands, in the first place make my tools and then from the raw materials make a musket with as much precision, exactness, and finished workmanship as belongs to any Musket which I have ever seen—and I have seen and examined with attention the muskets made both in this Country and the principal Countries of Europe. I have had more practical experience in

Musket making than any other man in America. . . . I did not undertake the manufacture of Arms, relying on the skill and experience of any man or number of men I might employ. All my workmen without an exception, were . . . and have always been almost wholly of my own instructing. I am indebted to no man for planning or executing any part of my Machinery. I have always directed in person the intire detail of the business both as to the forms and modes of working. The more difficult branches I have executed myself. After having pursued the business for fifteen years . . . my ignorance of the subject should be ascribed to a want of capacity rather than a want of experience!"

After this proud statement of his mechanical qualifications, Whitney pointed out his legal rights. He noted it "to be a clear principle that the nonfulfillment of a particular item of a contract does not vitiate the contract itself"; he advised Irvine (Whitney had consulted his lawyer, Baldwin, and his other well informed New Haven friends) that "I cannot comprehend how one party can have a *right* to *revoke* the contract, which does not equally appertain to the other party."

Once before, Whitney had had to fight to maintain his rights in a contract—to collect moneys lawfully due him—once before he had marshaled facts and courage and won; he would teach Irvine that, if he could have triumphed over the hostility of the southern planters, he would not take defeat now without a determined struggle.

Did Irvine suddenly sense the stature of the man whom he was trying to discredit? There is a wry acknowledgment of the position into which he had maneuvered himself when he summarized the situation for Armstrong and, indirectly, asked the Secretary for help: "Whitney's contract is vague on its terms, very advantageous to himself and the reverse to the Govt. . . . The best musket he could select, is exceedingly exceptionable. . . . He has not complied with his engagements as to time. . . . I have accordingly told him that I consider his contract at an end. He is in high dudgeon and we are at loggerheads; this I don't regard a straw. He has imposed on the Govt. and people long enough. I have informed him we do not want any more apologies for arms, having plenty such already."

As 1813 came to an end, Great Britain was able to take the war with the United States more seriously. When they had defeated Napoleon and forced his abdication, the British could spare troops to send to America. Immediately they prepared to intensify the war. None of this seems to have made the slightest impression on Irvine, sitting in his Commissary's Office in Philadelphia, intent on his own private war against Eli Whitney, whose factory in New Haven was making arms for the United States Army.

For several months everything was quiet on the surface. Irvine delayed doing anything while he tried to have Congress pass a law placing the public armories and private contractors under a single superintendent. Wadsworth warned Whitney of this: "A few experiments in relation to small arms as bold as have been made of late in the Organization and Discipline of our Armies, will give the finishing stroke to our Military Character." The bill was lost in the Senate—Senator David Daggett, one of the men who had signed his name to Whitney's original bond, had spoken against its passage. The winter months passed. When Whitney asked that an inspector be sent to examine the muskets, Irvine did not answer; he had taken his stand that Whitney had failed to deliver as he had agreed to in his contract.

Finally, Whitney took measure to force acceptance of the finished guns. In May he went to Washington and carried letters of praise and recommendation from Wolcott and Governor Tompkins of New York—both these men could speak personally of contracts undertaken and satisfaction given. On the 18th he addressed himself to Armstrong: "Immediately after entering into his present existing Contract with the U. States . . . he proceeded to erect, in addition to those which he had before in operation, two new sets of water-works, one at Salisbury and the other at Haddam, for forging the Barrels; but that owing to the severity of the succeeding winter, these Establishments did not get into effective operation as soon as was expected. In the mean time he was successfully employed in . . . laying in an ample supply of materials & going on with the other branches of the work. He has now on hand nearly a thousand finished muskets and the principal parts of from two to three thousand more in great forwardness." Since all this was done "solely for the purpose of supplying Arms to the Government," breaking the

contract "will subject the Subscriber to great losses and a total de-
rangement of his affairs"; he respectfully solicited the Secretary of
War "to make such dispositions and give such directions, as shall
enable him to proceed in the regular execution of his contract."

Whitney had come to Washington a few days too late. Irvine had
succeeded in convincing the Secretary of War that the proper course
was to request the Comptroller of Public Accounts "to report the
state of Mr. Whitney's accounts . . . to the end that a suit may be
brought against him for non-fulfillment." It was not to find such a
decision that Whitney had come all the way to Washington. For
six weeks he stayed on, intent on undoing what Irvine had committed Armstrong to do. He went from the Secretary of War's office to the Secretary of State's; and James Monroe, who remembered
how Jefferson had commended his genius, laid the matter before
President Madison, "with both of whom I had several interviews."
In the end he got the answer for which he had been looking: "The
Secty of War paid me the 5000 Dollars due me and directed Irvine
to send on a man to inspect the muskets—1000 of which were due for
delivery."

Poor Armstrong! His was the unenviable position of the commanding citadel for which opposing armies battle to capture and control.
Shaken in his trust in Irvine, his Commissary General, he solicited
an opinion of Whitney from Wadsworth, Chief of Ordnance. Wadsworth, in a long, scholarly argument, reassured Armstrong. "I think
his arms as good, if not superior, to those which have in general
been made anywhere else in the United States." He reminded the
Secretary that since the first contracts were given out "more men
have failed in consequence of abortive efforts to manufacture arms,
in proportion to the number engaged, than in any other branch of
manufacture attempted in this country. The business is not yet so
firmly established as to endure the incision-knife and caustic in cur-
ing its defects. Tampering and trying experiments with it will be
premature and hazardous until it takes firmer roots."

Every consideration—national security, contractual obligations,
technical factors, an established official leniency toward delivery
schedules, official regulations, the policy of encouraging domestic
manufactures—everything was on Whitney's side. Irvine had only

his vindictiveness and his need for vindication; he decided to bow to the storm so that he might still hold tenaciously to his position and purpose. When Armstrong ordered him to "let Whitney go on with his contract," Irvine snapped to attention, agreed with the order, and then, acting as if the change in policy had changed the situation, he stubbornly, monotonously repeated his old conclusions: "I would recommend that Whitney's Contract be rendered void. If not, please to inform & I will do the best I can!"

"The best I can": the words sounded ominously like a promise Irvine was making to himself to find some way to bring Whitney to terms. Coxe had said, "Patterns & Inspectors are of infinite consequence," and both sides knew the truth behind those words. Whitney, as well as Irvine, appreciated that the Secretary's decision had determined nothing but policy and that the policy could be circumvented and negated even as it was seemingly obeyed. Whitney, on his part, had learned from the sale of the gin rights to South Carolina that a sale was not a sale until one had received the cash. Until his moneys had been paid him, anything, at any stage, was possible.

Foreseeing that the proof and inspection would be the weapon used against him, Whitney asked Wadsworth what official regulations governed these steps. "The one regulation in the United States, bearing the Stamp of Authority, relating to the mode of proving Musket barrels," Wadsworth answered his query, was that "promulgated by the Secretary of War about the year 1798 and was literally translated from the French, the only difference being that which subsists between the avoirdupois & the French weights." He discussed minutely the quantity and potency of different powder charges, and added: "Within a past few years, I understand, there has been a deviation . . . which consists in *substituting the British proof charge of powder for Musket barrels in lieu of that prescribed by the regulation of 1798. . . .* This alteration I have not been able to trace to any competent authority. It . . . has probably taken place on the suggestion of some of the Inspectors, who have been employed in examining the Arms fabricated . . . on Contract. It has not been yet received at the Springfield Armory, where they still adhere to the regulation of 1798." In order to get outside the area governed by the Springfield Armory standards, Irvine suggested to the War Department that Whitney send his muskets to New York for inspection and proof. But on the point that the inspection was to be done at his manufactory, Whitney's contract was specific.

The careful preparations, the strategy and counterstrategy, are eloquent of the high stakes involved. Irvine was intent on removing the one person who stood between him and his ambition; Whitney was determined to save his manufactory—the child of his brain and hands, his sweat, his lonely purpose, his long years of concentrated effort. Both had pride; each wanted to maintain his preeminence in his own special world. The whole violent action, so tightly compressed, was like an explosion; it occurred during a few torrid days in August, 1814.

Irvine was not actually present. He was represented by Wickham and another inspector, H. H. Perkin. Both men—by word and letter—were advised of the special nature of the assignment: Wickham was told to take "powder with you of approved strength" (the strength of the powder used had not been standardized and varied considerably); and Perkin, warned that Irvine expected difficulty with Whitney, was directed to support Wickham, who would "give you my ideas generally in relation to Mr. Whitney's Contract, manner of inspection, &c." In addition, Irvine deliberately delayed a full month before sending the inspectors to New Haven. Did he hope thus to harass and infuriate Whitney to the point where he would throw up his contract?

The sound of the explosion can still be heard. "Wickham came here the evening before the last," Whitney wrote to Wadsworth on August 13th, the handwriting betraying the fury that still shook him, "apparently under the strong bias of prejudice & passion—he has left this place this morning still more under the influence of passion than when he came without doing anything. My embarrassment is very great—I have not time to write you in detail. . . . If you can prevail upon the Secretary to fix upon a fair proper and uniform mode of proving musket Barrels, you will render the public a great service & relieve me and many others from the most vexatious and ruinous embarrassment. . . . Immediate and great exersions will be made to induce the Secretary of War to establish the proof [greater than that prescribed by the regulations] which has improperly been presented by subordinate officers of the Govt. No time should be lost in your application. I wish for nothing but that which is fair and proper."

After agitated conferences with his attorney, Baldwin, Whitney wrote Wickham (though they were in the same house, Whitney, on Baldwin's advice, communicated only in writing), "I now again Repeat the tender of 1000 muskets to you for your inspection and delivery, agreeable to the terms of my contract . . . and hereby give you notice that if they are not now received, they will be hereafter, at the risque of the United States and that if they are destroyed by the enemy or fire, the loss must be theirs." Wickham's reply, sent back immediately, fills the scene that had taken place with the sound of cold fury: "I can only repeat to you what I have frequently done since my arrival." He insisted he would "make use of the Harpers Ferry proof charge, which are made use of at their Armory, at Phila also . . . with the exception of the Springfield Armory." He protested against the number of barrels "which you tendered on Saturday for proof in the presence of Judge Balding [Baldwin] and Mr. Bishop" because "you acknowledged to me this morning that they were not ready for proof. I propose leaving town at 2 oclock provided you will not agree to my propositions." He left at "a Quarter past two without receiving Mr. Whitney's reply."

What happened can be seen through the eyes of both men. Whitney wrote his version to Secretary of War Armstrong, and Wickham sent in a report, with his opinion of what would be the outcome, to Irvine. ("Were I compelled to inspect, pass & certify muskets agreeable to Mr. Whitney's construction of the contract, the U States had much better save the trouble and expence of an inspection by Taking Mr. W word for the quality &c of the arms.") The letters, long and detailed, continued the struggle and brought it right back to Armstrong. No longer was he called on to determine policy; now he had to provide ways to make certain his policy was carried out.

Whitney's letter of August 17th is less a letter than a brief. He told the Secretary that he asked Wickham the "Principles & Rules by which he proposed to be governed in the proof and inspection of the arms— He appeared to be averse to a free communication. I will state the leading views of Mr. Wickham so far as I understand them: with my objections thereto." And he summarized their differences: the strength of the proof charges, the variations in the caliber, and the responsibility for the cost of proof and inspection. Such technical disagreements were bad, but far worse was that Wickham, "as he himself acknowledges, received *instructions* by which his decisions . . . are to be regulated, and from which he feels himself bound not to make the least deviation; which instructions he refuses to submit to my inspection. . . . I can never while I retain my senses, under any circumstances, consent to be bound by an instrument, to which I am not a party—which I have never seen—and which I must never be permitted to see."

Whitney did not linger over the legal and technical aspects of their differences—such matters were for experts to discuss and resolve. He desired to make it very clear to Armstrong that he would not tolerate the climate created by Irvine and that behind his talk of methods to prove and inspect muskets Irvine was waging a nasty, unprincipled fight against Whitney personally. He repeated conversations with Wickham to illustrate the unfair treatment they had prepared for him. "I proposed the following case. Suppose we procure from the State of N.York a Box of the same identical Muskets refered to in the Contract, and I present you an equal number of Muskets precisely similar in form and quality, will you accept them? No, said he, unless they correspond with my ideas of what a musket ought to be. I then enquired of him whether . . . a musket might be made which would cost the maker from 25 to 40 dollars, and still that musket be conformable. . . . 'Yes,' said he, 'from 50 to 100 dollars' and remarked 'that muskets might be made at all prices from *five* dollars to *one hundred* Dollars each & all of them be exactly conformable in all respects to the model . . . made for the State of N York. From such a construction, it results that I have undertaken for a definite sum to perform a thing which is altogether indefinite, and am wholly at the mercy of the person who may be sent to receive the arms. . . . You will readily perceive the impossibility of my doing business with men under such circumstances and entertaining such views.

"It is reported here that the enemy have declared 'they will destroy my Manufactory let it cost what it will.' Whether such a declaration has actually been made or not, I consider the danger very serious and am, on that account, extremely anxious that the arms should be removed; tho I consider the 1000 Muskets ready for delivery now at the risque of the U States. They are well made and such as I contracted to make. . . . I hope you will think proper immediately to appoint some competent and unbiased person to receive the Muskets."

To Wadsworth, with whom he was joined not only in friendship but in common defense against Irvine, Whitney repeated the substance of his letter to Armstrong and spoke openly of his antipathy and fear. "This man Wickham seems to have set himself up as a Supreme Dictator as to everything relating to the Manufacture of Arms. As to Irvine, I consider him the mere mouthpiece of Wickham. . . . They have already ruined every private manufactory in the U States except mine by their impositions and exactions. . . . If I will submit implicitly to his dictations and promise never to dispute his authority in the future, he will proceed to inspect the Muskets & not otherwise. If I do not submit ruin is inevitable. My situation is truly embarrassing." This evaluation of the roles of Wickham and Irvine may well have been valid; or it might have reflected Whitney's growing fear at the power and determination shown by his enemies, his clash with Wickham having a more sinister expression than his earlier unpleasant encounter with Irvine. As when with Miller he had fought a conspiracy of the southern planters, so now (with Wadsworth's help) he struck out against this new conspiracy. For the second time Whitney battled to save for himself the fruits of his genius.

Four days later Whitney again wrote to Armstrong. Day after day the same situation persisted: the manufactory, geared to high production, was turning out musket barrels. He wanted to make it very clear that inspection fitted into the production schedule itself. "Musket Barrels are bored to the proper caliber—cut to the given length—ground so as not to exceed a given weight—breeched—and in that state, it is the universal practice, to prove them. Great inconvenience would result from proving them in any of the subsequent stages of their manufacture." Irvine knew this, and yet—what better instance could Whitney give of Irvine's outrageous, highhanded behavior?—almost ten months had passed since Whitney had notified him "that I should shortly have a number of Barrels ready for the proof—and requested him to inform me who would perform that service. To this request he has never thought proper to make any reply. After waiting some weeks for his answer, it became necessary that I should either discharge my workmen and stop the Manufactory, or adopt some method of proving the Barrels. As the former alternative would amount to an entire breaking up of the Manufactory, I adopted the latter.

"The Barrels of the 1000 Muskets which I have now ready for delivery, have all been proved by James Carrington Esq, who was specially appointed by the Secretary of War to prove the greatest part of the 10,000 Muskets which I formerly manufactured for the U States. . . . It is true that Mr. Carrington has not been specially appointed to prove the barrels made for my present contract— and therefore I do *not object* to the Barrels being proved over again, but as it was not my fault that the barrels were not proved at the proper time, I do object to my being subjected to the extra expence of proving the barrels over again, now the guns are finished. This extra expence will be at least $500 upon 1000 muskets."

The struggle was not over; rather it was getting worse, since, daily, the manufactory was finishing barrels that would need proving. And so Whitney ended his letter, not to report what had occurred but to remind Armstrong that this would be, until cured, a chronic condition. "I have several hundred Barrels in a proper state to be proved and the embarrassment arising from there not being some person, residing near the Manufactory, appointed to prove them, from time to time as they are prepared for that operation, still subsists."

The climax came swiftly. The official war against the British and Irvine's private war against Whitney—each going its own independent, unrelated way—collided. A few days after Wickham walked out of Whitney's manufactory, the "British came to Washington and *Blew Up Armstrong*." So Whitney, with a certain grim pleasure, summed up the events some years later. "The business of the Armories & contracts for arms was placed under the care of the Ordnance Dept. & I have heard nothing further from Irvine." (Josiah uttered sentiments common to New England when he wrote, "The late destruction of the City of Wash is Considered by all a National disgrace, at the same time it is thot the seat of Govt will in consequence be at Phila, and the interest of the Country so much improved by the change that the Loss of Wash will eventually prove a blessing to the country.")

Whitney never knew that Armstrong had ordered—the words were written on the back of Whitney's last letter to him—"Let Bomford * send a man of competent knowledge to prove Whitney's muskets. Let him prove 100 of the 1000—taking those to be tried from the heap. When proved—the arms should be sent to N.Y. without delay." Poor Armstrong! He was very glad to be relieved of his office. On September 27th James Monroe relinquished his Secretary-ship of the State Department and took over the demoralized post Armstrong had vacated.

Irvine had been defeated.

How thoroughly became clear over the next few months. A change could first be sensed in the War Department's attitude toward Whitney's manufactory, which, having stood off Irvine's attacks, became, in the glare of the appalling realities of the burning of the Capital and the bombardment of Fort McHenry, an establishment at once vulnerable and valuable. A Colonel Staples was dispatched to New Haven to install a shore battery because, "The British have lately captured the Revenue Cutter of this Port, which leaves us without the least floating defence whatever." (The thousand muskets which Whitney had feared might be captured by the enemy were bought and paid for by Governor Tompkins of New York; Whitney received his contract price, and New York assumed the costs of proving and transportation.)

In February, 1815, Congress passed an Act which embodied "all such provisions as the experience of the war had shown to be necessary." The activities and jurisdiction of the Commissary's Office and the Ordnance Department—both created in 1812—were finally given specific definition. "I have good reason to believe," Whitney wrote

* Major George Bomford (1782–1848) at that time was assistant Commissary General of Ordnance. Well educated and an able engineer, he became the outstanding authority on ordnance. Colonel Bomford was appointed Chief of the Ordnance Department on May 20, 1832.

to Colonel Roswell Lee, who was appointed to the Superintendency at the Springfield Armory, "that it was in consequence of the nefarious conduct of Wickham & Irvine that the business of the Armories & contracts for arms was put over into the charge of the Ordnance Dept. & it is nothing strange that Irvine should have a grudge against me as I certainly had no inconsiderable agency in deflating his abominable projects."

Whitney could not yet rejoice; he was not free of Irvine. Armstrong's directive of March, 1813, notifying him that Irvine had been entrusted with the supervision of his contract, had not been superseded. Quite soon Whitney would have another thousand muskets ready. Who would inspect them? And to whom should he apply to have this situation corrected? Men seemed to be flitting in and out of the office of the Secretary of War: James Monroe had left, and now Alexander Dallas had assumed the office in addition to that of Secretary of the Treasury.

Whitney wrote directly to James Madison, the President. "The Secretary of War has signified his willingness that the contract may go on; but . . . insists on leaving the business in the hands and under the control of Mr. Irvine." Whitney sent his correspondence with Irvine for the President to read, and asked "whether considerations of justice as well as delicacy towards Mr. Irvine may not render it proper that this business should be placed in the hands of some other officer or agent of the Government."

Peace had already come when, in June, 1815, the government paid Whitney for the first thousand muskets it received on his contract. From that time on he made regular deliveries and regularly received his moneys; the whole of the fifteen thousand was completed in July, 1822. Long, long before, manufacturing the muskets had become quite routine. James Carrington, who had proved and inspected the greater part of the muskets Whitney made on his first contract, stayed on to serve in the same capacity for the second. For his own use he transcribed from the Proof Book the number of musket barrels he proved: 14,158, the number burst, 606, and the cost involved, $833.

Out of Irvine's petty machinations, the United States, but newly entered on the production of small-arms, had been forced to define more exactly the function of agencies responsible for proper standards. In his efforts to attain his own end, Irvine had touched on a problem that has persisted to the present day, a highly controversial problem: public ownership of industries deemed vital to the national welfare. In his day, and long afterward, public ownership was limited to certain manufactories of arms for the nation. In the beginning Whitney, and only Whitney, argued for the private producer. Forty years later the pendulum had swung to the opposite extreme. The Secretary of War, Jefferson Davis, was asked to report to Congress whether it would not be "more economical, proper and advisable to cause all the arms of the United States to be made on contract."

After studying the situation, Davis concluded that the national armories worked cheaper and established the prices to be paid the private contractors but that private contractors constantly tried to improve the models and experimented with new materials and construction. Therefore, he felt it would be as inadvisable to make all the small arms by contract as it would be unwise to restrict their manufacture to national armories.

XVIII *The Rise of*

a *National Arms System*

A GOOD Musket is a complicated engine and difficult to make—difficult of execution because the
conformation of most of its parts corresponds with no regular geometric figure. Being familiarized to the musket from our earliest
childhood, we are not aware of its complexity, tho' each musket, with
Bayonet, consists of fifty distinct parts."

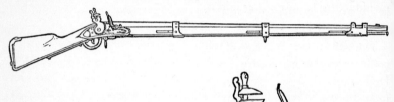

THE WHITNEY MUSKET MADE ON
THE CHARLEVILLE MODEL

These words, sonorous, suggestive, stand at the beginning of Whitney's request for the second contract for the government. They
stand apart from the context in which they were placed, claiming
attention; they stand outside the orderly line of facts marshaled for
the Secretary of War; they belong to Whitney's own particular
concentrated stream of thought. They are weighted with the long
brooding he had given to the shape and function and construction
and mass production of a musket. They defined a need. They formu-
lated, in positive terms, Whitney's way of saying that the lathe—

designed for turning an involved outer profile or for boring a true inner surface—could not cope with the irregular shapes demanded in the making of a musket. They referred to the major problem that had eluded solution: devising a tool to machine those parts which did not conform to a "geometric figure." By 1812 he had advanced far enough to phrase the requirements of a machine tool soon to be worked out and perfected—the milling machine.

Whitney bitterly resented Irvine's machinations because they robbed him of the time and freedom to think about this problem. Writing to Stebbins of those harassed years in which "a poor, pittiful, villianous piece of a thing, in the place of a public officer, set out systematically to break me up in the Manufacture of Arms," Whitney complained that he "prevented me from executing several projects which I had in view. . . . I have been so fortunate as to defeat his purpose. To accomplish this, however, has occupied a large portion of my time for mostly two years—& I regret that it should have been in his power to have cut so large a portion out of the little patch which constitutes the period of human existence."

The full measure of Irvine's defeat was not merely that Whitney could complete his contract, but that under the reorganized War Department for the first time he enjoyed fruitful cooperation with men concerned with the same problems. In this new atmosphere of shared endeavor, Whitney deserves high recognition because he made his milling machine quickly—and freely—available to the national armories.

The cooperation started as soon as he had freed himself from Irvine's jurisdiction, in June, 1815, and received permission to work under the Ordnance Department. Wadsworth conferred with "Mr. Prescott and Lt. Colonel Lee, the late and present superintendent at Springfield, with Mr. Stubblefield, the superintendent at Harpers Ferry, and with Mr. Whitney . . . [to] establish a pattern of a musket in our several armories, public and private [the want of which] has long been perceived. . . . No deviation from these patterns to be tolerated after the work now in hand shall have been finished."

Whitney knew all these men. Wadsworth was an old acquaintance, a classmate and friend of Miller's from Yale; he had served in the army at the time of the crisis with France, and resigned, when the country was "in prospect of peace"; for a few years he found it more remunerative and adventuresome to engage in Astor's northern fur trade, going back into the army when war was declared against Great Britain. Stubblefield had taken the post at Harpers Ferry that Dearborn had offered Whitney and, since their first meeting, at the Secretary of War's suggestion, their relations had been cordial and helpful. Roswell Lee, named Superintendent at Springfield (June 2, 1815), was a very capable, conscientious mechanic whom Whitney had employed, after Miller's death, to keep gins sold to important clients in operation. On Whitney's recommendation Wadsworth had taken him into the Ordnance Department—his long and distinguished tenure as head of the Springfield Armory was proof of his abilities.*

The letters that passed continually among them—official letters, mostly, to be found in the records of the Ordnance Department or the Springfield Armory—are compounded of business, shop talk, office rumors, and personal matters. Were there signs that the Connecticut iron ores were becoming exhausted, they acted together to investigate the Pennsylvania market. Did Lee hear that the government might recompense Simeon North for his improvement in pistols, he urged Whitney to apply for the same premium: "While I endeavor to be faithful to my trust, I feel disposed to aid in rewarding the *realy* meritorious." Lee and Whitney worked together in purchasing anything from wooden stocks to imported steel, in setting prices for contract work, and in lending each other the services of a skilled trip-hammer operator or bayonet maker for a few weeks or months.

Together they held a tight control over the labor market. "In a late struggle for the superintendence between the workmen and myself, I have discharged the following men," Lee wrote to Whitney, listing the malefactors; he also notified him when the wages at the Armory

---

* Running a national armory was an important administrative task for those days. More than 250 men were employed, and Wadsworth wrote to the Secretary of War that "to provide stock, tools and materials for keeping them employed; to preserve order, subordination and regularity of exertion . . . to retain every branch of the business in a relative state of progression with the rest, is a task very few men can be found equal to."

were to be cut. Or Whitney might ask Lee to hire some workers for him: "Smart men who will mind their own business. As for the cabolling, grumbling, trouble-making fellows I do not want them—having enough such already." Or Whitney, with considerable approval, reported to Lee: "Several of our workmen were taken rather suddenly with the Harpers Ferry fever and started this day week for that place. They have now returned home. I believe perfectly cured without the aid of medicine."

Concerted action among these men was not limited to setting the prices for raw materials, labor, and subcontractors. They were forever discussing technical details, and in this Whitney was their mentor. "If any alteration should be made in the Pattern Lock," Wadsworth wrote to Whitney after each part of the lock had been discussed and experimented with, "we ought to introduce the improved Bridle you invented some time ago, together with a Seer like Mr. Baker's and a better Seer Spring. I want you to undertake the construction of a Lock combining such properties, and as an inducement I presume it will be in my power to obtain for you something in the way of a Compensation for this, as well as the other Trouble you have had in this matter." Lee adopted the method Whitney had worked out to increase the efficiency of the trip hammer in welding barrels. "The trip hammers operate extremely well, the barrels now cost 30 cents less. The hammers can give 400 blows a minute."

A few years later Whitney offered Lee a machine for turning musket barrels. "If yours . . . should not answer the purpose I have one which I invented more than ten years ago which I am confident will answer well." And then, reacting to the injury he had suffered long before, when his cotton gin was pirated and he was impoverished, he added: "I would put it into operation if I could see any prospect of a fair remuneration for the invention & expence & risque of the Experiment. But the probability is that some person would contract to make the barrels & not only take advantage of my invention but intice away the workmen whom I had instructed in the use of the Machine before I could be half compensated for the expence of making it."

Exactly when Whitney made his milling machine cannot be deter-

mined. There was so much visiting between the men, so many conferences, so much demonstrating of new tools and methods, that
the written records are, at best, useful for their implications and suggestions. From the beginning Whitney had used "filing jigs" and
"filing fixtures"—work-holding, tool-guiding devices that imparted
a uniform degree of accuracy to successive pieces of work. Whitney's
skill in toolmaking was embodied in his jigs and fixtures; through
them his skill was transferred to each piece of work thus machined.
They were the basis of his system of interchangeable manufacture.
But more and more this controlled hand method became the bottleneck in producing individual parts—fully one-third of the operations
were of this nature. It was to solve this urgent problem that Whitney
developed the plain milling machine. At first glance it seems to have
derived from milling cutters used about 1780 by the great French
mechanic Jacques de Vaucanson. But the early French milling machines could not have had a strong influence on future designs, for
they were "rotary files," not true "tooth-type" cutters.

By 1818 Whitney had thought out and made his milling machine.
His first specific reference to it came only in 1823, when, forwarding
to Calhoun, Secretary of War "an improved Model of a Guard for
the Musket," he referred to milling. "Both ends of the Bow of this
Guard can be forged in a pair of matched Dies, each having a similar, circular, concave impression. Dies of this description are more
easily made & more induring than any other—they leave the fire in
a firm, solid state & the work more free from scales & *without any
fire*. Both ends of the Bow can then be finished by Milling or Turning, with more expedition & accuracy than those of the other form
can be filed." By that time milling operations were already common
at the Springfield Armory. A detailed cost analysis sent by Lee to
Bomford shows milling was routine both in shaping the muzzle and
milling and slitting the many screws which held the fifty parts solidly
together.

Whitney could look back, as he was finishing his second contract,
to the time when he had begun the "invention of new & complicated
machinery" and his system had been regarded "as altogether utopian."
Writing in 1821, when already few were left who remembered the
hesitating first steps of an infant industry, he recalled that he had
started his manufactory at almost the same time as the national

armories. "Mr Nicholson an experienced Gun Smith who had resided for some years in Philadelphia, was sent to the Armoury at Springfield to instruct them how to proceed in the execution of the work, & Mr Hoskins, an Englishman who had been thoroughly used to the manufacture of Arms in his native country was sent to erect & superintend the Establishment at Harper's Ferry. So strong are the prejudices of Education & force of habit that although several of the Machines & many of the improved modes of working, invented by your Memorialist had from time to time been introduced into the public Armories, it was not untill he had demonstrated the superiority of his System by a successful and uninterrupted experiment of ten years continuance, that it was adopted into the Public Armories. Since that period the quality . . . has been greatly improved without increasing the expence."

Twenty-five years! Whitney could remind the government officials that the road so many now used had been a path, but before there had been a path he had gone ahead to mark out a trail.

And Whitney could also look forward. In 1821, he went to Harpers Ferry, having been told of the "New System being adapted there." He would have been pleased to see how his principle was being developed and interested in the direction his work was taking; but "the Clerk who has been appointed to keep accounts relative to all the multifarious details arising out of the proposed new system, was then very sick."

The new system referred to was the work of John H. Hall, who in 1811 had been granted a patent for the first breech-loading firearm. In 1819 the government had given him a contract to manufacture his rifle so that its parts would be thoroughly interchangeable. All the equipment at Harpers Ferry was at his disposal, and he had only to concern himself with designing machinery to achieve the highest possible precision. In every way Hall profited by Whitney's work. The principle of interchangeability had been firmly established. Whitney had had to devise, by an elaborate system of guides, patterns, templates, gauges and jigs, ways whereby unskilled labor could reproduce faithfully and in large numbers a musket designed to be made by skilled craftsmen. In addition to a contract which bound him to a set time and a fixed price, Whitney was further hampered by having to conform strictly to a model not of his own making. Hall built his own model—designed for precise-machine production—and was weighed down neither by time nor price.

Many years later Eli Whitney Blake felt called upon to correct a false impression, which Hall himself had—knowingly or inadvertently—promoted, that lack of skill had prevented earlier mechanics from achieving the degree of interchangeability embodied in his rifles. "It is not a deficiency of skill, but the peculiar construction of the Musket, which has prevented the accomplishment of this object," Blake asserted. "Mr. Hall is himself the inventor of the Rifle which he manufactures, & the Government has with great propriety allowed him to form, fashion, model, & construct it in every respect according to his own good taste, judgement & discretion. He . . . has modeled & fashioned it with express reference to making it susceptible of being manufactured with such degree of uniformity & precision that the parts may interchange;—nor has he been limited . . . but from time to time as difficulties have occurred which he could not surmount by improvements in his machinery, he has obviated them by a change in the model of his Rifle." Not so the musket makers. "A model, got up by others without any reference to this object [interchangeability] has been placed in their hands to be copied. In the form & construction of the musket they have been permitted to exercise no discretion or judgement whatever, but on the contrary are forbidden to deviate from the model in any respect. . . . Certainly there are mechanicians among them who, with liberty to construct their own models & with the use of the Public purse, will do all for the musket that Mr. Hall has done for his rifle, in the way of making the Limbs to interchange, taking as the basis of their operations the system established by *Eli Whitney* & borrowing none of those peculiarities which may have been engrafted onto that system by the truly original & inventive genius of Mr. Hall." *

On August 1, 1822, Whitney reached an agreement with "Lt. Col.

---

* Henry M. Leland, the man who applied precision concepts and techniques to the automobile industry, had worked at the Springfield Armory during the Civil War and later at the Colt Arms—the two shops where the Whitney influence was greatest. It was the precision-machine work in those armories that gave him his basic orientation and experience. In 1906 he took three Cadillacs to London and, repeating Whitney's great demonstration with muskets, disassembled the cars, scrambled their parts, and then reconstructed three new automobiles. Here was proof that "a producer of the automobile had mastered the principle of 'interchangeability of parts.'" Ford became Leland's "most distinguished disciple."

George Bomford acting with the consent and under the direction of the Hon. J. C. Calhoun," to extend the fifteen thousand muskets manufactured under the terms of the second contract—the last of which he had only delivered to the government—by another three thousand: "For Two thousand of the said Three thousand Muskets the said Whitney shall be entitled to receive Thirteen Dollars each. . . . And that for the remaining One Thousand Muskets, he shall be entitled to receive only Twelve Dollars each. . . . Whitney shall deliver the said Three Thousand Muskets within Eighteen months from the date hereof."

Two weeks later, August 15th, Whitney signed his third contract—for 15,000 muskets—with the War Department. It differed from the preceding ones. Starting in January, 1824, it called for an annual delivery of three thousand muskets during the next five years. The model, over whose design the Ordnance Department and the heads of the public and private armories had fussed and consulted, the blessed offspring of many minds, became the standard musket for the Army. The price schedule was quite new. Whitney was to be paid at the rate of $12 per musket; but "it is provided that when the actual cost of manufacturing Muskets at the public armories shall be satisfactorily ascertained, that then the said Whitney shall be entitled to receive . . . the same sum to which the actual average Cost of manufacturing a Musket in the two Armories of the U States shall amount in lieu of the Twelve Dollars aforesaid, said Average cost to be ascertained within one year from the date thereof. It being fully understood . . . that the interest in the Entire Capital employed at the Armories, insurance against all risks, with the addition of such further percentage for wear and decay, as shall be sufficient to preserve the said Capital unimpaired, shall be charged as making a part of the Cost of Manufacturing arms at the United States Armories."

The contract vindicated Whitney's argument at several critical points. Bomford and Calhoun had accepted Whitney's method for determining actual costs; they also accepted as governmental policy "to renew contracts where former contracts have been satisfactorily filled, provided terms were as low as any other bids."

Stating Whitney's oft-repeated arguments in his own words, Bomford gave as the reason for this procedure that "without such inducements, contracts upon reasonable terms could not have been obtained; because the U States was the only customer the contractors could have. . . . In 1798, when the first attempt was made [to establish the manufacture of small arms] there were but few persons in the country acquainted with the business; and but one of these (Eli Whitney of Connecticut) who embarked in it succeeded; all the rest were either ruined by the attempt or found the business so unprofitable and hazardous as to induce them to relinquish it. In 1808, after the passage of the law making a permanent appropriation, a renewed attempt was made, and many of the contractors who were then engaged in the business have also failed. The steady support and patronage given by the Government since that time to the contractors whose skill, perseverance and capital saved them from early failure has resulted in the firm establishment of several manufactories of arms, and preserved to the country establishments of great importance to its security and defence."

The Ordnance Department had not only designed a new musket, it also made inspection and proof uniform. The *Regulations for the Inspection of Small Arms,* issued in 1823—the first official change in twenty-five years—described each step in detail and established the standards inspectors were "strictly enjoined to conform to." Designed to achieve precision and uniformity, the tolerance permitted them was, by modern standards, but little advanced from the "thickness of an old shilling" that Wilkinson had obtained fifty years before when making Watt's cylinder. The *Regulations* instructed the inspector to "stretch a line through the barrel, and apply it to at least four sides of the bore, to ascertain if the interior is straight." Limit plug gages verified the caliber of the bore: "The small plug should pass freely through the barrel, and the large plug should not enter its whole length. If the barrel will not receive the small plug, or if it will admit the large plug, the barrel will be rejected." Point by point, the barrels and locks, the stocks, the mounting, the ramrods and bayonets were carefully examined and subjected wherever possible to a set of gages.

By the third contract Whitney undertook to make muskets that would pass such rigid inspection and proof; his profit was to be had by operating more efficiently than the national armories. To this new problem he was committed.

XIX   *Catherine and Henrietta*

ONCE Catherine Miller had written, "My heart was never formed to hear of the sudden death of any person of my acquaintance." At the very time Whitney was most harassed by Irvine, his brother wrote to him that "our friend Mrs. Miller died on the 2nd [of September 1814] with a fever after an illness of Six days." That, Josiah wrote, was all that he had heard.

When is death not sudden? Two years before, Kollock had pleaded with Whitney to abide by his oft-repeated promise to visit Georgia; he had warned him not to postpone too long. Whitney had understood the full meaning of Kollock's admonition—how does one tell such things to the heart?

Two years; an opportunity forever gone: this was a large part of the price Whitney had paid to defeat Irvine. "It seems to be invariably decreed that disappointment shall be my perpetual lot," Whitney had written Catherine just the February before she died. "I calculated to have set my affairs in order, provided for those who depend on me for bread and before this time have paid my expences to Georgia. But . . . my whole property and business, in which I have made large expenditures, has been thrown into a state of complete confusion and uncertainty by an upstart coxcomb of a public officer, who has no moral sense and not above half common sense. With a large stock on hand, no funds on hand, and a hundred persons dependent on me—I can assure you these are very serious embarrassments. As soon as these can be shaken off to allow me a respite to come to Georgia and return you may expect to see me there if I do not stay more than one week." And now he reread her answer to him—the last but one of her letters—in which she lamented

Whitney's "disappointments of every kind but more particularly the Old one of Seven Years standing." Seven years since he had seen her —seven years!

During the first of those years, she had been impatient: "I pray you to say in your next when I may expect you. . . . My patience is out— You will say that I have no right to be vexed with you—but I say I have—and I will be vexed with you and so good night—I cannot help adding God bless you notwithstanding." Afterwards she chided him, and gently upbraided him: "I write this letter merely to complain to you, and of You— In the first place I complain of the breach of Promis contained in your last letter saying 'that you would write to me *often*— Especially if you were sick.' Now shall I go farther and make my Own angry comments? or what I believe will be a better course—to leave the matter to your Own Conscience—which I hope will give you some smart twinges—and Make you remember how disappointed I am every Friday which brings not with it some account of you."

Scattered throughout her letters, her anger against him lies in ambush, concealed and ready to wound. She never called him heartless or suggested that he had become forgetful or mercenary; she merely repeated an adjective that had been used—by his brother Josiah, or her daughter Louisa, or their mutual friend Goodrich—in order to be able to tell him how she had silenced the voice that dared make such an accusation within her hearing. The little scenes, as she reported them to her dearest friend, Mr. Whitney, always concluded with her loving defense of him, her constancy in believing his promises, her unwavering faith in his friendship for her.

Catherine Miller was a great lady in a day when ladies expressed themselves within the formulae of their class. It is told how Aaron Burr called on her when he traveled southward after his fatal duel. ("The feelings of the whole community are agonized beyond description. . . . Our friend fell by the first fire," Wolcott had written of Hamilton's death.) And since she and Burr were among the few who had stayed through the winter at Valley Forge, she offered him the hospitality of her house; but, to rebuke him for having killed her friend Alexander Hamilton, she herself left. Not even her sure style, her aura of charm could blind Kollock's medical eye to the fact that suddenly she had grown old—old and tired and negligent. That was why he had warned Whitney (as 1812 began) that Catherine was "enfeebled & is descending into the vale of years." Twice widowed, she spent her last years among the multifarious complications willed her by the two active men who had died still young and in the midst of activities. There was the estate of General Greene and there was Miller's estate; there was the Yazoo purchase, the ginning business with Whitney, the several side ventures engaged in with Josiah Whitney. These had all to be settled and apportioned among the Greene children, now grown up and, save for Louisa, the youngest, now married.

More and more the unhappy, unloving hand of Louisa can be felt, manipulating her mother's decisions, embittering Catherine first against one child, then another. Catherine had been brought to disapprove of her daughter Cornelia's marriage to Edward Littlefield; there is a glimpse of Catherine—how dreadfully changed!— arranging to have her son-in-law, who had decided to leave Dungeness for distant Tennessee, "arrested and detained in Savannah with *his wife, children, Negroes,* Waggons etc etc for a number of days, . . . to give Bonds to be answerable for his Proportion of any Demands that might hereafter come against the Estate of Genl. Greene." Josiah, who heard of the incident from Georgia friends, added the local reaction "—all of which was thought to be an Ill-natured act on the part of Mrs. Miller—" and commented that "Mrs. Miller's friends in Rhode Island generally are of the opinion that she has been Hard and unkind to all her children except the youngest."

Finally Louisa tried to step between her mother and Whitney. She transposed the tone of anger she had heard her mother use and keyed it to her own pitch. But where Catherine's displeasure had been a surface vexation, an arch pique employed to whet her friend's affection, a sentiment intensified to bridge the intervening miles, Louisa's discontent became an ugly weapon. To Whitney it was indistinguishable from Irvine's animosity. It did not woo him, rather it brought to the fore the bitterness he felt toward those who would attack him. "I confess I felt wounded by the threat contained in the letter of my worthy friend Louisa," (Whitney wrote directly to Catherine, disregarding the daughter who must have suggested that "the only method of settling the affairs of M & W is by a suit at Law.") "I propose to set out for Georgia. To be arrested on my arrival there and held to bail & be subjected to the fatigues vexations & torments of travelling five or six thousand miles to attend a Georgia Court, is a situation of all others I should wish to avoid."

Catherine, unaware how she had been betrayed by her daughter's attitude, was aghast. She cried out: "The idea you suggest of going to Prison gives a shock to my heart, . . . good god what has this world come to? I who have always loved you and still love you . . . is it *Me* that is to put you in Prison. . . . No dear Whitney Your own Mother would not shield you from every Evil with more tenderness or More anxious solicitude than your sincere friend Cath Miller." But Whitney never did get to Georgia; for even as Louisa was trying to uproot the delicious friendship for Catherine that had flowered in his heart for twenty years, he was forced by Irvine's strategy to stay on in New Haven.

The pathetic crisis Louisa had concocted was dispelled by Catherine's words. Closer than ever before she hugged his friendship and her disappointment to her heart. Her last letter to Whitney, written two months before she died, showed that the bond between them had never been broken and that to the very end her warm charm stayed with her. "You will see by this that My salvation as to this world rests intirely upon the success of the Yazoo—that Yazoo which for so many years has been the torment of My life. . . . We have a party of Eighteen to eat Turtle with us tomorrow—I wish you were the nineteenth our first begins to flow in upon us. . . . I long for you and a few other friends to partake with us—Our Crops look well. . . . I am sincerely your friend C Miller."

And now she was gone—she who from the time he had left college had commanded and dominated his affections. All that was left him was her letters. Who had ever reached out to him in words as Catherine had? "As we have not heard from you this week, I begin to fear your poor head does want the lap of friendship to rest upon— if not the lap of Venus—I wish to god my dear friend you were married. . . . I am prepared to love any woman who would make you happy.

". . . . I am provoked for letting you take off My picture and have a good mind to come by way of N Haven to get it from you.

". . . . Never—Never shall I Cease Considering you My Son— and never never Cease lamenting that you were not born so.

". . . . I wish also to whisper other secrets in your Ear—which I certainly should do if you were seting by me—for it is true what Louisa says that I would *tell you* Every thought of my soul—I also wish to consult you about finishing my house. . . . I comfort myself sometimes in looking at your picture and mentally conversing with it—and sometimes in the Lover stile give it a kiss.

". . . . You see how little I can do without you—and I can see how much I could do—if I had your advice and assistance for a month. . . . Save my life in saving your own—for I find I can not comfortably be in this world if you are not of it.

". . . . Your picture ornaments my toilet table— It is every day looked at and some times kissed—that is to say when you are sick."

Catherine's letters to Whitney still pulse with her emotion; it can be felt under her conglomerate, instant outpourings. Her impulse gives life to the details of friendship, business, family, trips, affection, personalities, marriages, lawsuits, conviviality, crop estimates, advice for his health, the weather, births—details rush out indiscriminately. Her moods provided color and variety; she was gay, imperious, loving, hurt, provoked, forgiving, delighted, solicitous. Written long, long ago by a woman in her mid-fifties, they are alive and carry the sound of her voice. How potent they must have been when they were still warm from her hand! If time has not affected their power, distance could hardly have touched them, and Whitney, reading them, was held by the heart that penned them.

Had Whitney, in his grief for Catherine, forgotten that he had other friends? In May of 1815, Stebbins wrote him; the brevity of his note, its direct demands make it clear that he had heard of Mrs. Miller's death and was worried by Whitney's silence. "This sheet is only to salute you as one of the few friends, faithful, worthy, and beloved whom this dreary world has given me and whom I shall never recollect without gratitude that I have known them. Take up your pen and tell me whether any thing good or bad has fallen your lot, beyond the ordinary course of things."

Whitney had badly needed just such a summons from Stebbins. It gave "a sort of fillup to my resolution & I now sit down, on Sunday afternoon, after church, the weather being very pleasant, to comply with your request & gratify my own wishes." He then summarized the Irvine fight that had engrossed him for more than two years. He did not mention Catherine or Louisa or his thwarted efforts to go South, but he implied much when he mentioned that his health "had been bad for the winter past. I was confined to my room for more than six weeks."

Was it health or mourning that kept Whitney shut in his room, alone?

Illnesses—the causes, the cures—provide one of the sharpest lines dividing Whitney's time and the present. Sometimes, from descriptions, it is possible to suggest a modern medical diagnosis, so that one can safely assume that General Greene died of a heart attack, or that Paine, when he disgusted Whitney by his convulsive efforts to drink wine, suffered from Parkinson's disease. But what was the "Hypo" which afflicted Whitney in his youth and to which his sister so casually referred? Yellow fever, dysentery, influenza, and many other names were properly given to epidemics that recurrently held a town or a whole region in sickness and death. But with what was Whitney afflicted when he wrote to Stebbins, half truthfully, half jestingly, in the fall of that year, that he was "still affected tho' not so much distressed as I have been with the same epedemic Disorder which has now become almost universal in this part of the country. It is a singular circumstance that I find my stomach every morning filled with *Salt Water*. Yet I always sleep at least twenty feet above the highest *Tides*—I can, moreover, assure you upon my honor that I have neither swallowed any part of *Tom Jefferson's Salt Mountain* nor committed adultery with *Lotts Wife*. Now if you can explain this phenomenon I shall pronounce you a great Philosopher."

The recital of aches and pains has a certain morbid charm; it also presents such intimate scenes as to erase the long, intervening decades. A little mealtime drama becomes vivid when Catherine recounts how "My ever dear Mr. Miller when I first knew him was dreadfully afflicted with an assid stomach. . . . I prevailed upon him to live cheafly upon beef—and no vegetables, his bread was Crakers —by these attentions to his diet he recovered sound health and good spirits." Similarly, no adjective Whitney could use presented as lonely a picture as his account of his self-administered doctoring.

"I speak from experience," he wrote to Stebbins, who complained of a troublesome knee, "having been myself several years exercised with a bad feversore—where the bone was seriously affected. Many are the hours which I have spent in rubbing my leg with my hands & numerous are the instances in which I have relieved myself from a pain which was so severe as to prevent me from sleeping. Move your hands with a moderate velocity & a moderate degree of pressure. . . . Continue it for half an hour & repeat it several times in each 24 hours. This will press forward & force the animal fluids thro' the vessels in which they ought to circulate. If at the same time you bathe your knee in some kind of ardent spirit, it will not be amiss. . . . Something to lubricate & in some cases something to relax (perhaps Opadilack)—Opadilack, I take it, consists of Soap Camphor & a little laudanum.* Wash your limb for ¾ of an hour with strong *Soap Suds* . . . the alkali of the soap will aid the water to dissolve the matter of perspiration which may have become indurated and sealed up the pores of the skin. Animal health & life cannot long continue if the pores of the skin are obstructed—sick *pigs* are plunged in soap suds & scrubbed & almost always cured. I think in most cases of sick children this simple remedy would be equally efficacious."

But Whitney did not, in his letters to Stebbins, linger long on illness. Like the rest of New Haven, he was, that summer of 1815, actively engaged in building. "In addition to my ordinary business of manufacturing Arms, I shall be occupied this summer in erecting some additional buildings near my manufactory."

He made detailed inquiries of Stebbins about lumber—the quality and price, quantities and freight costs from Wiscasset to New Haven. "I suspect that the principal part of the Lumber which we get at N Haven comes from that part of Maine," Whitney wrote, and described the quantities that had been used. "About two years ago N

---

* The first pharmacopoeia, written by Doctors John C. Warren and James Jackson for the Massachusetts Medical Society, was published in 1808.

Haven folks were seized with a violent ferver for pulling down their Meeting Houses & Building New Ones. Since which there has been a very handsome New House erected nearly on the site where the Old Brick stood. Fair Haven is pulled away & a new one nearly finished in its place. The New Episcopal Chirch is placed directly south west of the State House & in a line with the other two houses of Worship; which are Brick. . . . They are all Elegant Buildings & the three when finished will have cost about one hundred thousand Dollars. In addition to these a considerable number of new Dwelling Houses & Stores have been put up in the town.

"Give me a particular account of One Judge Stebbins, who I understand lives in your part of the Country. He has been for a long time an old friend of mine."

Stebbins's tone, so light and warm, had smoothed the way for Whitney to renew correspondence with him; his letters rambled on, deceptively simple, a remark or a question inserted so as to give no offense. It was the blandest kind of talk, spoon-fed to a stricken heart. Did Whitney confine his remarks to procuring Maine shingles, Stebbins cautioned him that "*Shingle weavers,* their appellation with us, cheat by habit, and are cheated in their pay by habit; good pay would do something towards getting good shingles"; then disarmed Whitney with his forthright statement, "I would rather correspond with you on business, than not at all"; and at the end, prodded him, "When you are quite at liesure, tell me what you are about; and what and where you are building—and anything else—short metre, or long."

Keeping the same easy, leisurely manner, Stebbins ventured to say something important—hidden in his banter was concern and advice for his friend. "When I wrote you . . . about lumber and things in general, I had in my head the notion of your building a mighty country seat, outhouses & inhouses, in the pleasant prospect of East-Rock: and such a notion, including a notion that you had renewed your gallantry, and some foolish girl was going to take the pig for the sake of the stye, set me out of all reasonable calculations."

The months passed, the aimless, innocuous exchange continued. Stebbins confessed "to be very sober and sentimental, I do love such letters, provided always they are from folks that I love." In February,

1816, Whitney proudly noticed in the "Boston Weekly messenger, which I received regularly that 'the Honbl. Josiah Stebbins Esq' was by a very unusual Majority Elected one of the Gov's Council . . . from which I infer he is now in Boston. . . . I presume your knee is better or you would not have travelled to Boston." Stebbins's reply inquired about Whitney's method for warming rooms. (Warming was the best they could have hoped for, and would be several degrees under heating.) Whitney had worked out a special kind of fireplace: "They have a cast-iron *hearth* or pavement under the fire. The Jambs should be either cast iron or hewn stone because I know of nothing else which will last & appear well. . . . My fireplaces to which you allude answer well—they equal my expectations— I am fully satisfied with the principle as I stated to you when here."

And then, casually slipped in among suggested treatments for aging bones, smoky fireplaces, and passing mention of town doings and Council duties, Stebbins wrote, on November 29th, 1816: "I am glad to learn that your *secular* business has been compelled to give way long enough for you to contract matrimony. I hope it may be a contract worth the making. You know I was ever an oddity, going by the rules of contraries. Others would say a congratulation conjugal would hardly do to mix with an inquiry about smoke & flues and chimney backs; But I say, what is so natural to connect as marriage and housekeeping?"

"Married. January 6th [1817], In Bridgepoart, Eli Whitney, Esq. of Hamden to Miss Henrietta F. Edwards, daughter of the Hon. Pierpont E." That is all to be found on Whitney's marriage. Stark, laconic, impersonal, the newspaper item states the salient facts; but the host of questions which would be asked by even the most incurious, still sound, unanswered. Whitney's letter to Stebbins announcing his impending marriage, with whatever details he included for his friend's eye; the letters he sent to his sister Elizabeth and his brother Josiah, telling them of his projected step—of these not one remains among his papers.

Henrietta Edwards was thirty-one when she married Whitney. He was twenty years her senior, a friend of her father's; he was someone she had known since she was a little girl.

Although no evidence exists for assessment, it could be assumed that Henrietta was on the frightening threshold of becoming a spinster and seized an opportunity to be mistress of her own home. Equally well it might be assumed that it was difficult for Pierpont Edwards's daughter to relinquish the elegant, urbane home of her father, a center that attracted men of learning, men of power, to become the wife of a young man, untried and perhaps unfitted for that brilliant world. Or, if one would view the marriage as the culmination of a romance, it might be that as a young girl she had found Whitney endowed with such excellencies that she would have none other and that she bided her time convinced that a day would come when he would find her, the daughter of his friend, desirable. Without facts, any theory is possible, any premise tenable.

Whitney's position is clearer. For twenty years, perhaps, Catherine's image so possessed him that even when he had established himself financially and could have married, he was unable to give himself to another woman. Only Catherine's death could end the spell; once it was broken, the part within him that had resisted Catherine healed and sought the home he craved and which before had been impossible. Was Henrietta old? She was but half Catherine's age. Like her, she was by blood and breeding and participation of the great world in which he now moved. Whitney, at fifty-one, was looking for the mother of the children that had so long been denied him —and in Henrietta he found her.

Pierpont Edwards's friendship had aspects to which Whitney had to adjust. As the son of the great Jonathan Edwards and the great-grandson of the mighty Solomon Stoddard, he belonged to the highest New England aristocracy. In his own person he was intelligent, cultured, and charming; a successful lawyer. His home—always described as a mansion—was a New Haven landmark, and his hospitality was dispensed on a grand scale. The more charitable people called his conduct erratic—a way of saying that in his thoughts, his actions, his way of life, he followed his own standards and was not obedient to those prevailing. In that Federalist stronghold he was an active Jeffersonian; in a land solemnly committed to steady habits he freely spent the large sums he earned on fine foods and lusty women. "Respectable" was the only adjective not associated with his

name; he seems to have tried deliberately to efface all memory of
the austerity and sanctity of the frontier mission in Stockbridge where
his boyhood was spent—everything but his father's massive intellec-
tuality and integrity.

Edwards early discerned Whitney's great talents: he was one of
the ten men who signed the bond the government required; and to
his friend James Madison, Secretary of State, he described Whitney
as "a gentleman very highly respected by all who know him and considered here as a very able Mathematician & the first mechanical
genius in New England." Whitney was grateful for Edwards's support, honored to be counted among his friends, and delighted by
his brilliance and learning. Under the aristocratic bearing he recognized the stubborn, dedicated fighter who in the end led his party
to victory over the entrenched oligarchy. Yet he could write to Stebbins in 1802, when Edwards was a widower, "P. Edwards has broke
up housekeeping, lives at Wallingford with his Doxy." (This must
have been Mary Tucker, whom he subsequently married.)

Henrietta was fourteen at the time of her mother's death (1800),
and she may then have gone to live with her older sister Susan, who
had married Samuel William Johnson and lived in nearby Stratford.
In 1806 her father was appointed Judge of the District Court and
took up residence in Bridgeport. Whether she moved there with him,
or whether she alternated between her sister's home and her father's,
is impossible to know. But it was in Bridgeport that she and Whitney
met again—he was accustomed to call on Judge Edwards when in
his vicinity; it must have been there that he asked her to marry him—
for he passed through Bridgeport on a trip to Philadelphia late in
the autumn of 1816; * and it was from her father's home that they
were married in January, 1817. To Henrietta, his wife, Whitney gave
the same abiding devotion that had characterized his relationships as
son, brother, and friend.

* A letter Whitney wrote on December 25th, 1816, says that he "returned home
. . . from Philadelphia, after an absence of nearly six weeks. I was one of the
persons deputed by the Citizens of N. Haven . . . to solicit the location of the
U. States Branch Bank at this place & was in Phila. attending to the business of
that appointment before the Citizens of Hartford began to make any movement."

xx *Into New Hands*

I<small>N</small> May, 1818, Whitney felt he could no longer attend to everything himself. He asked young Eli
Whitney Blake to spend his vacation in New Haven to aid him in
"getting on with my affairs which have been so numerous, embarrassing and oppressive that I am almost driven to delirium. I find
that it is absolutely impossible for me to accomplish one half of that
for which there is the most pressing necessity." The affairs which,
curiously enough, suddenly overwhelmed Whitney were not the
patterns for a new, cast-iron pump commissioned by Wolcott, nor
the intricate chemical apparatus required by Professor Silliman, nor
even his own milling machine, which occupied much of his attention;
they were concerned with the long-delayed, final settlement of the
Miller & Whitney ginning business.

Preparing for the settlement might have induced a reaction of
subdued melancholy, reviving memories of a quarter of a century
before, when Whitney and Miller and Catherine Greene had merged
their fortunes and destinies to create Miller & Whitney. Of the three,
Whitney alone was now alive. The firm had ceased functioning
long ago, and Whitney could have been annoyed at being asked to
retrace details intricate and half-forgotten—but the sums involved
were significant. Whitney's excited anxiety seems to have been the
measure of how deeply he was disturbed at the prospect of having
Catherine's executor, Russell Goodrich, present in New Haven.

Two months later he again entreated Blake to help him: "I am
exceedingly pressed with other business—more than I can do, but
if there is no other way I shall dismiss my workmen & relinquish
all other business until this, with the Estate of Miller is settled. . . .

I have for many years been distressed by the situation in which I have stood relative to the Estate of Miller. A large amount will be claimed from me, which in equity & good conscience I ought not to pay—but now is the time & the best time to settle this business—& I would rather sacrifice three thousand Dollars than it should remain unsettled another year. Mr. G. . . . will be very impatient & is in many respects a difficult man to do business with; but on the whole it is vastly better for me to close it with him, than with any other person connected with Miller's Estate." *

The final settlement of December 5, 1818, is a coda—it introduces, surprisingly, the "principal points about which we disagree"; it offers the last statement made by the participants in the complex affairs of the firm.

For five days the referees—Simeon Baldwin for Whitney, Nathaniel Rossiter for Goodrich—heard the arguments, examined the "accounts & books and the several claims of each partner" before they resolved the disagreements. Whitney, they found, was entitled "to his expences & compensation for five journeys at the rate of two thousand Dollars each & for one by water & for a shorter time, one thousand, making the whole eleven thousand Dollars." That Whitney should have put in such a claim reveals that the fatigue of those dreary annual trips had never been forgotten. Long before, he had written Stebbins: "The fates have decreed that I shall be perpetually on the wing. Wild Goose like I spend my summers in the North & at the approach of winter shape my course for the regions of the South. But I am an unfortunate goose. Instead of sublimely touring thro' the aerial regions with a select corps of faithful companions, I must slowly wade thro' the mud & dirt, a solitary traveller."

Whitney's second major claim was not unexpected. Miller's Yazoo gamble had always aroused mixed reactions in Whitney; at the beginning he had questioned the cost to them in cash and credit and good will, later he had assessed the amount lost by having the animosity of the Georgia planters transferred to their enterprise, and most recently he was aware that whereas Miller & Whitney had been penalized, Miller's estate had profited hugely when, in 1814, Con-

* See Appendix C and Appendix D.

gress appropriated $8,000,000 to compensate the Yazoo speculators, who, at most had laid out but $500,000. These reasons influenced the referees to award him damages to "the sum of Fifteen Thousand Dollars." This amount and $11,054, the sum given to each of the partners, can be considered the profit Whitney received from Miller & Whitney.

The few figures mentioned in the final settlement indicate that the moneys taken in by the firm added up to about $90,000, while its total costs for manufacturing the machines, installing and maintaining the ginneries, legal fees, and traveling expenses, came close to $47,000. On the face of it, this would seem not an insignificant return. There is no indication of how much Miller (and the Greene estate) actually had invested at any one time; but an estimate can be had from Miller's statement, made in 1799, when ginning had come to a complete standstill, that "in making, perfecting and bringing into use this valuable invention, we have expended more than $20,000 not more than one half of which have our profits * yet returned to us." It seems fair to assume that at that point the investment lay somewhere between $10,000 and $12,000; at that time it could be written off as a dead loss and Miller & Whitney dismissed as a spectacular failure.

This situation continued with no relief—it might even have grown worse as the firm required further expenditures for legal services—until Whitney closed the South Carolina sale at the beginning of 1805. From then on, Miller & Whitney's finances swung to the other extreme—$14,060.85½ in royalties from North Carolina, an unspecified amount from Tennessee, and damages from Georgia were welcome additions to the ledger sheets. The change was sudden; more than three-quarters of the total income came in the final two years, and transformed a twelve-year history of struggle and loss into an eventual profit.

It was this timetable of loss and profit that made Whitney seek to have his patent rights extended, as it was for this same reason that

---

* The profits might—though it does not seem likely—refer to the only figures relating to income other than that derived from the arrangements made with North and South Carolina: $4,322 collected by Goodrich at an unknown time from unknown sources, $1,100 for gins sold to a Mr. Hardin, and $4,175.65 taken in by Miller at the Mulberry Grove ginnery.

the southern congressmen thwarted his petitions. Whitney knew that had the Circuit Court sustained him in the beginning or, at the end, had Congress renewed his patent, his returns on his invention would have been greatly increased. This was the yardstick by which he measured the failure of Miller & Whitney.

When the settlement was finished and Miller & Whitney had become just a name, Goodrich and Whitney, their differences adjudicated, were aware that "these things and these times have passed by; and other folks and other times, have succeeded."

Miller & Whitney, the small, adventuresome firm that had pioneered modern business, was soon forgotten. Forgotten too was the small independent farmer who had seized on the gin. Both had been succeeded by something of different magnitude and composition: a society that rested on cotton cultivation and because of this dependence developed its own economy, its special political and social structures, its particular mores and ethics and myths; a society where wealth and power came from a single-minded devotion to the growing and ginning of the green-seed short-staple cotton; a society convinced that the plantation system and slavery were imperative.

Because of the critical part Whitney inadvertently played in slavery's consolidation and expansion, his omitting any reference to it is striking. During his early years such silence is understandable, for until he went to the South he had had little or no contact with it. It must seem that he deliberately did not choose to consider it in terms of good and evil. It was the same kind of reasoned inaction, of refusing to take sides that had characterized his avoidance of political partisanship. Business has always been concerned with the rituals of ethics, the scrupulous observing of contractual obligations, not with its dogmas, man's relation to man.

How ironic that Stiles, who abominated slavery and labored to end it; who in Newport, where slaves were a valuable commodity, had helped found the American Colonization Society; and later in New Haven had continued his agitation—that Stiles should be the one to send Whitney South! In June of 1792 Stiles recorded his joy at the news that "Mr. Wilberforce advocated a Bill in Parliament for total abolition of slavery—amended to gradual Abolition—passed 150 Majority. Wonderful." By contrast the situation in America was

not bright: "Lately an insurrection of 6 or 700 Negroes in Virginia
East Shore. Where will this end?" That same year, in September,
Stiles urged Whitney to accept the teaching position in South Carolina; it was he who introduced Whitney, the ablest engineer of his
day, to Mrs. Nathanael Greene, at whose plantation he invented the
cotton gin which fastened slavery on the nation.

Blake, who had come on a temporary basis to help his uncle prepare for the Miller & Whitney settlement, stayed on, taking over
much tedious detail, assuming greater and greater responsibility in
the manufactory, as Whitney increasingly suffered from illness.

"My health has been very poor for two months past," he had written Josiah in November, 1820. "In addition to my other infirmities
I have for the last five weeks been struggling with an unusually
severe attack of influenza. For a week past I have been almost wholly
confined to my house. . . . It is almost nine weeks now since my
manufactory has been wholly stopped—during which time I have
been anxiously engaged in rebuilding the Dam. This has been an
arduous task, especially considering my bad state of health—and
it will be now, I expect, ten Days before the works will be in operation. . . . I wish you *not to fail* to send me a Barrel of *good cran-
berries.*"

It was at this time that Whitney endorsed Ithiel Towne's lattice-
truss wooden bridge, a structure that was to become a commonplace
feature of the New England scene. The first one built (1823) was
covered, and its one-hundred foot span crossed Mill River at Whitney's manufactory. Whitney recommended it because "its simplicity,
lightness, strength, cheapness & durability are, in my opinion, such
as to render it highly worthy of attention."

In January of 1821 he announced to his brother the glad tidings
that "We had a Son born on the 24th Nov. [Eli Whitney, Jr.] He has
never had a sick hour—Thrives very well &, of course, is a very promising boy. . . . My family & our friend here are all in good health—
my own health not so good as it was some weeks ago." *

* This is the only birth date of any of Whitney's four children that can be
stated with certainty. Frederick C. Pierce, in *The Descendants of John Whitney*,
does give Nov. 13, 1817, as the date of the first daughter, Frances Edwards, but
omits any date for the second daughter, Elizabeth Fay (named for Whitney's

Early that June Whitney heard that his good friend Wadsworth had resigned as head of the Ordnance Department and that Colonel George Bomford had been named to succeed him. This change did not mean a renewal of the struggle for power, but was made necessary by the fact that his friend had been forced, by illness, to quit. Whitney went to Washington, partly on business—to meet with Bomford and John C. Calhoun, the Secretary of War—and partly to satisfy himself that Wadsworth was not suffering from inattention and neglect. Whitney knew what it meant to be without family or proper home; he brought his dying friend back to New Haven and "located him in very comfortable lodgings at the house of Elisha Lewis, where he will probably remain till his fate is decided. I am not without hope that he may recover, but I think the chance is much against him." Summer passed and autumn came in violently —the great September gale blew down hundreds of chimneys as though they had been cornstalks—and the Indian summer days that followed—golden but short and sad—witnessed the swift ebbing of Wadsworth's strength. Though Whitney himself was ill enough so that he could "attend to business but very little," he visited him daily and was with Wadsworth when he died. "He retained his senses & the recognition of his Friends until a few hours before his exit." Whitney was gratified that "the funeral which took place yesterday, was very respectably attended."

"As to myself," Whitney wrote Stebbins as 1822 was starting, "my health is but indifferent—much as it has been for two or three years past. I live in the town of N Haven and continue to carry on my Manufactory as heretofore. I contrive many new mechanical projects—& execute but few of them—much fewer than I should if my health was good. My family are, & have uniformly been blessed with good health—I have four children—the third is a son, the other three are Daughters—they are all now in perfect health. I live in a small hired house, where it would give me *large pleasure* to see you."

---

mother). Whitney, in a letter dated April 8, 1819, mentions "the situation of my family" as an excuse for his not having answered earlier; it would seem safe to assume that she was born in March, 1819. For the third daughter, Susan Edwards (named for her mother's older sister), Pierce gives January, 1821—obviously an error. She was probably born in December, 1821; she died when she was only twenty-one months old.

His words have the quiet contentment of a traveler who has re-turned to familiar scenes of which he dreamed when far from home in strange, distant lands. In the invention of the cotton gin, in the countless devices he had created to carry out his system of mass production, he has satisfied the demands of his society and his own genius; here, in the hired house with Henrietta and his four children, he had happily fulfilled the long-postponed needs of spirit and body. He had established his own family.

1822 had come in with a serene happiness—it ended in a pro-longed, discordant crash of pain. "On the 22nd July I left this Place [New Haven] for Washington City," Whitney wrote to his brother at the beginning of September. "I sustained the journey as well as I expected—the first 14 days after I arrived there, my health was as good as it has been at any time for two years past. I returned to this place on the 22nd Aug. & suffered much on the journey home —for the last three weeks my health has been very poor—I am however more comfortable than I was a fortnight ago. My success in the accomplishment of the business which carried me to Wash-ington was equal to my expectations, which were not great. I have made some engagements relative to the manufacture of muskets which it will require five or six years to fulfil & tho' the terms are not such as to afford much profit—it is better than to let my works lie still."

Always Whitney had been a fighter. He had fought to get his education, he had fought the southern planters for his patent rights, he had fought to save the manufactory from Irvine; and now, with the same steadfastness, the same courage, the same optimism, he fought to live. His five years of happy marriage, his still young children, his third contract just entered on made him struggle to sur-mount pain and replenish his own diminishing strength. Only an old warrior would have stayed on, fighting his great suffering.

Denison Olmsted, professor of Natural History at Yale, who wrote a short biography of Whitney in 1832 and called on many friends to embellish the bare outline of Whitney's achievements, relied on "a near friend and eye witness" for the sequence of Whitney's last illness. "In September, 1822, immediately after his return from Washington, he experienced the first attack of his complaint, which immediately threatened his life. [Whitney was suffering from an enlargement of the prostate gland—a condition that was then recognized but for which there was no cure.] For three weeks he suffered paroxysms of pain, of from thirty to forty minutes continuance, severe beyond description. These were repeated six or eight times in every twenty four hours. For six weeks he was confined to his room, at the end of which time he was able to walk about the house, and to enjoy the society of his friends."

During the following months Whitney alternated between the dread attacks that held him in a vise of pain and periods of comparative ease when he could enjoy the sweetness of the life around him. In mid-November he wrote Josiah that "my health has improved since I wrote you last & I think is improving tho' I am still confined to my House. . . . Judging by the price which you pay for my wine, I think you are disposed to have me live rather extravagantly. . . . We shall be very glad to see you here whenever you can make it convenient to come. Your sister Henrietta, has lately taken the strange freak into her head of offering you to every Old Maid she sees— They all say yes—& thank'y too. I have no doubt that they will, every one of them, be greatly disappointed—& that she will get herself into a sad scrape." It is the postscript that suddenly makes the sick room, the doomed man, the happy innocence of his children, the gracious sunlight of that late fall afternoon fuse into an unforgettable picture: "Fanny and Elizabeth have just returned from school & Fanny says 'give my Love to Uncle Josiah & tell him he must come & see me—' Elizabeth [in the serious solo of a two-and-a-half-year old who listens and repeats her older sister's words] 'Give my Love to uncle Josiah & tell him I want to see him very much.'"

In January, 1823, he had a bad relapse. Eli Blake, who the previous summer had married, settled in Whitneyville so that he could supervise the manufactory for his uncle. For a week it was feared that Whitney could not survive; but he did. James Carrington, the inspector, wrote to Lee at the Springfield Armory that "his mind seems much more occupied with the cares and business of this world than with any apprehensions respecting the future." A few weeks later he noted that "Mr. Whitney is supposed to be better and is in fact more comfortable, but yet suffers much and is very apprehensive that he has got to suffer more."

And then, as soon as he was granted some relief, his children were in his room. A friend of Josiah's "called this afternoon about an hour & an half before sunset & brought the little Books which you are so good as to send. They were all greatly delighted & have been wholly occupied with them till they went to bed. Eli could not consent to go to bed without taking his into bed with him—Fanny & Elizabeth have directed me to give 'their love to Uncle Josiah & tell him they thank him very much for the beautiful Picture Books which he has been so kind as to send—& that they will try to keep them nice & clean till he comes to N Haven again.'"

Back and forth, back and forth the indicator swung erratically between the extreme of pain and the quiet pleasures of children and family. If, as he once said, it was like suffering "the rack of the Inquisition," he examined his particular rack as earlier he had studied the intricacy of the musket. In this he was helped by his doctor, Nathan Smith, one of the great men of his profession. The fifth graduate of the Harvard Medical School, he had subsequently studied at Glasgow, Edinburgh, and London; he started the Dartmouth Medical School, later established a medical department at Bowdoin, and came to Yale in 1821 to organize the medical school there. Of him Oliver Wendell Holmes said that he did not occupy "a chair, but a whole settee of professorships"—teaching anatomy, surgery, chemistry, and clinical medicine. Dr. Smith told Whitney exactly what his condition was, and Professor Silliman, who was a frequent visitor, remembered that Whitney "examined with great care and coolness the best medical writers on his disease; he inspected their plates, . . . he critically recorded such facts in his case as interested him the most and . . . acted rather as if he himself had been the physician than the patient. During this period, embracing at intervals several years, he devised and caused to be constructed various instruments for his own personal use."

Silliman was awed by a mind strong and heroic enough to mobilize its creative gifts to solve a desperate problem. "Nothing that he ever invented, not even the cotton gin, discovered a more perfect comprehension of the difficulties to be surmounted, or evinced more efficient ingenuity. . . . From his sick bed he wrote both to London and Paris for materials important to his plans, and he lived . . . to apply them in the way that he had intended. He was perfectly successful, so far as any mechanical means could afford relief. . . . I urged Mr Whitney, and the late Dr. Smith [he died in 1829], his attending physician, to make sure of these inventions * while it was possible, but I believe no record was ever made of them, and it is but too probable that the instruments were lost."

The years of his last illness saw no decline in his extraordinary mental powers. It might have been then, when he was confined so closely to his room, and noticed how his children naturally wanted to explore where they were not supposed to, that he designed bureaus which removed temptation from the very young: the drawers were opened or locked by a single key in the top drawer. The mechanism is the same as that found in every modern business desk where one drawer locks and opens all the others.

In the summer of 1824, the superintendent of the Springfield Armory asked his advice on a series of problems, and Whitney, who had "for two or three days been more comfortable," apologized that he could only "make some desultory remarks." He noted that "it is five or six years since I originated the plan of driving a trip hammer by a Belt or Strap. [Lee had suggested refinements in the 'space between the Cogs or Cams.']. . . . It is found in practice to answer remarkably well & I have no doubt that it is a very great improvement. I believe that a hammer of 500 to 1000 wt. may in most situations be driven by a belt with great advantage—upon the Principle a number of hammers, say 8 or 10, may be operated by one wheel with great convenience. . . . This principle opens a great field for improvement in the hammer itself & renders every moving power applicable to driving hammers with great advantage & convenience.

"I have a further invention for drawing, forging & fashioning Metals which is based on a principle entirely new & from which I have great expectations. If my life should be spared . . . I shall test the principle by actual experiment in the course of this present year.

* It is most probable that Whitney designed a flexible catheter for his use. Benjamin Franklin, about 1784, is said to have made the first one.

If it answers my expectations it will form a new era in the business of forging Iron & Steel. . . . When will you be here? I wish to converse with you on several different subjects. My health is very infirm otherwise I would come to Springfield."

His life was not spared him. In November, young Letitia Morse wrote to her gifted husband Samuel, to whom Whitney and his wife had sat for their portraits, that Mr. Whitney's "disorder has taken a different turn and is attended with considerable fever. Dr. Smith who seldom speaks discouragingly, told Mr. Silliman last week that if Mr. W wished to make any arrangement as to his worldly affairs, now was the time, for he was past medical aid. Mrs. Whitney's children have been threatened with the croup, they are getting better but the alarming illness of Mr. W weighs heavily upon her spirit. Father and Mother called there this afternoon but saw none of the family." On that same afternoon Whitney's will, which Simeon Baldwin had drawn up after several discussions, was signed in the presence of witnesses.

Terrible days and nights dragged out into weeks. Susan Johnson, who came to be with her younger sister, wrote to her husband of such a day and night. "Mr. Whitney continued quite comfortable until four in the morning, when he had a slight chill which was followed by a pain in his head, but that mitigated and there was a prospect of a quiet day, but soon after noon he grew rapidly worse, and the evening passed in a very distressing manner. Between 9 and 10 there was every appearance that a dissolution was at hand, his distress was very great, and he did not know his wife. This was agonizing to her, and she was obliged to leave the room; he continued in this state till ½ past 11 when his fever mittigated and his mind was clear and calm but very feeble.—he was however so comfortable, that Henrietta persuaded me to go to bed, and I lay down with my clothes on about 12. I was not called up—Dr. Smith sat up untill one, and Henrietta and Mr. Sabin by turns the rest of the night—and he was tolerably quiet. About 8 this morning he had another severe ague, which the Doctor found he could not support, but it had gone off and the fever is now increasing and we know not what the next hour may bring. The Dr. says he may live thru the day and probably will

—but thinks he will not continue thru the night. There now seems no interval of ease to him."

Still he was not ready to die. Pain, fever, delirium were pushed aside for moments of clarity and concentrated thought; he had made his will, but its terms did not satisfy him. It almost seems as though for six weeks he held off death so that he might make his final wishes equitable and just. The long codicil that he signed on Friday, January 7, 1825, expressed these final wishes; it also insured the continuity of his manufactory. [See Appendix E.]

He died the next day. "To the last," Silliman wrote, "he maintained the observance of order and proper attention to his person."

Whitney's death only marked the end of the first phase of the business he had established. Its continuance was assured by the energy and competence of his two nephews, Philos and Eli Blake, to whom, during their childhood and youth, he had been a father. In the mass production of muskets, they made the critical transition from those manufactured under Whitney himself to those manufactured by the Whitney method. Under their guidance the momentum generated by the man who had founded the system never slackened; the manufactory remained productive until its direction could be assumed by the gifted, the able, and equally ambitious Eli Whitney, Jr.

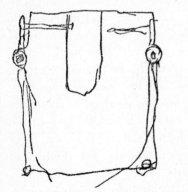

"This sketch was made by Mr. Whitney but a few days before his death, & is believed to be the last sketch ever made by him.—" (Eli Whitney Blake)

The American Scene
after Eli Whitney

Consider Whitney's life and work. His talent for originality, his ambitions, and his solid, merited success are easily encompassed; equally understandable are the directions and limitations imposed by the needs of his society and the tools which previous artisans had put into his hands—consider all this, and add the colors proper to his personal pilgrimage, and still his life and work appear remote. They seem to have been finished long ago; they are even pervaded by the condescending quality of quaintness. These are tricks wrought by time and modern complexities.

His career had been short—only thirty years of intensive effort—but it was to have a long sequel.

Whitney began his work in a nation newly formed, a nation whose founders (save only for the West-Indian-born Hamilton) sought to perpetuate an independent yeoman agriculture and an energetic commercial trade—economies in which they had been reared and in which they had prospered. Just twenty years after the Constitution had been adopted, Whitney completed his first musket contract, and the two streams of force flowing from his work were ready to help reshape American society—two streams destined to come into partial conflict. Eli Whitney of the cotton gin, which gave to the southern plantation system and chattel slavery dominion over hundreds of thousands of square miles, was also Eli Whitney of the standardization of machined parts, which gave to the North, and eventually the whole nation, a dynamic industrialism—a quantity production of inexpensive goods that lifted the standard of well-being, and a uniformity of consumption that went far to knit the population into a homogeneous whole. From the one stream of force came national disunity; from the other came progressive integration.

Implicit in many of his letters is his awareness of the sharp difference between Georgia and Connecticut, between white cotton fields and whirring shops, between the agrarian ideas of Governor James Jackson and the Hamiltonian aims of Secretary Oliver Wolcott. When his final illness gave him time for contemplation, did he wonder about the future of these diverse segments of America? Whitney had not intended to affect the ultimate destiny of the South —but he had; he had not intended to remake the national economy and outlook—but to that, too, he had contributed significantly.

There was drama at Mulberry Grove when Whitney (the Yankee schoolmaster, as he must have been called by the planters who visited there) put a few bolls of upland cotton into his crude, makeshift model, turned the crank, and demonstrated to Miller and the assembled Greene family how the fiber could be torn from its green seeds. That moment proclaimed the future cotton belt, three hundred miles wide and reaching fifteen hundred miles deep to the 97th meridian; sun and rain and heat in proper proportions for cotton's growth set it apart and made it a region distinct, a region which within half a century would arrogate to itself the privileges (it even claimed the divine right) of king of the world's commerce. The gin turned cotton cultivation into a Golconda; in time the crop required more than 25,000 gins.

But in 1793 the cotton belt was still primitive wilderness. The Indians, respectful of the land, had hardly touched the broad bands of towering, tasseled canebrakes that marked the rivers or the unending forests of its upland. Magically, the gin slashed down the canebrakes and leveled the trees; cotton fields were planted and harvested; and then, as the soil's wealth was soon spent, the fields were abandoned and left to clothe themselves poorly in foxtail and broom sedge. For planters bought land as they might a hoe or gin—cheaply, and with the expectation of wearing it out. Here and there a voice protested the wave of migration that from Virginia to Texas passed over the country like a devastating scourge. At once man formed a new adjustment to the land, and the white race made a new adjustment to the black race.

The cotton gin, finding the plantation in decline, revitalized it, and the plantation system carried slavery across vast areas; slavery spread from the Ashley-Cooper to the Trinity River. The cotton plantation gave the Negro a new value; slavery, which had been dying out, was resuscitated; suddenly it possessed a vigorous and aggressive life. By 1830 cotton had overspread the Georgia-Carolina uplands and pushed deep into neighboring states. When Whitney first traveled across South Carolina, the upland counties were but 5 per cent Negro; when he died the slave population approached 50 per cent. By 1850 King Cotton ruled Alabama and Mississippi, and plantations filled the Delta country of Louisiana and Arkansas; by 1860 the plantation lorded it over eastern Texas. The plantation system dominated the economy—though nine-tenths of the southern cultivators were small proprietors—as the planter regime spoke out for the Lower South—though not one-third of the southern whites had an economic stake in the system.

The planter regime was more than a way of making money: it was a way of life; it organized society around the "peculiar institution" and created a well defined cultural outlook. Its prevailing aristocratic tone could be partly traced back to feudal Europe, and its romanticism was imported, novel by novel, from Sir Water Scott. It stridently reiterated the doctrine of the "inherent inferiority" of large human groups—a justification which Whitney's New England found abhorrent; its assurance expressed itself in maintaining high prices paid for slaves, prices that forced Virginia to become, as Jefferson's grandson bitterly declared, "a *negro* raising state for other states; she produces enough for her own supply and six thousand for sale"; it was hostile to industry and trade, and openly contemptuous of the greasy mechanic and the counter-jumper; its intellectual apologist, Fitzhugh, seriously proposed that workers in English and New England cotton mills "should be made slaves of the owners who must give them support and kindly treatment."

No regime was ever more static. It resisted political change, theological change, economic change, social change. Criticism made it touchy, and it loftily demanded to be left unmolested; it was limited, self-satisfied, caught by the image of its own picturesqueness, rejecting the untidy, confusing rush of the Northern and Western World.

As with his invention of the cotton gin, so also his contract for muskets with standardized, interchangeable parts ushered in events remarkable and far-reaching. In Whitney's work, manufacturing gins had been the antecedent necessary to project quickly and surely the possibilities of mass-producing muskets. Had he not lost in the factory fire "several machines that were used for different purposes"; simple machines, no doubt, yet specialized and designed for a uniform output? The machines which he mentioned in his arresting proposal to Wolcott, three years later, were even then, in an inner vision, already made. The delay which beset him in fitting up his manufactory with machines was the same kind of perplexing and irritating delay met with in "tooling-up" American munitions plants in 1941–1943. Once the machines were installed, once the tooling-up was completed, the problem was solved; production came with a rush.

The concept of standardizing parts so that they would be interchangeable did not originate with Whitney alone. Yet, independently, he conceived the idea, as did also Leblanc and Bentham and Brunel. Here the question of priority is misleading—independent invention by three widely separated men is not unique. What can be asserted is that in America Whitney was the first to make the concept into an industrial system.

He laid a primitive but broad foundation; on it, part by part, was built the industrial edifice which has made the United States. After Whitney comes a procession of men who developed his initial masterly achievement. Samuel Colt's first sizable order for revolvers was produced in the Whitney Shops (the management having been but recently assumed by Whitney's son), where special machinery was devised to make the intricate parts of the six-shooter. Isaac M. Singer's mass-produced sewing machines were young industrial America's first calling cards left in homes throughout the world; their accuracy of performance, delicacy of finish, and numerous parts set a level of achievement never before attained. Cyrus H. McCormick and his rivals mass-produced agricultural implements that revolutionized northern farming. The new shoe machinery of Lyman Blake manufactured footgear in quantity and in time to equip the armies of Grant and Sherman. Each utilized the skills of his predecessors, each added

Whitney's Short Description
of the Gin

The principal parts of this machine are 1. The Frame. 2. the Cylinder. 3. the Breastwork. 4. the Clearer and 5. the Hopper.

I. The frame, by which the whole work is supported and kept together, is of a square or parallelogramic form, and proportioned to the other parts as may be most convenient.

II. The Cylinder is of wood: Its form is perfectly described by its name, and its dimention may be from six to nine inches in Diameter and from two to five feet in length. This Cylinder is placed horizontally across the frame, leaving room for the clearer on one side and the hopper on the other. In the Cylinder is fixed an iron axis which may pass quite thro', or consist only of gudgeons driven into each end. There are shoulders on this axis to prevent any horizontal variation and it extends so far without the form as to admit a winch at one end, by which it is put in motion and so far at the other end as to receive the whirl by which the clearer is turned. The surface of the Cylinder is filled with teeth set in annular rows which are at such a distance from each other as to admit a cotton seed to play freely in the space between them. The space between each tooth in the same row is so small as not to admit a seed nor half a seed to enter it. These teeth are made of stiff Iron wire, driven into the wood of the Cylinder. ["Steel wire would perhaps be best if it were not too expensive," say the specifications in the Long Description]. The teeth are all inclined the same way and in such a manner that the angle included between the tooth and a tangent drawn from the point into which the tooth is driven, will be about 55° or 60° Degrees. The gudgeons of the Cylinder run in brass boxes which are in two parts one of which is fixed in the wood of the frame and the other is confined down upon the axis with screws.

III. The Breastwork is fixed above the cylinder parallel and contiguant to the same. It has transverse grooves or openings thro' which the rows of teeth pass as the cylinder revolves, and its use is to obstruct the seeds while the Cotton is carried forward thro' the grooves by the teeth. The thickness of the breastwork is two and half or three inches and the under side of it is made of iron or brass.

IV. The Clearer is placed horizontal with and parallel to the Cylinder. Its length is the same as that of the Cylinder, and its diameter is proportioned by convenience. There are two four or more Brushes or rows of Bristles fixed in the surface of the clearer in such a manner that the ends of the bristles will sweep the surface of the Cylinder. Its axis and boxes are similar to those of the Cylinder. It is turned by means of a band and whirls; moves in a contrary direction from the Cylinder by which it is put in motion and so far outruns it as to sweep the cotton from the teeth as fast as it is carried thro' the Breastwork. The periphery of the whirls is spiral and the band a broad strap of Leather.

V. One side of the Hopper is formed by the Breastwork, the two ends by the frame and the other side is movable from and towards the Breastwork so as to make the hopper more or less capacious.

The cotton is put into the Hopper, carried thro' the Breastwork by the teeth, brushed off from the teeth by the Clearer and flies off from the Clearer with the assistance of the air, by its own centrifugal force. The machine is turned by water, horses, or in any other way as is most convenient.

There are several modes of making the various parts of this machine, which together with their particular shape and formation, are pointed out and explained in a description with Drawings.

Letters from Robert Fulton and Oliver Evans Relating to Patent Laws

Whitney was not alone in feeling that the existing Patent Law offered inventors neither protection nor incentive. Among his papers he kept letters from Robert Fulton and Oliver Evans, two outstanding inventors of the day; their words made him feel that they shared his anger and dissatisfaction.

Fulton wrote to Whitney on April 4, 1811:

You justly remark that in proportion to an Invention being beneficial to the public, unprincipaled individuals feel interested in depriving the Inventor of his mental property, of this, you, Sir Richard Arkwright and Watt have had more experience than any other men, and you have done more for mankind; Our courts, are beginning to see the importance of holding out encouragement to men of inventive powers by guarding their rights, but to this end Inventors and patentees must combine to defend themselves against the many.

After taking up and laboring through the difficulties of the steamboats, a subject which was universally ridiculed as impracticable, After proving their practicability & utility to the world and accomodating the public with a conveyance from New York to Albany which for elegance conveniance and Rapidity is superior to any conveyance on this globe, And which should be considered an ornament to the arts in our country. A Company of speculators at Albany without the least mechanical knowledge without the least pretention to Invention, have Built two boats in which they have copied me exact, with a hope that the imperfection of the law will permit them to run and earn money to contend with us in law until the suit be decided. To prevent which I am about to apply for an Injunction and sought your case as one in point. As my suit will be a conspicuous object and one of magnitude all artists and inventors are highly interested in the decision. I shall perhaps be under the necessity of soliciting your kindness to attend as evidence of the boats being copies from me.

The inventors did combine, as Fulton suggested. The next October, Whitney heard from Oliver Evans:

Having heard that Doctr. Mitchell has expressed his doubts of the patent bill ever being passed by Congress unless some active man in behalf of the Patentees attend the Congress to urge it—

Some of us Patentees have undertaken to make up a purse to employ Counsel to attend as our Agent for the purpose and Mr James Ray Counselor at law . . . who appears to have made the patent law his particular study we think proper to engage him

Mr Robert Fulton will give Certain $200 and in case of success to obtain a law for 21 years 150$ more and for a law for 28 years 150$ more making 500$

Thus Robert Fulton certain $200 for 21 yrs 150 for 28 yrs 150—500

O Evans do——	200 do——	150 do——	150—500
George Clymer do——	50 do——	50 do——	50—150
Evans [Oliver's son] do——	33-⅓ do——	33-⅓ do——	33-⅓-100
	483-⅓	383-⅓	1250

We wish to make up 6 or 700$ Certain about 1200 for success to obtain a Law for 21 years and 2,000$ for [letter torn] patentees 28 years

We will thank you to throw in your mite. It must be done by a few that have began to receive something for their inventions the others can pay nothing and we must rely on them to refund us a part if they please if not we must bear it ourselves but try what you can get

I am strongly inclined to beleive the Bill will never be passed without such exertions altho I beleive that no law was ever passed that will prove so beneficial.

Whitney left no record indicating whether he subscribed to the inventor's lobby fund for which Evans was soliciting, nor does it appear that anyone joined him when he appeared before Congress in July, 1812, to argue for a revision of the law.

Statement of the Referees:
Miller & Whitney Final Settlement

We the subscribers referees mutually chosen & appointed by Eli Whitney of New Haven on the one part, & Russel Goodrich as Executor of the last will & testament of Phineas Miller late of Georgia deceased of the other part,—to hear and award on certain controversies subsisting between them relative to the settlement of the concern of the late copartnership between the said Eli Whitney & the said Phineas Miller under the firm of Miller & Whitney as by the annexed submission Dated Dec.^m 5, 1818 appears, having accepted the appointment & taken on ourselves the burthen of an Award; met & heard the parties with their exhibits on the said first day of s.^d Dec.^r & from day to day until this fifth day of the same month, & having carefully examined the articles of copartnership between the said Miller & Whitney & their accounts & Books & the several claims of each partner on the firm, so far as they had become the subject of dispute or controversy between the parties to said submission—and taking as the basis of our proceedings the adjustment and statement amicably made between the said Eli Whitney & the said Russel Goodrich & which they agreed to before us, we find thereby, that the said Phineas Miller had received of the company property & ought to be debitted therefor the sum of .... Dol. 22632.65
& that he has assumed & paid of the
company debts to the amount of 2584.76

leaving a balance of company funds of 20047.89 in the hands of said Miller. And the said Russel Goodrich claimed a further allowance in favour of said Miller of Dol. 3859.81 cts. being the amount of sundry balances, transferred from the cash account of Miller & Whitney to the private Book of said Miller, against the s^d Miller & Whitney—and we are of opinion & do award that the same be allowed as a credit to the said Miller for so much advanced by him in cash for the use of Miller & Whitney and upon the further claim of the said Russel Goodrich that an allowance to the said Miller be made of the balance of sundry accounts transfered directly from the journal of Miller & Whitney to the private books of said Miller & there setled which balance amounts to Dol. 1196.28 cents we are of opinion & do award that the same be allowed as a further credit to the s^d Miller as so much paid by him on account of Miller & Whitney—which two sums thus allowed amount to Dol 5056.09 & being deducted from the amount of company funds in his hands as stated above leaves the balance in his hands fourteen thousand nine hundred & ninety one $\dfrac{80}{100}$ Dollars.

It also appears by said statement & is agreed by & between the parties that the said Eli Whitney had received of the company property & ought to be debited therefor, Dol 63,984.81 Cts. of which he paid over to the said Phineas Miller Dol 10,000—which makes part of the sum in his hands, and that said Whitney had assumed & paid of the company debts etc to the amount Dol 23986.—and the said Whitney claimed an allowance for his expenses & compensation for six journeys to the Southern States on the business of the company stated at Dol 15000 & the s^d Goodrich insisted that he was entitled to his expenses & nothing more & the said Whitney also claimed such Damages as the referees should award against said Miller for a breach of the articles of copartnership by entering into extensive land speculation, which he contended deprived the company of his, said Millers, services & funds, subjected it to expensive agencies, & injured its concerns more than the value of s^d Millers interest therein; which claims the said Goodrich also resisted & we the said referees, having fully heard the parties on said claims, do find that the said Whitney is entitled to his expenses & compensation for five journeys at the rate of two thousand Dollars each & for one by water & for a shorter time one thousand, making in the whole eleven thousand Dollars & we do award that said Whitney be allowed that sum therefor—and we also find that said Whitney is entitled to Damages on account of said Millers breach of the articles of copartnership as aforesaid to the amount of 7500 Dol from said Millers share in the funds of s^d Company: we therefore award that double that sum viz. the sum of Fifteen thousand Dollars be charged to s^d Company against their funds in the hands of said Whitney which being deducted leaves a balance of company funds in his hands of four thousand Dollars. It also appears to us & on the agreement of the parties we find that the said Russel Goodrich in his individual capacity & as agent for s^d concern is indebted to the late firm of Miller & Whitney in the sum of Three thousand one hundred & sixteen Dollars & twenty one cents, for so much of the funds of the said company now in his hands and that there are no other Debts either on Book or by Note or otherwise which are of any value, or can be considered as collectable, & it is further agreed by the parties that they know of no other funds or property belonging to said company & that no debts are due from said company. We the said referees therefore find that the funds of said Company consist of the balances found as aforesaid, viz.

In the hands of said Miller at his decease .... 14991.80 cts.
In the hands of said Whitney 4000.00
In the hands of s^d R. Goodrich & due from him 3116.21

making in the whole .... 22108.01 cts.

which sum ought to be divided in equal shares yielding to each copartner . . . . 11054. Dollars and to effect the same, that the said Whitney, in addition to the four thousand Dollars now in his hands, is entitled to collect, receive & retain, the said sum of Three thousand one hundred and sixteen $\frac{21}{100}$ Dollars, due from said Goodrich as agent as aforesaid, & the remaining sum of three thousand nine hundred thirty seven $\frac{79}{100}$ Dol from the estate of said Phineas Miller. And we do accordingly award that the said sum of Three thousand one hundred & sixteen Dollars and twenty one cents when collected from Russel Goodrich be retained by said Eli Whitney, and we do further award that the said Eli Whitney recover, have & receive from the estate of the said Phineas Miller the sum of Three thousand nine hundred & thirty seven Dollars & seventy nine cents: And that this award shall be final & conclusive between the parties, & shall end all controversies & mutual claims subsisting, or which may arise between them, respecting said agreement or articles of copartnership, & the construction thereof, & all accounts subsisting between them relative thereto, and of all claims & demands which either party has or may have on the other relating to s^d copartnership or any thing respecting the same.

In witness whereof We the said referees have hereunto subscribed our names in the City of New Haven this fifth day of Decr A. D. 1818.

SIMEON BALDWIN
NATHANIEL ROSSITER } Referees

Remarks Relating to Whitney and the New Haven Bank

The final settlement of Miller & Whitney contained the findings of the referees; but the "accounts & books" are missing, and approximation and inference based on a few scattered notations collected at that time to substantiate the opposing claims must be offered in lieu of exact, verifiable figures. It is important to consider the New Haven Bank, on whose books Whitney is listed among the first stockholders as the owner of twenty shares valued at $4,000. The date is October, 1795.

From Whitney's papers his purchasing with his own funds such a sizable block of stock at that time is utterly inconceivable. Only three years before he had been graduated from college, still dependent on his father's generosity; he had borrowed money from New Haven friends to go South and there had foregone the salary as tutor offered by Mr. Dupont and stayed on as Catherine Greene's guest to make a model of the gin. For $1,000 he had sold Miller a half-interest in a valuable invention in order to finance himself and his workshop. He had delivered the first gins to Mulberry Grove in May, 1794; the factory was destroyed in March, 1795; and, by the end of that year, between the illegal gins and the suspicion of the British spinners, Miller & Whitney was close to bankruptcy. Whitney had succeeded in borrowing money to rebuild his workshop, but during the next two years neither he nor Miller could raise the fare to get him to England. With what, then, could he have purchased the stock? His ownership cannot indicate Whitney's financial status at that time; rather, it is most probable, Whitney permitted the use of his name for the purchase of the stock so that in the face of the limitations set by the bank's charter a particular group of men could secure control of the bank.

On a page in a notebook (undated, and subsequent entries are without proper sequence) Whitney wrote: "Account of Miller & Whitney's Debts Assumed by E. Whitney 1798," and under it "Amt. due N. H. Bank—$4685"; under this is his notation, "Interest 7 years & 2 mos.—$2913.30." The total is $7,598.30. This entry, with its legend of Whitney's borrowing from the New Haven Bank, raises more questions than it answers. When did he get the loan? At what date did he make the entry? One can only surmise that it was made in 1818, when, going through his papers with young Blake, he collected all disbursements relating to the ginning venture to document his claims at the final settlement. Other pages in the notebook contain the following headings: "Land Concern P[hineas] M[iller] & J. C. N[ightingale] to Miller & Whitney; Phineas Miller to E. Whitney; P. Miller to Miller & Whitney; Miller & Whitney in acct with Eli Whitney Cr[editor]; Estate of Genl. Greene in acct with Miller & Whitney; Jno. C. Nightingale to Miller & Whitney." As Whitney wrote Blake, when soliciting his help, "These concerns are intricate, numerous & difficult."

What significant dates span the interest that ran for "7 years & 2 mos?" The time when he received his first advance from the government on his musket contract (August, 1798) to the time when he was notified that South Carolina had paid the whole purchase price (October, 1805) covers a period of seven years and two months.

It seems reasonable to suppose that getting the advance from the government gave Whitney assurance that he would be able to discharge his personal obligation; the contract, by its terms, would be completed within two years—and Whitney hoped to make a substantial profit. But actually it was the then unforeseen sale to South Carolina that provided him with the required cash. Of the $22,418 Adam Gilchrist advised him the State had paid, Whitney instructed Wolcott to transfer $15,000 to his account; the remainder, unaccounted for in any record, would cover the bank loan and interest charges.

How Whitney, without any personal assets in 1798, could have obtained such a large loan might be explained by his receiving permission to pledge the stock bought in his name as collateral on the loan. The New Haven merchants judged him a good risk.

Estate, Will, and Codicil of Eli Whitney

Not Whitney's estate, which was impressive, nor the will by which he extended his protecting care to his widow and three children distinguishes Whitney from other rich, responsible men of his period. The codicil, framed with his last living strength, provided his manufactory with trained and devoted supervision; it became the instrument by which the system he had pioneered remained intact and functioning without interruption.

Whitney left considerable wealth. The inventory of his estate made a year after his death, was appraised by Baldwin, his lawyer, Elisha Munson, an astute New Haven merchant, and James Carrington, the government inspector who later became Whitney's foreman; the total for the items listed was $63,085.37. (They had written off the $18,200 Whitney had paid for 174 shares of Eagle Bank stock as a loss. Nine months after his death the bank failed.) Not included in the inventory were other items of value: his personal property, his "Plate and all household articles & implements; my Horse, Chaise & Sleigh, with the articles belonging to the same; . . . also my Watch & all my wearing apparel; . . . my Books, except Rees's Cyclopedia, the Repertory of Arts and Manufactures and such others as relate to the Physical sciences which I give to my son Eli & leave in her care to be delivered to him," which were given without inventory to his wife; nor did the inventory include almost $70,000 Whitney held in personal notes—he, who had known the anguished need to borrow, seemed never to have refused a loan to friend or workman, associate or relative. Also missing was an appraisal of a most valuable but intangible part of the estate—the gun manufactory's goodwill and earning capacity. How could they assess its worth? At best the arms trade was uncertain; Whitney's illness had injured the business; the executors had been forced to ask the government to postpone the first delivery under the new contract for two years, from January, 1824, to January, 1826; and the capacity of his nephews to continue the work still had to be proved.

The importance of his estate, even with those sizable omissions, can best be judged by a measuring stick scaled to times when a skilled New England millwright or carpenter earned $1.25 a day and the roster of rich New Yorkers included the merchant Archibald Gracie (worth $45,000) and the iron dealer Peter P. Goelet (worth $79,000).

Of the appraised amount, the manufacturing plant accounted for almost one-half the inventory: $20,000 was the valuation placed on the two hundred acres containing the Mill Rock site, with three old houses, a new barn, five stone dwellings built for workmen, and worth $1,250 each, "beautifully constructed, and arranged and a stone store; while the "water privileges, Dam, Bridge, Manufacturing and other buildings and appurtenances thereon exclusive of Machinery" added another $9,500. Real estate and investments—houses and lots in New Haven, "one sixth part of the distillery on Water Street," a small tract of salt meadow, a piece of woodland, a half-interest in a paper mill with its acreage, "millseat privileges and appurtenances"—accounted for $22,000. The balance consisted of farm stock, farm tools and, as the lengthy, detailed inventory shows, materials, tools, and machines used in manufacturing.

From this precise accounting of the contents of the factory at the time of his death, a picture of the arms establishment can be pieced together. It complements Silliman's allusions to a canal Whitney constructed "to take the water from the dam to the forging shop," or the stone work laid in cement composed "of a mixture of iron rust and siliceous and micaceous sand, derived from the grinding of the gun-barrels and other pieces of iron," or the two "buildings for fuel: the one for charcoal, and the other for mineral coal. . . . These store-houses stand by the side of the mountain and at its foot, and by excavating a road in the bank above, the coal carts are driven up to the gable end . . . and their loads are discharged into them by simply tipping up the cart."

He must have continued to use one of the three old houses as his office; there he kept the master jigs and fixtures, patterns and molds and gages, and supplies of rasps, chisels, augurs, and files of all lengths and shapes—smooth, round, square, bastard, whipsaw. The machine and filing shop shared a building; the list mentions "lathe tools, Milling tools & nitching Machine, Drilling machine: caps & appurtenances, Large cast iron Shears New, Screw Machine & apparatus, Stamping Machine 7 tools, 2 Polishing Machines, Breeching vice & tools, Stake & block for Cutting files"—most of the costly items. In another two-story building, the "stocking shop," were quantities of wood and metals, stores of old copper and copper tubing, fence pickets, pine boards and mahogany, English blistered steel, Milan steel and Russian iron, a huge pile of bullhide leather, a box of asphalt, glue by the pound, squares of glass for replacement, a grindstone with frame and crank—more than a hundred separate articles. A forging shop had seven pairs of bellows, anvils for swedging, "I Set Bayonet forging tools, I Set tools to make tumblers, Heading Stake with five heading tools." A lumber yard stacked with piles of cedar posts and timber blocks was situated between the coal houses and the "White Stone Store." This, with two additional ones —the "Barn Store in New Township" and the "Wooster Store in New Township"—held great quantities of cordage, castings, gun stocks, seasoned boards for musket boxes, supplies of milled screws, a Rumford cooking apparatus, and "33 large 33 less and 33 small boxes supposed to contain 66 cotton-gins"—a motley assortment of articles used or discarded, supplies for a going concern, imperfect parts rejected and junked.

In his will Whitney discharged certain obligations clearly and directly. He stipulated that on the house to be built for his widow the large sum of $6,000 was to be spent. No. 80 Elm Street was to be a mansion. He and Henrietta had lived in a "hired house" at 275 Orange Street, though for some years he had planned to erect a suitable home and had bought the lot. He provided a handsome yearly allowance for his family, designated which business properties his son was to inherit and what moneys his daughters would receive on marriage, and arranged an annuity for his sister and cash bequests to her daughters. Other obligations, other properties were not so easily arranged.

In January, 1823, serious illness showed Whitney that he could no longer postpone discussing these problems with his lawyer. Minutes made by Baldwin of their conversation reveal Whitney's concern:

> He lamented that so much of [his property] was in real & unproductive estate. He said he had long intended to make some provision for his Nephews, particularly Philos & Eli W. Blake—but he was desirous rather of placing them in a situation to earn for themselves, than to give them much outright—& with that in view he had been repairing the works at his manufactory & intended to complete the repairs & begin work & to add some new machinery & let them in as partners together with Capt. [Jacob] Whiting upon the new contract which they soon expected to commence.

Over the next two years, Whitney's plans crystallized; the day before he died, having resolved the problems, he signed the codicil to the will.

The codicil was a grand proposal to the nephews to carry on the business and complete the third contract—15,000 muskets to be delivered at the rate of 3,000 a year.* Whitney's terms were so advantageous, and made the nephews party to such benefits, that, even had they not remained out of loyalty, self-interest would have dictated their continuing. Eli Blake, who had assisted his uncle during his last illness, and in the unsettled period after his death managed the arms factory and met the first delivery date of 500 guns as stipulated, only confirmed his position when, with Philos, he entered into an agreement with the executors and trustees. This agreement, made on September 23, 1828, gave legal form to the provisions suggested by Whitney. Each nephew was to receive an annual wage of $400 plus a yearly advance of $500 against profits, and, on final settlement, two-ninths of the profits made on the contract. They were expected to make all routine repairs. On their part, the trustees were to furnish an adequate working capital, and pay

---

* Account books and balance sheets have disappeared. On December 17, 1830, Eli Blake accounted to the trustees for 10,500 muskets: 1,000 delivered in 1827, 3,500 in 1828, 3,000 in 1829, and the final 3,000 in 1830. Since this statement does not include 500 guns delivered on January 1, 1826, the 4,000 muskets remaining on the contract, for which there is no record, might have been delivered between that date and August, 1827, the date Blake's statement begins.

for any extraordinary repairs necessitated by "fire, flood, or any act of God." The Blakes knew how substantial were the moneys they might expect; their combined advances of $1,000 a year would be more than covered by their four-ninths of the profits.

The Blake brothers showed how careful, how thorough had been their uncle's teaching. Not only did they capably execute the contract, they sought to improve the individual parts as before them Whitney had constantly done. It was to justify this—continuing Whitney's unceasing efforts to better the workmanship—not to boast of their abilities, that animated their telling a trustee, "The bolts, screws, and wipers which have been made at this Establishment latterly are far superior to those made at any other establishment either public or private."

Whitney's judgment was vindicated by the success with which the Blakes, brought up to understand mechanical arts and business practices, fulfilled the terms of the contract. Their account, submitted to the trustees, for the period covering August 12, 1827, to November 23, 1830, states that of the $134,031 paid by the government for 10,500 muskets, the costs aggregated $91,200. This schedule of items—it is not bookkeeping in the modern sense of indicating profit and loss, but rather a record of transactions: purchases, rentals from mill houses, wage payments, interest rates, farm expenses, miscellaneous expenditures and receipts—indicates that the margin of profit was $42,831. Under the agreement it was divided, giving four-ninths, or almost $19,000, to the estate, and the same amount to Philos and Eli Blake. Jacob Whiting received one-ninth. Whitney's estate profited as handsomely as did his nephews.

A Note on the Bibliography

The core of this study is the collection of Whitney's papers which Eli Whitney's great-granddaughters have deposited at the Yale University Library. Though many original Whitney letters have been located elsewhere, the bulk of significant and revealing material still was to be found among the family papers—letters, letter books, notebooks, ledger sheets, college papers and diplomas, a miscellany of scribbled notations, copies of memorials addressed to political leaders, Whitney's comments on newspaper clippings (including a stack of lottery announcements!), business papers, real-estate transactions, and his own sketches for tools and machines.

Out of this store of riches, Olmsted and Hammond and Blake have selected letters and used them completely or in part—choice titbits to whet the appetite—to present the major outlines of Whitney's achievements. Their studies have indicated Whitney's place in the development of the United States, depriving us of the excitement of unknown surprises; it has remained our task to try to give the full texture and minor relevant facets of Whitney's life and work.

Historians can be grateful to Henrietta Whitney, the widow. She knew her husband's greatness. It was she who asked Stebbins to return her husband's letters to her for safekeeping; it was she who prompted Elizabeth Whitney Blake, Simeon Baldwin, Denison Olmsted and Benjamin Silliman to record those aspects of Whitney's life which they knew intimately; it was she who requested that his mechanical drawings and business papers be rescued from the manufactory where they lay neglected. But gratitude is edged with suspicion. In the forty-five years of her widowhood (she died on April 16, 1870), she alone had access to the material. The abundance of business letters makes one wonder if the paucity of personal letters

317

was not contrived. How much did she deem it her right to destroy? Why, for example, is Whitney's letter to Stebbins announcing his marriage missing? As she was convinced that her husband's struggles and triumphs belonged to American history, so she must have felt justified in withholding certain areas of his life—she was quite successful in her efforts to see that she remained little more than a name.

It is pleasant to find among the papers a note written by Eli Whitney Blake, then eighty-seven, to his cousin Eli Whitney, Jr.: "Among these papers are 18 letters of our grandfather written by him to your Father at a most interesting period of his life [1791 to 1795]. Your Father, as you know, was to me all that a father could be; & for this reason I prize these letters of his very highly; but I think it more proper that they should be transmitted to posterity in your branch of the family."

Because this study's principal reliance has been on unpublished material, reference footnotes would have only clogged the text. It has been thought best to list page by page the letters quoted under *Sources of Letters Quoted,* pages 333–338. For the convenience of the student, it includes a few significant quotations found in published material.

The following manuscript collections yielded additions to the original Whitney material; the books listed were used to give proper order, meaning, and emphasis to Whitney's background and problems. One is forced to search far and wide to feel at home in the comparatively neglected, strange new world of early American technology. The host of memoirs and histories covering the period are of little value to Whitney's biographer, for they do not mention the inventor, though he moved in the circles which they describe. The writers, agitated by other problems and struggles and achievements, found nothing to note about a respected man preoccupied with tools and technology, machines and industrial methods. In fact, the word "technology" was itself compounded by Jacob Bigelow about the time of Whitney's death.

MANUSCRIPT COLLECTIONS

Connecticut Historical Society
  Wolcott Papers
  Jeremiah Wadsworth Papers
  Collections. 14 vols. 1860–1912.
Connecticut State Library
  Whitney will, codicil, and inventory.

  Connecticut Archives. Finance and Currency.

  Analysis of the accounts of the United States armoury at Springfield, Mass., showing cost of manufacturing muskets, with objections by the legal representatives of Eli Whitney estate on allowances made by the Springfield armoury under a contract with Eli Whitney for 1822. 1828.

  Carrington, James. Account of the musket barrels inspected & proved at the manufactory of Eli Whitney from Aug. 19, 1814, to May 18, 1821.

  Agreement or order made by Pierpont Edwards, James Hillhouse, and Charles Chauncey, who sold to Eli Whitney of New Haven, Conn., the mill, mill place appurtenances and privileges thereto, in town of Hamden, Conn., called Todd's mill, granting Eli Whitney the power and privilege to take possession of the premises and buildings thereon that have been in possession of William Fowler and others. Sept. 17, 1798.
Georgia: Minutes of the Circuit Court, Savannah, Georgia. April, 1793–April, 1798, 1798–1806, 1806–1816. 3 vols.
  Record Room, Superior Court, Chatham County.
Georgia Historical Society, Savannah
  Georgia newspapers
Historical Society of Pennsylvania
  Seven Eli Whitney MS letters, 1803–1824.
Library of Congress. Division of Manuscripts
  William Thornton Papers
  Samuel F. B. Morse Papers
  James Madison Papers
  Thomas Jefferson Papers
Massachusetts Historical Society. MS Letters:
  Jefferson to Monroe, Nov. 14, 1801.
  Eli Whitney to Josiah Whitney, Jan. 23, 1809.
  Whitney to Jefferson, Nov. 24, 1793.
New Haven Colony Historical Society
  Dana Collection

Leffingwell Letters, Vol. P
MS letter, Whitney to Ithiel Towne, Dec. 26, 1820.
MS letter, E. W. Blake to James Goodrich, Dec. 12, 1829.
New York Historical Society
Rufus King Papers. Vols. 26, 38, 71.
Oliver Wolcott Account Books. 2 vols. MS, 1808–1815.
General Henry Dearborn. Copies of letters and orders, MS, 1812–1813. 2 vols.
Alexander Hamilton and Aaron Burr Duel Correspondence.
New York Public Library. Manuscript Room
Oliver Wolcott Letterbook, 1803–1808.
Miscellaneous
Box: New York State, Gov. Tompkins file.
Box: South Carolina counties, miscellaneous subjects.
MS letter, Tench Coxe to James Monroe, Dec. 2, 1819.
Princeton University Library. Manuscript Room
Letter, Jefferson to Sullivan, Oct. 8, 1809.
United States. National Archives
General Records of the Department of State
Miscellaneous Letters, Jan. to Dec., 1809, Jan. to Dec., 1810. Record Group No. 59.
Naval Records
General Letterbook No. 4 (Aug. 26, 1800 to Sept. 16, 1801), No. 5 (Sept. 21, 1801 to Aug. 31, 1802), No. 9 (Aug. 1, 1807 to May 13, 1809).
War Records Division
Office of the Secretary of War. Letters Received. W-Miscellaneous.
Office of the Adjutant General. Post Revolutionary War Collection, War of 1812 Manuscripts.
Office of Chief of Ordnance. Letters Sent, 12 vols., 1812–1825. Contract Book I.
Springfield Armory Records. Letters Sent, 5 vols. (1799–1828), Letters Sent Miscellaneous, 5 vols. (1813–1823), Letters Received, 5 Boxes.
United States. Records of the Census Bureau. Census of Manufactures, 1820. Whitney's reply to questionnaire.
Yale University Library
Baldwin Collection: Notes on Eli Whitney's Will, Letter to Mrs. Whitney, 1847
Blake Family Collection
Bushnell Papers: "E. W. Blake and His Contributions to Science," MS
David Daggett Collection

Eliot Family Collection

Hillhouse Family Collection

Memoirs of the Class of 1792, Yale College by Rev. Timothy Mather
Cooley

Morse Family Collection

Records of the New Haven Collector's Office

New Haven Fire Insurance Company

New Haven Papers

Benjamin Silliman's "Reminiscences" and "The Wild Pigeon" letter

Dr. Nathan Smith Papers and notebook

Ezra Stiles "Literary Diary"

Miscellaneous Whitney items

PUBLISHED MATERIAL

Adams, Henry, *History of the United States* (1801–1817). 9 vols. New
York, 1921.

American Journal of Science, The, more especially of minerology, geology
and the other branches of natural history; including also agriculture
and the ornamental as well as useful arts. Conducted by Benj. Silliman, M.D. 2nd ed., Vol. I. New York, 1819–1846.

Atwater, Edward F., *History of the City of New Haven.* New York, 1887.

Bagnall, William R., *The Textile Industries of the United States.* Cambridge, 1893.

Baines, Edward, Jr., *History of the Cotton Manufacture in Great Britain.*
London, 1835.

Baldwin, Ebenezer, *Annals of Yale College.* New Haven, 1831.

Baldwin, S., *The First Century of the Connecticut Academy of Arts and
Sciences, 1799–1899: A Historical Address.* New Haven, 1901.

Barber, John W., *Historical Collections of Connecticut.* New Haven, 1838.
———, *History and Antiquities of New Haven.* New Haven, 1856.

Bates, Edward C., *The Story of the Cotton Gin.* Reprinted from the *New
England Magazine* issue for May, 1890, by the Westborough Historical Society, 1899.

Bathe, Greville and Dorothy, *Oliver Evans: A Chronicle of Early American Engineering.* Philadelphia, 1935.

Beard, Charles A., *The Economic Basis of Politics.* New York, 1947.
———, *Economic Origins of Jeffersonian Democracy.* New York, 1915.

Benét, Stephen V. (ed.), United States Ordnance Department: *A Collection of Annual Reports and Other Important Papers, Relating to the
Ordnance Department, Taken from the Records of the Office of the
Chief of Ordnance, from Public Documents and from Other Sources.*
4 vols. Government Printing Office, Washington, D.C., 1878–1890.

Bigelow, J., *Elements of Technology*, taken chiefly from a course of lectures delivered at Cambridge, on the application of the sciences to the useful arts. 2nd ed. Boston, 1831.

Bishop, Abraham, *Georgia Speculation Unveiled*. Hartford, Conn., 1797.

Bishop, J. Leander, *A History of American Manufactures, from 1608 to 1860*. 2 vols. Philadelphia, 1861–1864.

Blake, Henry F., *Chronicles of New Haven Green from 1638 to 1862*. New Haven Colony Historical Society, New Haven, 1898.

Blake, William P., *History of the Town of Hamden, Connecticut*. New Haven, 1888.

———, *New Haven Colony Historical Society Papers*, Vol. V. New Haven, 1894.

Bolles, Albert S., *Industrial History of the United States*. Norwich, Conn., 1879.

Bowers, Claude G., *Jefferson in Power*. Boston, 1936.

Bramson, Roy T., *Highlights in the History of American Mass Production*. Detroit, Mich., 1945.

Brasch, F. E., "The Royal Society of London and Its Influence upon Scientific Thought in the American Colonies," *Scientific Monthly*, XXXIII (1931).

Brown, H. B., *Cotton*. 2nd ed. New York, 1938.

Burkett, C. W. and Poe, C. H., *Cotton*. New York, 1906.

Burlingame, Roger, *Backgrounds of Power: The Human Story of Mass Production*. New York, 1949.

———, *Engines of Democracy: Inventions and Society in Mature America*, New York, 1940.

———, *March of the Iron Men: a Social History of Union Through Invention*. New York, 1938.

Byrn, E. W., *The Progress of Invention in the Nineteenth Century*. New York, 1900.

Cairnes, J. E., *The Slave-Power*. New York, 1862.

Calder, Isabel Macbeath, *The New Haven Colony*. New Haven, 1934.

Callender, Guy S., *Selections from the Economic History of the United States* (1765–1860). Boston, 1909.

Carroll, Charles, *Rhode Island: Three Centuries of Democracy*. 4 vols. New York, 1932.

Clark, Victor S., *History of Manufactures in the United States*. 3 vols. New York, 1929.

Clarke, Louise B., *The Greenes of Rhode Island*. New York, 1903.

Cochran, Thomas C., and Miller, William, *The Age of Enterprise*. New York, 1942.

Cohen, I. Bernard, *Science, Servant of Man*. Boston, 1948.

————, "Science and the Revolution," *Technology Review*, XLVII (1945), No. 3.

————, "Science and the Civil War," *Ibid.*, XLVIII (Jan., 1946), No. 3.

Cole, Arthur H., *The American Wool Manufacture*. 2 vols. Cambridge, Mass., 1926.

Commons, John R. (ed.), *History of Labour in the United States*. 4 vols. New York, 1918–1935.

————, *A Documentary History of American Industrial Society*. 11 vols. Cleveland, Ohio, 1910–1911.

Condorcet, Marie Jean Antoine, *Outlines of an Historical View of the Progress of the Human Mind*. London, 1795.

Connecticut. *Report of the Secretary of State Relative to Certain Branches of Industry*. Conn. House of Representatives. Doc. 26, May Session, 1839. Hartford, 1839.

Cooper, Thomas, *Some Information Respecting America*. 2nd ed. London, 1795.

Cotton-Textile Institute, Inc. *Cotton from Raw Material to Finished Product*. 3rd ed. New York, 1944.

Coulter, Ellis Merton, *Georgia: a Short History*. Chapel Hill, N.C., 1947.

Coxe, Tench. *View of the United States of America*. Philadelphia, Pa., 1794.

————, *Essay on the Manufacturing Interest of the United States*. Philadelphia, Pa., 1864.

————, *Report of the Committee of Commerce and Manufactures on Various Memorials . . . Praying for Legislative Patronage to Several Domestic Arts, Trades and Manufactures*. Philadelphia, Pa., 1804.

————, *A Statement of the Arts and Manufactures of the United States of America for the Year 1810*. Philadelphia, Pa., 1814.

————, *Memoir of Feb. 1817 (and of Dec. 1818) upon the Cotton Wool Cultivation, the Cotton Trade, and the Cotton Manufactures of the United States*. Philadelphia, Pa., 1817 and 1818.

Crawford, M. De C., *The Heritage of Cotton: The Fibre of Two Worlds and Many Ages*. New York, 1931.

Cummings, Joseph B., *Address on the Occasion of the Celebration of Municipal Centennial of the City of Augusta. Georgia Historical Quarterly* Vol. I. Savannah, Ga., 1917.

Cuningham, C. E., *Timothy Dwight, 1752–1817*. New York, 1942.

Dampier, W. C., *A History of Science and Its Relations with Philosophy and Religion*. 3rd ed. New York, 1943.

Day, Clive, *The Rise of Manufacturing in Connecticut, 1820–1850*. Connecticut State Tercentenary Commission. New Haven, Conn., 1935.

De Bow, J. D. B., *The Industrial Resources of the Southern and Western States.* 3 vols. New Orleans, 1852–1853.

De Forest, H. P., and Bates, E. C., *The History of Westborough Mass.* Published by the town. 1891.

Dexter, Franklin B., *Biographical Sketches of the Graduates of Yale College* (1701–1815). 6 vols. New York, 1885–1912.

————, *Biographical Notices of Graduates of Yale College,* 1816–1884. New Haven, 1913.

Deyrup, Felicia J., *Arms Makers of the Connecticut Valley: A Regional Study of the Economic Development of the Small Arms Industry, 1798–1870.* Smith College Studies in History, Vol. XXXIII. Northampton, Mass., 1938.

Dick, Oliver Lawson, ed., *Aubrey's Brief Lives.* London, 1950.

Dickinson, W. H., and Jenkins, Rhys. *James Watt and the Steam Engine.* Memorial volume prepared for the Committee of the Watt Centenary Commemoration at Birmingham, 1919. Oxford, 1927.

Dictionary of American Biography, Allen Johnson and Dumas Malone, eds. 21 vols. New York, 1928–1937.

Dodd, William E., *The Cotton Kingdom.* New Haven, Conn., 1921.

Donnell, E. J., *History of Cotton.* New York, 1872.

Durfee, W. F., *The History and Modern Development of the Art of Interchangeable Construction in Mechanism.* American Society of Mechanical Engineers. New York, 1893.

Dwight, Benjamin W., *The History of the Descendants of John Dwight of Dedham, Mass.* Vol. 2. New York, 1874.

Dwight, Theodore, Jr., *The History of Connecticut from the First Settlement to the Present Time.* New York, 1840.

Dwight, Timothy, *Statistical Account of the Towns and Parishes in the State of Connecticut.* New Haven, 1811.

————, *Travels in New England and New York.* 4 vols. Edinburgh, 1823.

Earle, Edward M. (ed.), *Makers of Modern Strategy.* Princeton, N.J., 1944.

Edwards, E. E., "American Agriculture—the First 300 Years," U.S. Dept. of Agriculture, *Yearbook of Agriculture,* 1940. Washington, D.C., 1941.

Ellet, Elizabeth F., *The Court Circles of the Republic.* Hartford, Conn., 1869.

————, *The Women of the American Revolution.* Vol. I. 1848.

Encyclopedia Americana.

Encyclopaedia Britannica, 11th ed.

Encyclopaedia of the Social Sciences.

Encyclopédie ou Dictionnaire raisonné des Sciences, des Arts et des

Métiers. 17 vols. Paris, 1751–1765. *Supplément à l'Encyclopédie.* 4 vols. Amsterdam, 1776–1777.

Evans, Oliver. *The Young Millwright and Miller's Guide.* 4th ed. Philadelphia, Pa., 1821.

Faulkner, William, *The Portable Faulkner,* ed. Malcolm Cowley. New York, 1946.

Fitch, Charles H., *Report on Manufactures of Interchangeable Mechanism.* U.S. Census, 1880. Volume on Manufactures, Washington, D.C., 1883.

Floyd, Dolores B., Mulberry Grove Plantation near Savannah. Mimeographed and distributed by the Savannah Chamber of Commerce. (Extracts made by the author's consent from the lengthy documented article, typewritten and bound, in the library of the Georgia Historical Society, 1936.)

Forbes, Harriette M., *The Hundredth Town. Glimpses of Life in Westborough, 1717–1817.* Boston, 1889.

Fuller, Claud E., *The Whitney Firearms.* Huntington, W.Va., 1946.

Fuller, Grace P., *An Introduction to the History of Connecticut as a Manufacturing State.* Smith College Studies in History. Northampton, Mass., 1915.

Garrison, Fielding H., *Introduction to the History of Medicine.* Rev. ed. Philadelphia, Pa., 1929.

Georgia: A Guide to its Towns and Countryside. American Guide Series. Athens, Ga., 1946.

Georgia. Journal of the House of Representatives for the year 1800.

Gibbs, George, *Memoir of the Administrations of Washington and John Adams,* ed. from the papers of Oliver Wolcott, Secretary of the Treasury. 2 vols. New York, 1846.

Glover, John G., and Cornell, William B., *The Development of American Industries.* Rev. ed. New York, 1941.

Goodrich, S. G., *Recollections of a Lifetime.* 2 vols. New York, 1856.

Goodwin, C. L., *The Trans-Mississippi West, 1803–1853: A History of Its Acquisition and Settlement.* New York, 1922.

Gras, N. S. B., and Larson, H. M., *Casebook in American Business History.* New York, 1939.

———, *Industrial Evolution.* Cambridge, Mass., 1930.

Gray, L. C., *History of Agriculture in the Southern United States.* 2 vols. Washington, D.C., 1933.

Graydon, Alexander, *Memoirs of a Life Chiefly Passed in Pennsylvania, Within the Last 60 Years.* Harrisburg, Pa., 1811.

Green, Constance M., *Holyoke, Massachusetts: A Case History of the Industrial Revolution in America.* New Haven, 1939.

Green, Constance M., *History of Naugatuck, Connecticut.* New Haven, 1948.

Greene, George Washington, *The Life of Nathanael Greene.* 3 vols. New York, 1867–1871.

Guest, Richard, *History of the Cotton Manufacture, with a Disapproval of the Sir Richard Arkwright's claim to his Inventions.* 1823.

Halévy, Elie. *A History of the English People in 1815.* 3 vols. (Pelican Books) London, 1937–1938.

Hamilton, Walton H., and Adair, Douglass. *The Power to Govern: The Constitution—Then and Now.* New York, 1937.

Hammond, M. B., "Correspondence of Eli Whitney Relative to the Invention of the Cotton Gin," *American Historical Review,* Vol. III, No. 1. October, 1897.

———, *The Cotton Industry: An Essay in American Economic History.* Part I: "The Cotton Culture and the Cotton Trade." American Economic Association. New York, 1897.

Handlin, Oscar, and Mary F., *Commonwealth: A Study of the Role of Government in the American Economy, Massachusetts, 1774–1861.* Studies in Economic History, New York University. New York, 1947.

Hansen, Marcus L., *The Atlantic Migration, 1607–1860.* Cambridge, Mass., 1940.

Haraszti, Zoltàn, "John Adams Flays a Philosophe: Annotations on Condorcet's Progress of the Human Mind," *William & Mary Quarterly,* 3rd series, Vol. VII, p. 225.

Harte, C. R., *Connecticut's Iron and Copper.* Annual Report Connecticut Society of Civil Engineers. New Haven, 1944.

Hartley, Rachel M., *The History of Hamden, Connecticut, 1786–1936.* Hamden, Conn., 1943.

Hay, Elzy, "The Cotton Gin and Its Inventors," reprinted from *Scientific American* (n.d.), in *De Bow's Review.* New Orleans, May–June, 1870.

Heitman, Francis B., *Historical Register and Dictionary of the United States Army.* 2 vols. Washington, D.C., 1903.

Von Helmhotz, Hermann, *Popular Lectures on Scientific Subjects,* transl. E. Atkinson. 2 vols., 1st Series. London, 1901.

Henderson, Archibald, *Washington's Southern Tour, 1791.* Cambridge, Mass., 1923.

Hicks, James E., *What the Citizen Should Know About Our Arms and Weapons.* New York, 1941.

———, *Notes on United States Ordnance.* 2 vols. 1940.

Holland, Josiah G., *History of Western Massachusetts.* 2 vols. Springfield, Mass., 1855.

Holmes, Abiel, *The Life of Ezra Stiles*. Boston, 1798.

Howe, Henry, *Memoirs of the Most Eminent American Mechanics*. New York, 1844.

Hubbard, Guy, "Development of Machine Tools in New England," *American Machinist*, Feb. 14, 1924. 13th article.

Humphreys, F. L., *Life and Times of David Humphreys*. 2 vols. New York, 1917.

Hutcheson, Harold, *Tench Coxe: A Study in American Economic Development*. Johns Hopkins University Studies in Historical and Political Science, New Series, No. 26. Baltimore, 1938.

Iles, George, *Inventors at Work: With Chapters on Discovery*. 2 vols. New York, 1906.

———, *Leading American Inventors*. New York, 1912.

Jaffe, B., *Men of Science in America: The Role of Science in the Growth of Our Country*. New York, 1944.

Jefferson, Thomas, *Writings;* ed. H. A. Washington. 9 vols. New York, 1853–1855.

———, *Writings;* ed. Paul Leicester Ford. 10 vols. New York, 1899.

Johnston, Edith D. "The Kollock Letters, 1799–1850," *Georgia Historical Quarterly*, 1946.

Jones, Charles C., Jr., *The History of Georgia*. 2 vols. Boston, 1883.

Keir, Robert M. *Manufacturing*. New York, 1928.

Keith, H. C., and Harte, C. R., *The Early Iron Industry of Connecticut*. Reprinted from 51st Annual Report of the Connecticut Society of Civil Engineers, New Haven, 1935.

Kendall, Edward Augustus, *Travels Through the Northern Parts of the United States in the Years 1807 and 1808*. 3 vols. New York, 1809.

Kingsley, J. L., *A Sketch of the History of Yale College in Connecticut*. American Quarterly Register, Vol. VIII. Boston, 1836.

Kirby, R. S., *Inventors and Engineers of Old New Haven*. A series of six lectures given in 1938 under the auspices of the School of Engineering, Yale University. New Haven Tercentenary Publications. New Haven Colony Historical Society. New Haven, Conn., 1939.

Knight, Lucien L., *Georgia's Landmarks, Memorials, and Legends*. 2 vols. Atlanta, Ga., 1913–1914.

Kraus, M., "Scientific Relations Between Europe and America in the Eighteenth Century," *Scientific Monthly*, Vol. LV, 1942.

Krout, John Allen, and Fox, Dixon Ryan, *The Completion of Independence, 1790–1830*, Vol. V, *A History of American Life*. New York, 1944.

Lewton, F. L., *Historical Notes on the Cotton Gin*. Smithsonian Report for 1937. Washington, D.C. (Publ. 3478).

Livermore, Shaw, *Early American Land Companies: The Influence on Corporate Development*. New York, 1939.

Lodge, Henry Cabot (ed.), *The Works of Alexander Hamilton*. 12 vols. New York, 1904.

Lovell, Caroline C., *The Golden Isles of Georgia*. Boston, 1932.

McCrady, Edward, *The History of South Carolina in the Revolution, 1780–1783*. New York, 1902.

McCulloch, John Ramsay (ed.), *A Select Collection of Early English Tracts on Commerce*. London, 1856.

McMaster, J. B., *A History of the People of the United States*. 8 vols. New York, 1883–1913.

Mach, Ernest, *The Science of Mechanics*, transl. from the German by Thomas J. McCormack. 4th ed. London, 1919.

Mantoux, Paul, *The Industrial Revolution in the Eighteenth Century*. Rev. ed. transl. by Marjorie Vernon. New York, 1929.

Mason, G. C., *Reminiscences of Newport*. Newport, R.I., 1884.

Mechanics' Magazine Museum Register, Journal and Gazette. Saturday, Sept. 29, 1832.

Melish, John, *Travels Through the United States of America in the Years 1806 and 1807, and 1809, 1810, and 1811*. London, 1818.

Miller, Perry, *Jonathan Edwards*. New York, 1949.

Mitchell, Broadus, *The Rise of Cotton Mills in the South*. Baltimore, Md., 1921.

Morse, Jedidiah, *The American Universal Geography: or a View of Present State of All the Kingdoms, States, and Colonies in the Known World*. 2 vols. Boston, 1805.

———, with Richard C. Morse, *The Traveller's Guide or Pocket Gazetteer of the United States*. 2nd ed. New Haven, 1826.

New Haven Chamber of Commerce. *Economic and Industrial Survey*. New Haven, 1939.

New Haven Colony Historical Society Papers.

Niles' Weekly Register, ed. Hezekiah Niles, 1811–1826.

North, S. N. D., and Ralph, H., *Simeon North. First Official Pistol Maker of the United States*. Concord, N.H., 1913.

Olmstead, Frederick Law, *Journey in the Seaboard Slave States*. New York, 1861.

Olmsted, Denison, *Memoir of Eli Whitney, Esq*. New Haven, 1846.

Parsons, Francis, "Ezra Stiles of Yale," *New England Quarterly*. June, 1936.

————, *Six Men of Yale.* New Haven, 1939.

Parton, James, *Life of Thomas Jefferson.* Boston, 1874.

Paine, Thomas, *Writings;* coll. and ed. Moncure Daniel Conway, 4 vols. New York, 1896.

Perregaux, Charles et Perrot, F. Louis, *Les Jaquet—Droz et Leschot.* Neuchâtel, 1916.

Pharmacopoeia of the Massachusetts Medical Society, The. Boston, 1808.

Phillips, Ulrich B., *Life and Labor in the Old South.* Boston, 1929.

Pierce, Frederick C., *The Descendants of John Whitney.* Chicago, 1895.

Pitkin, Timothy, *A Statistical View of the Commerce of the United States of America: Including also an Account of Banks, Manufactures, and Internal Trade and Improvements.* New Haven, 1835.

Polé, William, *Life of Sir William Fairbairn.* London, 1877.

Purcell, Richard J., *Connecticut in Transition, 1775–1818.* The American Historical Association. Washington, D.C., 1918.

Ramsay, David, *History of South Carolina.* 2 vols. Charleston, S.C., 1809.

Redford, Arthur, *The Economic History of England* (1760–1860). London, 1931.

Rees, Abraham, *Cyclopedia or an Universal Dictionary of Arts and Science.* 41 vols. Philadelphia, 1822.

Rhode Island: A Guide to the Smallest State. American Guide Series. Boston, 1937.

Rice, Franklin P., *Vital Records of Westborough, Mass.* Worcester, Mass., 1903.

Rice, William R., *The Leicester Academy Centenary, 1884.* Worcester, Mass., 1884.

Roe, Alfred S., *More Old Houses in Westborough, Mass. with Their Occupants.* Westborough Historical Society, 1908.

Roe, Joseph W., *English and American Tool Builders.* New Haven, 1916.

————, *Connecticut Inventors.* Tercentenary Commission of the State of Connecticut. Published for the Tercentenary Commission by the Yale University Press. New Haven, 1934.

————, *Interchangeable Manufacture.* Excerpt from Transactions of the Newcomen Society. Speech read at the University Club, N.Y., and at the Royal School of Mines. London, 1937.

————, "Machine Tools in America," *Journal of the Franklin Institute,* Vol. CCXXV, No. 5. May, 1938.

Sawyer, Charles W., *Firearms in American History.* 3 vols. Boston, 1910.

Scarborough, William, "Sketch of the Life of the Late Eli Whitney with Some Remarks on the Invention of the Saw Gin," *Southern Agriculturalist,* Vol. V, No. 8, August, 1832.

Scherer, James A. B., *Cotton as a World Power: A Study in the Economic Interpretation of History.* New York, 1916.

von Schultze-Gavernitz, G., *The Cotton Trade in England and on the Continent,* transl. O. Hall. London, 1895.

Seybert, Adam, *Statistical Annals: Embracing Views of the Population, Commerce, Navigation, Fisheries, Public Lands, Post-Office Establishment, Revenues, Mint, Military and Naval Establishments, Expenditures, Public Debt and Sinking Fund of the United States of America.* Philadelphia, 1818.

Sharpe, Philip B., *The Rifle in America.* 2nd ed. New York, 1947.

Sheffield, Lord John, *Observations on the Commerce of the American States.* 6th ed. London, 1784.

Shlakman, Vera, *Economic History of a Factory Town: A Study of Chicopee, Massachusetts.* Smith College Studies in History, Vol. XX. Northampton, Mass., 1935.

Silliman, Benjamin, *An Address Delivered Before the Association of the Alumni of Yale College in New Haven, August 17, 1842.* New Haven, 1842.

———, *An Oration Delivered at Hartford on the 6th of July, A.D. 1802.* Hartford, Conn., 1802.

Smiles, Samuel, *Industrial Biography: Iron Workers and Tool-Makers.* London, 1863.

———, *Men of Invention and Industry.* New York, 1885.

———, *Smeaton and Rennie.* London, 1904.

——— (ed.), *Autobiography of James Nasmyth.* London, 1883.

Smith, Adam, *An Inquiry into the Nature and Causes of the Wealth of Nations.* 5th ed. 3 vols. London, 1789.

Smith, Margaret Bayard, *The First 40 Years of Washington Society,* ed. Hunt Gaillard. New York, 1906.

Smith, Walter B., and Cole, Arthur H., *Fluctuations in American Business, 1790–1860.* Cambridge, Mass., 1935.

South Carolina: Journals of the House of Representatives.
Journals of the Senate.
Report of a Joint Committee. Feb., 1804.

Stearns, Charles, *The National Armories.* 2nd ed. Springfield, Mass., 1852.

Stevens, William Bacon, *A History of Georgia.* 2 vols. New York, 1847.

Stiles, Ezra, *The Literary Diary of Ezra Stiles,* ed. F. B. Dexter. 3 vols. New York, 1901.

Stokes, Anson, *Memorials of Eminent Yale Men.* 2 vols. New Haven, 1914.

Struik, Dirk J., *Yankee Science in the Making.* Boston, 1948.

Swank, James M., *History of the Manufacture of Iron in All Ages, and Particularly in the United States from Colonial Times to 1891.* 2nd ed. Philadelphia, 1892.

Sward, Keith, *The Legend of Henry Ford.* New York, 1948.

Taylor, Frederick W., *The Principles of Scientific Management.* New York, 1911.

Taylor, George R., *The Transportation Revolution, 1815–1860* (Vol. IV of *The Economic History of the United States*). New York, 1951.

Thomas, E. S., *Reminiscences of the Last Sixty-Five Years, Commencing with the Battle of Lexington.* 2 vols. Hartford, Conn., 1840.

Thompson, Holland, *From the Cotton Field to the Cotton Mill.* New York, 1906.

———, *The Age of Invention: A Chronicle of Mechanical Conquest.* New Haven, 1921.

Tompkins, Daniel A., *The Cotton Gin: The History of Its Invention.* Charlotte, N.C., 1901.

———, *Cotton and Cotton Oil.* Charlotte, N.C., 1901.

———, "Cotton and Its Uses," *Manufacturer's Record.* Supplement, Nov., 1895.

Tompkins, Daniel D., Governor of New York, 1807–1817, *Public Papers.* 3 vols. Albany, N.Y., 1902.

Tryon, Rolla M., *Household Manufactures in the United States, 1640–1860.* Chicago, 1917.

United States: American State Papers.
    Class III, Finance. 3 vols. Washington, D.C., 1832.
    Class V, Military Affairs, 1789–1819.
    Class VI, Naval Department, 1794–1825.
    Class VIII, Public Lands. 2 vols. 1809–1824.
    Class IX, Claims, 1790–1823.
    Class X, Miscellaneous. 2 vols. 1789–1823.

———, *Diplomatic Correspondence of the United States from the Signing of the Definite Treaty of the Peace . . . to the Adoption of the Constitution.* 4 vols. Washington, D.C., 1837.

———, Patent Office:
History of the Patent Office from 1790 to 1877. Washington, 1877.
List of Patents Granted by the United States, April 10, 1790, to December 31, 1836. Washington, 1872.

———, McLane, Secretary Louis, *Report.* Executive Document 30. 22nd Congress, 1st session. Washington, D.C., 1832.

———, *Woodbury Report on the Cultivation, Manufacture and Foreign Trade of Cotton.* House Document 146, 24th Congress, 1st session. Washington, 1836.

Usher, Abbott Payson, *The Industrial History of England.* Boston, 1920.

———, *A History of Mechanical Inventions.* New York, 1929.

Vance, Rupert B., *Human Factors in Cotton Culture: A Study in the Social Geography of the American South.* Chapel Hill, N.C., 1929.

Wailes, B. L. C., *Report on Agriculture and Geology of Mississippi.* Philadelphia, Pa. 1854.

Walton, Perry, *The Story of Textiles*. Boston, 1912.

Wansey, Henry, *An Excursion to the United States of North America in the September of 1794*. Salisbury, England, 1798.

Ware, Caroline, *The Early New England Cotton Manufacture*. Boston, 1931.

Ware, Norman, *The Industrial Worker, 1840–60*. Boston, 1924.

Weeden, W. B., *Economic and Social History of New England, 1620–1789*. 2 vols. Boston, 1890.

Wharton, Francis, *The Revolutionary Diplomatic Correspondence of the United States*, Vol. V. Washington, 1899.

White, George S., *Memoir of Samuel Slater, the Father of American Manufactures*. Philadelphia, 1836.

White, Martha (ed.), *Westborough and Northborough*. 1902.

Whitney, Eli, *The Oration on the Death of Mr. Robert Grant, Member of the Senior Class . . . Aetat. XXIII*. New Haven, 1792.

Williams, Eric, *Capitalism and Slavery*. Chapel Hill, N.C., 1944.

Williamson, Harold F. (ed.), *The Growth of the American Economy*. New York, 1946.

Wolf, A., *A History of Science, Technology, and Philosophy in the Eighteenth Century*. London, 1938.

Woodworth, Joseph V., *American Tool Making and Interchangeable Manufacturing*. New York, 1911.

Woolsey, Theodore D., Wells, David A., Knight, Edward H., and others, *The First Century of the Republic, a Review of American Progress*. New York, 1876.

Woolsey, Theodore S., *The Old New Haven Bank*. New Haven Colony Historical Society, Vol. VIII, May 19, 1913.

Wright, Carroll D., *The Industrial Evolution of the United States*. Meadville, N.Y., 1897.

Young, T. M., *The American Cotton Industry*. New York, 1902.

NEWSPAPERS

Connecticut Papers:
 Connecticut Herald
 Connecticut Journal
 Connecticut Post
Georgia Papers:
 Columbia Museum & Savannah Advertiser
 Republican & Savannah Evening Ledger
 Southern Sentinel and Gazette of the State. Augusta
 Georgia Gazette
 Gazette of the State of Georgia
 Georgia Republican & State Intelligence

Sources of Letters Quoted

[Unless otherwise specified, the letters are from the
Whitney Papers, Yale Library.]

Phillips to EW, Jr., 2 April, 1865, ix;
EW to Stebbins, 9 Nov., 1802, 1;
EW to Stebbins, 21 Sept., 1787, 25;
EW to father, 5 April, 1791, 38-39;
father to EW, 21 July, 1790, 39; father
to EW, 8 March, 1791, 39; father to
EW, 21 May, 1792, 39; letter unsigned,
undated, 40; EW to Josiah, 25 Sept.,
1792, 44; EW to father, 26 Sept., 1792,
44-45; EW to Stebbins, 8 Oct., 1792,
46-47; Miller to EW, 20 Sept., 1792,
48; EW to father, 17 Oct., 1792, 48;
EW to Stebbins, 17 Oct., 1792, 48;
Stebbins to Mrs. Whitney, 7 April,
1825, 48; Catherine to EW, 1808-
1814, 50-51; Catherine to EW, 27 July,
1809, 51; Greene to Clarke (Henderson, *Washington's Southern Tour*,
1791, p. 232), 53; Greene to Clarke
(Greene, *Life of Nathanael Greene*,
Vol. 3, p. 352), 53; EW to Stebbins, 1
Nov., 1792, 55-56; EW to father, 11
April, 1793, 57; EW to Stebbins, 11
April, 1793, 57-58; EW to Stebbins,
1 May, 1793, 58; father to EW, 16
Aug., 1793, 59; EW to father, 11 Sept.,
1793, 59; EW to father, 11 Sept.,
1793, 66-68; EW to Jefferson, 20 June,
1793, 69; EW to Jefferson, 15 Oct.,
1793, 72-73; Jefferson to EW, 16 Nov.,
1793, 74-75; EW to Jefferson, 24 Nov.,
1793, 75-77; EW to Stebbins, 22 Dec.,
1793, 77-78; Goodrich to Wolcott, 25
Nov., 1794 (Gibbs, *Administration of
Washington and Adams*, Vol. I, p.
128), 79; EW to father, 30 March,
1794, 79-80; EW to Timothy Pitkin,
8 July, 1796, 94; Miller to EW, 13
Dec., 1797, 94; EW to Wm. Wallace, 7
June, 1799, 94; eight letters between
EW and Adam Babcock, 22 Nov.,
1810, to 10 Jan., 1811, 94; Miller to
Hamilton, 19 Jan., 1803 (M & W

2:215-231), 96; Miller to Pierce Butler,
20 March, 1795 (M & W 1:59), 97;
M & W to ——, 98; Miller to EW, 8
March, 1796 (M & W 1:51-57), 98;
Miller to Toole, 17 May, 1794 (M & W
1:2), 99; M & W to Mayront, 20 March,
1798 (M & W 2:29), 99; M & W to
Shields, 4 Nov., 1794 (M & W 1:8),
99; *ibid.*, 99-100; M & W to Fowler,
2 March, 1798 (M & W 2:14), 100;
M & W to Russell, 20 Oct., 1794 (M &
W 1:10), 100; M & W to Mayront, 20
March, 1798 (M & W 2:29), 101;
ibid., 13 Dec., 1798 (M & W 2:92-
93), 101; M & W to Russell, M & W to
Durkee, 20 and 25 Oct., 1794 (M & W
1:10-15), 101-102; M & W to ——, 25
Oct., 1794 (M & W 1:16), 102; Miller
to Toole, 11 May, 1794 (M & W 1:1),
102; M & W to Randolph, 28 June,
1794 (M & W 1:3), 103; EW to father,
17 Aug., 1794, 103; Stiles, *Diary*,
3:531, 104; M & W to Toole, 20 Oct.,
1794 (M & W 1:13), 104; Miller to
EW, 25 Oct., 1794 (Olmstead, *Journey*,
p. 20), 104; EW to father, 20 Nov.,
1794, 104; Kollock to Whitney, 1805,
105; M & W to Waring, 29 Dec., 1794
(M & W 1:25), 106; Whitney to Miller, 25 Dec., 1795, 106-107; Miller to
Whitney, 6 April, 1797, 107; EW to
father, 22 March, 1795, 108; M & W to
Russell & Ammadon, 22 Jan., 1795
(M & W 1:41), 108; EW to father,
op. cit., 108-109; EW to Miller, 16
April, 1795 (*Georgia Gazette* 638),
109; EW to father, 2 Nov., 1795, 109;
Miller to EW, 11 April, 1795? (Olmstead, *Journey*, pp. 21-22), 110; EW
to Miller (*Georgia Gazette* 638), 110;
M & W to Shields, 22 Jan., 1795 (M &
W 1:25), 111; M & W to Bacon &
Woodruff, 30 April, 1799? (M & W

2:138-144), **111-112**; M & W to Toole, 30 March, 1797 (M & W 1:115-116), **112**; *Georgia Gazette,* 7 May, 1795, **114**; *So. Sentinel and Gazette of the State,* 21 May, 1796, Augusta, **114**; M & W to Chas. Jackson, 22 April, 1798 (M & W 2:66), **114**; M & W to Hamilton, 19 Jan., 1803 (M & W 2:215-231), **115**; EW to Stebbins, 7 March, 1803, **116**; Miller to EW, 8 Sept., 1797, **116**; EW to father, 20 Nov., 1794, **117**; Miller to EW, 25 Nov., 1795? (Olmstead, *Journey,* p. 22-23), **118**; EW to father, 2 Nov., 1795, **118**; *Georgia Gazette,* 26 Nov., 1795, **118**; EW to Miller, 25 Dec., 1795, **119**; Miller to EW, 31 Dec., 1795 (M & W 1:35), **119**; Hopkins to EW, 22 July, 1796, **120**; EW to Stebbins, 22 Dec., 1796, **120**; 8 Jan., 1797, **120**; Miller to EW, 8 March, 1796 (M & W 1:51-57), **120**; Miller to EW, 2 Dec., 1796 (M & W 1:88-90), **120**; Miller to ——, 4 Dec., 1796 (M & W 1:92), **120**; Miller to EW, 11 May, 1797 (M & W 1:147-154), **122**; Miller to —— (M & W 1:141), **123**; Miller to Uriah Tracy, 12 Dec., 1797 (M & W 1:232), **123**; Miller to Johnson, 7 Nov., 1800 (M & W 2:185), **123-124**; Wadsworth to Joshua Coit, 12 Dec., 1797 (M & W 1:237), **124**; M & W to Alexander, 23 Oct., 1798 (M & W 2:89), **124**; M & W to Jones, 15 Oct., 1799 (M & W 2:172), **124**; M & W to Nel, 15 April, 1797 (M & W 1:125-126), **124-125**; M & W to Tracy, 12 Dec., 1797 (M & W 1:230), **125**; M & W to Bacon, 15 Aug., 1799 (M & W 2:157-158), **125**; M & W to Durkee, 5 Jan., 1796 (M & W 1:38), **125**; M & W to Toole, 10 Nov., 1796 (M & W 1:79), **125**; M & W to Wallace, 10 Nov., 1796 (M & W 1:84), **125**; M & W to Wallace, 20 March, 1798 (M & W 2:27), **125**; M & W to Wallace, 16 April, 1798 (M & W 2:60), **125**; Miller to EW, 26 March, 1797, **126**; 21 July, 1797, **126**; 7 July, 1797, **126**; M & W to Russell, 26 Nov., 1797 (M & W 1:213), **126**; Miller to EW, 19 Jan., 1799, **126**; M & W to Hamilton, Maker & Co., 17 Dec., 1798 (M & W 2:98-99), **126**; M & W to Kinloch, 17 Sept., 1798 (M & W 2:85), **127**; Miller to EW, 25 May, 1797, **127**; M & W to Goodrich, 27 Feb., 1799 (M & W 2:125), **127**; Miller to EW, 31 Dec., 1795 (M & W 1:27-34), **128**; Miller to EW, 3 Dec., 1795 (M & W 1:27-34), **129**; EW to Stebbins, 1 Nov.,

1792 (see pp. 55-56), **130**; Miller to EW, 31 Dec., 1795 (M & W 1:27-34), **132**; EW to Stebbins, 22 Dec., 1796, **132**; Miller to EW, 20 March, 1797, **132-133**; Miller to EW, 6 April, 1797, **133**; 8 Sept., 1797, **133**; EW to Stebbins, 15 Sept., 1797, **133**; EW to Miller, 7 Oct., 1797, **133-135**; Williams to EW, 27 May, 1798, **136**; Chester to EW, 19 March, 1798, **137**; EW to Wolcott, 1 May, 1798, **138**; Treasury Dept. to Col. North, 20 June, 1798 (Wolcott Papers, MS Letterbooks, Vol. 34, Conn. Hist. Soc.), **142**; Wolcott to EW, 16 May, 1798, **143**; EW to Baldwin, 27 May, 1798, **143**; copy, EW proposals to Sec. Treas. 2 June, 1798, **143**; *The Report and Estimate of Tench Francis, Purveyor of Supplies,* 7 June, 1798, **145**; *Articles of Agreement,* 14 June, 1798, **145**; EW to Stebbins, 27 Nov., 1798, **146-147**; Miller to EW, 21 July, 1797, **147**; 19 Jan., 1799, **147**; M & W to Brown, 10 Aug., 1799 (M & W 2:153-155), **148**; EW to Stebbins, 19 Jan., 1799, **148**; M & W to Jones, 22 Oct., 1800 (M & W 2:179), **148**; Miller to EW, 4 Sept., 1801, **150**; EW to Stebbins, 22 Nov., 1801, **151-152**; EW to Stebbins, 20 Dec., 1801, **152-153**; EW to Josiah, 27 Dec., 1801, **153**; deSaussure to Wolcott, 28 Dec., 1801 (Wolcott Papers, MS Letterbooks, Vol. 16, Conn. Hist. Soc.), **153-154**; M & W to Legislature of S.C., 11 Dec., 1801, **154**; M & W to Goodrich, 24 Jan., 1802 (M & W 2:212-214), **154**; M & W to State of S.C., 16 Feb., 1802, **154**; EW to Josiah, 27 Dec., 1801, **154**; EW to Stebbins, 10 June, 1802, **155**; EW to Stebbins, 9 Feb., 1805, **156-157**; EW to Stebbins, 1 Jan., 1803, **157**; EW to Miller (Olmstead, *Journey,* p. 38), **157**; M & W to Hamilton, 19 Jan., 1803 (M & W 2:215-231), **157-158**; EW to Pinckney, 8 Dec., 1802, **158-159**; Hamilton to EW, 30 Nov., 1804, **159**; EW to Stebbins, 6 March, 1803, **160**; M & W to Goodrich, 14 March, 1801 (M & W 2:197), **161 n.**; EW to Stebbins, 7 March, 1803, **161 n.**; EW to Stebbins, 7 March, 1803, 15 Oct., 1803, **162**; Baldwin to Mrs. Whitney, 1847? (*ibid.*), **162**; EW to Madison, 1 Nov., 1803, **162**; Pendleton to Pinckney, 1 Nov., 1804, **162**; EW to Stebbins, 15 Oct., 1803, **162**; EW to Egan, 18 Jan., 1804, **163**; EW to Dearborn, 26 Jan., 1804, **164**; EW to Egan, 18 Jan., 1804,

3 Jan., 1818 (Nat. Archives, War Dept., SAR, Letters Rec'd.), 269; EW to Calhoun, 20 March, 1823 (MS letter courtesy Penrose Hoopes), 270; price list, U.S. Armory at Springfield, 1823 (Nat. Archives, War Dept., SAR, Letters Sent, Vol. 4), 270; EW to Calhoun, 9 July, 1821, 270-271; Eli Blake to editors of *National Intelligencer*, July, 1835 (Yale), 272; agreement between EW and Bomford, 1 Aug., 1822 (Nat. Archives, War Dept., Office Chief Ordnance, Contract Book 1), 272-273; contract between EW and Bomford acting for Calhoun, 15 Aug., 1822 (*ibid.*), 272-273; American State Papers, Class 5, Military Affairs 11, 1819–1825, p. 599, 273-274; Catherine to EW, 31 Oct., 1808, 275; Josiah to EW, 22 Sept., 1814, 275; EW to Catherine, 14 Feb., 1814, Catherine to EW, 16 April, 1814, 30 Nov., 1808, 7 March, 1809, 3 April, 1811, 275; Wolcott to King, 12 July, 1804 (N.Y. Hist. Soc., King Papers, Vol. 26), 276; Kollock to EW, 12 Feb., 1812, 277; Josiah to EW, 11 Sept., 1813, 277; EW to Catherine, 29 Aug., 1813, 277-278; Catherine to EW, 19 Oct., 1813, 5 July, 1814, 12 Oct., 1809, 278; *ibid.*, 5 July, 1809, 3 April, 1811, 8 May, 1811, 20 June, 1811, 279; Stebbins to EW, 20 May, 1815, 279-280; EW to Stebbins, 4 June, 1815, 5 Nov., 1815, 280; Catherine to EW, 2 Feb., 1809, 280-281; EW to Stebbins, 12 Nov., 1815, 4 June, 1815, 281; EW to Stebbins, 5 Nov., 1815, 281-282; *ibid.*, 4 June, 1815, 282; Stebbins to EW, 21 Oct., 1815, 19 Nov., 1815, 282; EW to Stebbins, 11 Feb., 1816, 20 March, 1816, 283; Stebbins to EW, 29 Nov., 1816, 283; *Connecticut Herald*, 14 Jan., 1817, 285; Edwards to Madison, 27 Oct., 1801, 285; EW to Stebbins, 10 June, 1802,

285; EW to Lee, 25 Dec., 1816 (Nat. Archives, War Dept., SAR, Letters Rec'd.), 285 n.; EW to Eli Blake, 12 May, 1818 (Blake Coll.), 286; *ibid.*, 21 July, 1818, 286-287; Baldwin & Rossiter, 5 Dec., 1818, 287; EW to Stebbins, 15 Oct., 1803, 287; M & W to Brown, 10 Aug., 1799 (M & W 2: 154), 288; Russell Goodrich to EW, 16 Jan., 1819, 289; EW to Josiah, 10 Nov., 1820, 290; EW to Towne, 26 Dec., 1820 (New Haven Colony Hist. Soc.), 290; EW to Josiah, 9 Jan., 1821, 290; EW to Lee, 8 April, 1819 (Nat. Archives, War Dept., SAR, Letters Rec'd.), 291 n.; *ibid.*, 23 Aug., 1821 (Misc. Letters 1813–1823), 291; *ibid.*, 17 Sept., 1821 (Letters Rec'd.), 291; *ibid.*, 10 Nov., 1821, 291; EW to Stebbins, 2 Jan., 1822, 291; EW to Josiah, 9 Sept., 1822, 292; *ibid.*, 11 Nov., 1822, 293; Carrington to Lee, 14 Jan., 1823 (Nat. Archives, War Dept., SAR, Misc. Letters 1813–1823), 293; *ibid.*, 30 Jan., 1823, 294; EW to Josiah, 9 Feb., 1823, 294; Carrington to Lee, 14 Jan., 1823 (*op. cit.*), 294; Olmsted, *Memoir*, p. 71, 294-295; EW to Lee, 2 Aug., 1824 (Nat. Archives, War Dept., SAR, Letters Rec'd.), 295-296; Letitia to Morse, 22 Nov., 1824 (Morse Papers, LC MSS Div., Vol. 9), 296; Susan Johnson to husband, 18 Dec., 1824, 296-297; Olmsted, *Memoir*, p. 75, 297; Fulton to EW, 4 April, 1811, 305; Evans to EW, 29 Oct., 1811, 306; Baldwin and Rossiter, 5 Dec., 1818, 307-309; Lee to Carrington, 22 Dec., 1825 (Nat. Archives, War Dept., SAR, Letters Sent), 315 n.; Blake to Goodrich, 12 Dec., 1829 (Leffingwell Letters, New Haven Colony Hist. Soc.), 316; Blake to EW, Jr., 18 Dec., 1882, 318.

Index